D1245166

SURVEY MANUAL FOR TROPICAL MARINE RESOURCES

2nd Edition

SURVEY MANUAL FOR TROPICAL MARINE RESOURCES
2nd Edition

Edited by S. English, C. Wilkinson and V. Baker

**AUSTRALIAN INSTITUTE
OF MARINE SCIENCE**

Townsville
1997

The first edition of this manual was published in 1994 on behalf of the ASEAN-Australia Marine Science Project: Living Coastal Resources by AIMS, with funds provided by the Australian Agency for International Development (AusAID). The following organisations have provided additional support to AIMS for the publication of this 2nd edition.

Environment Agency, Government of Japan   The World Bank   **IUCN** The World Conservation Union

 South Pacific Regional Environment Programme   International Tropical Marine Resource Centre

 Sida   Swedish International Development Cooperation Agency   Ecole Pratique des Hautes Etudes, Moorea

 Fondation Naturalia Polynesia, Tahiti

National Library of Australia Cataloguing-in-Publication data:

Survey manual for tropical marine resources.

2nd ed.
Bibliography.
Includes index.
ISBN 0 642 25953 4.

1. Marine resources - Research - Tropics. I. English, Susan A. (Susan Anne), 1951-. II. Wilkinson, Clive. III. Baker, V.J. IV. Australian Institute of Marine Science. V. ASEAN-Australia Marine Science Project.

333.952072013

Cover photographs by the Australian Institute of Marine Science.

To order copies of this manual write to the Australian Institute of Marine Science, P.M.B. No. 3, Townsville Mail Centre, Qld, 4810 Australia or contact the Institute via the internet on http://www.aims.gov.au.

Foreword

The first edition of the Survey Manual for Tropical Marine Science was published in 1994. Since that time the usefulness of this manual has been demonstrated in many countries throughout the world, while the need for the monitoring of change in the world's tropical coastal habitats has become more important than ever.

The need for coastal monitoring is especially strong in countries where people make substantial use of nearshore forests and seafood for their day-to-day living requirements of food, shelter and energy. However, the sustainable development of coastal resources requires comprehensive public education and often strong management action in order to prevent irreversible decline in water quality or loss of coastal habitats.

Public education and management action must be built on a solid foundation of knowledge about our natural and modified coastal ecosystems. The methods described in this manual are therefore relevant and directly applicable in tropical countries seeking to collect this information.

The sampling protocols were developed during the highly successful ASEAN-Australia Marine Science Project: Living Coastal Resources. They have been refined and tested by the participants in that project through extensive field sampling programs. This project demonstrated the benefits of adopting standardised approaches to data collection and storage in order to promote national and international cooperation, comparative studies of ecosystems and a support base for the more inexperienced students beginning work in this field. Scientists from Australia, Indonesia, Malaysia, the Philippines, Singapore and Thailand have all made valuable contributions.

During December 1991, in recognition of the extensive development and testing of these survey methods in developing countries, they were selected for use in monitoring coral reefs and mangrove forests by a meeting of experts in Monaco (UNEP-IOC-WMO-IUCN Meeting of Experts on a Long-term Global Monitoring System of Coastal and Nearshore Phenomena Related to Climate Change).

In 1994 Australia, France, Jamaica, Japan, the Philippines, Sweden, United Kingdom and the United States formed the International Coral Reef Initiative (ICRI). Representatives from more than 40 countries met the following year in the Philippines and identified four major thrusts for ICRI: coastal management; capacity building; research and monitoring; and, regular reviews of progress towards sustainable management of coral reefs and related ecosystems.

The research and monitoring component of this initiative is being addressed by the Global Coral Reef Monitoring Network (GCRMN), which was formed in 1996 under the co-sponsorship of the IOC, UNEP and the IUCN, with financial support from the governments of the United States and Australia.

The GCRMN has adopted the coral reef monitoring methods in this manual as the 'standard methods' for global reef monitoring and will recommend this survey manual to all participants in the network. These global programs cannot succeed without a degree of standardisation in monitoring protocols, and the survey methods described here make this possible

The first edition of this Survey Manual has been very successful. I recommend this significantly improved second edition. It contains information on new technologies and recent literature, making it the most comprehensive survey manual of its type available.

Dr Russell Reichelt
Director
Australian Institute of Marine Science

Table of Contents

Preface

The initial concept of using simple repeatable methods to allow comparison of data across regions has been a significant step towards a regional understanding of marine ecosystems. This, the second edition of the Survey Manual for Tropical Marine Resources, builds on the foundation established by those who moulded the concept into an agreed set of sampling protocols during the early workshops of the ASEAN-Australia Living Coastal Resources Project in 1984. The efforts of this group provided a framework for data collection which has been applied throughout the ASEAN region and has been acknowledged internationally with the adoption of these protocols for global studies.

Since the manual was first published in 1994, it has been widely used to survey and monitor coastal resources. This edition includes improvements to the text, which incorporate feedback from those who are using the methods in the field. It also includes more recent literature.

The database in the first edition specifically used dBase™ structures. While the overall structure of the database is still valid, recent advances in database software are reflected in the move to a more generic structure for the database. In addition, the database has been revised to better describe the methods presented in the text. It should be noted, that while the recommended structure will facilitate the transfer of data between research groups, the database can also be expanded to accommodate specific data needs of individual research groups.

As technologies advance and equipment becomes less expensive and more accessible, new methods can expand on those presented in the earlier edition. This edition, includes a section describing video transects (Appendix II). If a video camera and the ancillary equipment is available and well-supported by service operators, the technology provides a useful method to complement or replace the Line Intercept Transects.

Acknowledgements

In preparing this manual there are many who deserve thanks. Clearly a large part of this acknowledgment goes to many of our colleagues working at the Australian Institute of Marine Science (AIMS) and in the ASEAN region. Dr Suraphol Sudara provides inspiration and energy to many who are directly and indirectly involved in the assessment and management of the coastal zone in the ASEAN region. This manual is in itself recognition of his influence and enthusiasm.

Specifically, in relation to the preparation of this publication, thanks go to Marietta Eden for the illustrations, and Terry Done, Lyndon De Vantier, Katarina Fabricius, Emre Turak and J.E.N. Veron for the colour photographs.

Very special thanks goes to Maylene Loo (National University of Singapore) who provided much valuable input to this edition, and to the following:

❏ **Coral Reefs** - Debbie Bass (Australian Institute of Marine Science) and Russell Babcock (University of Auckland, New Zealand).

❏ **Mangrove Ecosystems** - Barry Clough (Australian Institute of Marine Science), and Ong Jin Eong and Gong Wooi Khoon (Universiti Sains Malaysia).

❏ **Soft-bottom Communities** - Peter Arnold (Museum of Tropical Queensland, Australia) and Helen Yap (University of the Philippines).

❏ **Seagrass Communities** - Warren Lee Long (Queensland Department of Primary Industries, Australia).

❏ **Coastal Fisheries** - A. Sasekumar (University of Malaya).

INTRODUCTION

This survey manual has been developed to facilitate assessment of the status of coral reefs, mangrove forests, seagrass beds and soft-bottom communities and their associated flora and fauna in a repeatable and relatively inexpensive manner. The methods describe a minimum standard which will provide baseline data that can be expanded to suit more specific needs of the sampling. Data collected using these methods provide reliable information on the current status of tropical coastal ecosystems and allows comparisons over regional and global scales.

In order to detect changes in the status of coastal resources, sampling must be undertaken regularly over extended periods of time. Similarly, sampling conducted in many sites, over a variety of spatial scales, will permit comparisons within and between regions and allow the assessment of "regional" status and the scale of changes detected in the ecosystems resources.

Importance of coastal ecosystems: Tropical coastal ecosystems are particularly important for millions of people around the world as they provide both subsistence and cash-crop fisheries and other benefits, such as wood from mangrove forests. These ecosystems also contain a high biodiversity of animals and plants and form the basis for valuable tourism industries, with potential for ecotourism activities and discovery of new biochemical products.

The present outlook for many of these valuable resources is of great concern. Their status is declining through over-exploitation, pollution and conversion to other uses. The current rates of use of coastal resources are unsustainable. More than 25% of all production occurring within ocean upwellings and tropical marine shelf areas is consumed by humans, and overfishing has affected coral reef areas in at least 73% of countries bordering these ecosystems (World Resources Institute 1996). It is estimated than half of the world's mangrove forest resources have already been destroyed (World Resources Institute 1996) and as much as 70% of the world's coral reefs will be functionally lost within 40 years, unless effective management is implemented (Wilkinson 1993). In addition to direct and inadvertent stresses caused by human use, another threat looms over these resources through changes in global climate. Rising sea levels, increases in temperatures, and a possible increase in the incidence of storms could add to the serious stresses already evident through human use. An accurate and objective assessment of the true status of coastal resources is not possible, because of a serious lack of long-term monitoring data (Pearson 1981, D'Elia *et al.* 1991, Robertson 1992). The aim of this manual is to make such assessment possible through the repeated use of the methods outlined and analyses of the resulting data.

Surveying coastal resource status: Surveys of coastal resources provide information on the distribution and abundance of the animal and plant communities. The information obtained can be used to determine the status of that ecosystem and for comparisons at regional or global scales.

Before commencing sampling, it is important to recognise that there is considerable natural variation within marine ecosystems, both spatially and temporally. Any sampling program will be more effective if you have a basic understanding of the biology of the animals and plants: do they change behaviour or migrate during the day/night cycle; do tides have a major influence on behaviour; and what happens when they are reproducing? For example, fish may move in and out of the survey area depending on the state of the tide, hence, sampling at different times during the tidal cycle may affect the estimate of the fish abundance at the sample site. Temporal variability is also an important factor when undertaking surveys of populations which have short generation times, since their abundance can change considerably in a few months. Sampling at different times (e.g. January and March) in successive years may indicate a natural change in species numbers in a soft-bottom community, but without knowledge of the generation time of the species this could be interpreted as a decline in abundance of that species at the sampling site. On the other hand, surveys of the large, structural components of a community, such as corals and mangrove trees, may show less short-term variation, than more mobile organisms.

Knowledge of the biology of the animals and plants being surveyed will help the researcher understand the differences observed in an ecosystem at different sampling scales. In order to accurately describe the communities in an ecosystem, survey programs should be designed to minimise differences caused by the sampling itself (see Chapter 7). It is necessary to conduct regular monitoring to detect changes and suggest causes of change in a resource over time.

Monitoring change: The principal coastal resources in the tropics - coral reefs, mangrove forests, seagrass beds and soft sediment communities - all show considerable natural variability in time, as well as space. Predictable environmental changes, such as tidal cycles and seasonality, account for some of this variability. However, coastal ecosystems also undergo considerable changes because of natural disturbance. Unpredictable events like cyclonic storms, or biological interactions like outbreaks of disease or predators (e.g. the crown-of-thorns starfish), can cause dramatic changes in the community structure of an ecosystem. If the major structural features such as corals, mangrove trees or seagrass bed are damaged, the effects may persist for many years.

Human activities may also result in impacts on coastal ecosystems. In order to identify human-induced (anthropogenic) changes, it is essential to distinguish them from natural variations. Human impacts can be managed, whereas attempts at controlling natural changes may be futile or undesirable. The effects of disturbances like storms, or clear felling of mangroves, or some forms of pollution, have immediate impacts on the ecosystem. However, other impacts (both natural and human-induced) may be cummulative, resulting in gradual changes to an ecosystem e.g. climate change and contaminants such as pesticides.

A well-designed monitoring program can be used to distinguish between natural and human-induced variability so that management strategies can be developed and tested.

Developing a monitoring program: The first action in developing a long-term monitoring programme is to state the objectives. This will guide the selection of methods, sites and times of sampling. It is important to select sites for monitoring that are representative of the system as a whole. Accessibilty of sites, while an important consideration, should not be the primary reason for site selection - the closest site may not be the best. Similarly, 'pristine' sites will provide useful reference ('control') information but only if there are corresponding data from impacted sites. All site selection should be made following a preliminary overview of the area or through the use of a 'Pilot' program (see Chapter 7), especially if the purpose is to answer local questions. The number of sites chosen for monitoring will necessarily be a balance between collecting the maximum amount of information and the amount of resources and time available. The monitoring program should be designed around a series of sites that can be visited on a regular basis, e.g. every year. Chapter 7 considers the steps necessary to develop a sound monitoring program.

The effectiveness of surveying and monitoring can be enhanced if remote sensing data are available. Analysis of digital images provides useful information for site selection. For coastal vegetation sites (mangroves and seagrass), it is possible to define the vegetation composition and extent. Changes in the species composition and distribution can then be monitored over time. The ASEAN-Australia Living Coastal Resources project has effectively integrated the Australian remote sensing package microBRIAN with on-ground surveys to estimate the area covered by mangrove forests and seagrass beds and assess their species content and condition. Coral reef satellite surveys are limited to reef flats, because it is difficult to assess the deeper parts through the water.

A well-designed database is an essential component of long-term monitoring (see Chapter 8), because large amounts of data must be efficiently stored for later analysis and comparison. The data must be entered soon after collection and immediately checked for integrity and consistency. This will ensure early detection of errors which might otherwise jeopardise the usefulness of the whole database. The database should be tested early in the project to ensure that the data can be reliably retrieved for analysis. A valuable procedure is to extract data from the first set entered and apply a range of potential analyses. Careful design of the database will ensure that data can be entered quickly, accurately and consistently and that the effort spent in the field is not wasted. A suggested database structure has been included at the end of each chapter. This structure was proved useful in the ASEAN-Australia Living Coastal Resources project which has used the data to provide regional scale information of coastal resources in the ASEAN region (Wilkinson *et al.* 1994).

Conclusion: The establishment of a monitoring program will permit the objective assessment of coastal resources. The use of comparable and consistent methods will enable comparisons to be made over large spatial and temporal scales in order to detect large-scale environmental changes, such as global climate change. The methods in this survey manual have been developed and extensively tested by ASEAN and Australian scientists in both locations. They should be applicable in all regions, possibly with minor modifications to account for local conditions.

References

D'Elia, C. F., R. W. Buddemeier and S. V. Smith (1991). A workshop on coral bleaching, coral reef ecosystems and global change: report of proceedings. Maryland Sea Grant College Publication no. UM-SG-TS-91-03, University of Maryland, College Park. 49pp.

Pearson, R.G. (1981). Recovery and recolonisation of coral reefs. Marine Ecology Progress Series, **4**: 105-122.

Robertson, A.I. (1992). Concluding remarks: research and mangrove conservation. pp. 327-329. In: A.I. Robertson and D.M. Alongi (editors) "Tropical Mangrove Ecosystems". American Geophysical Union, Washington, D.C. (Coastal and Estuarine Studies No. 41). 329pp.

Wilkinson, C. R. (1993). Coral reefs of the world are facing widespread devastation: can we prevent this through sustainable management practices? Proceedings 7th International Coral Reef Symposium, Guam. Vol. **1**: 11-21.

Wilkinson, C.R., S. Sudara and L.M. Chou (editors) (1994). Proceedings Third ASEAN-AustraliaSymposium on Living Coastal Resources, Volume 1, Status Reviews. Australian Institute of Marine Science. 454pp.

World Resources Institute (1996). "World Resources 1996-97. A Report by The World Resources Institute, the United Nations Environment Programme, the United Nations Development Programme and the World Bank". 384 pp. Available on-line at http://www.wri.org

CHAPTER **CORAL**
2 **REEFS**

General Introduction

Coral reefs are complex ecosystems with high biological diversity that occur in shallow waters throughout the tropics. The reefs support productive fisheries which provide an essential source of protein. Their proximity to the coast exposes coral reefs not only to subsistence pressures but also to other human induced (anthropogenic) stresses such as pollution (industrial, chemical and sewage) and sedimentation (land clearing, reclamation, mining). Given the potential economic impact of continued degradation of the world's coral reefs, suitable monitoring programs are required to detect any degeneration and to facilitate the development of effective management plans to ensure the future viability of these resources.

Despite the complexity and high biological diversity of these ecosystems they are not stable, indeed they are sensitive to disturbance and are highly variable. Causes of natural variability range from obvious disturbances, such as cyclones or typhoons, to less obvious factors such as variability in the levels of recruitment. Long-term quantitative studies of coral reefs are necessary to distinguish human impacts on reefs from natural variability in community structure.

In fisheries, much of the natural variation is associated with recruitment of young fish to the exploitable stock. Variability in recruitment has been found to be a major source of uncertainty in fisheries management. Because of this, effective, long-term management of coral reef ecosystems must include studies of recruitment processes. While studies of recruitment in commercial fisheries are limited by the ability to detect the rate at which new individuals enter exploited populations, in coral reef ecosystems it is possible to detect recruits soon after settlement.

This chapter deals with the description of coral and coral reef fish populations. The methods presented are selected because they use inexpensive, accessible equipment. Most methods require minimal expertise to provide useful data for the description of reef communities, and monitoring for management (although expertise in the identification of fish species is required for visual census). The importance of *Acropora* species are reflected in the methods. This group are the predominant reef-building corals of the Indo-Pacific in terms of number of species and contribution to coral cover in most reef biotopes and hence the methods have provided an opportunity to give some focus to these species.

Implementation of the methodology described in the manual will provide baseline and temporal data for regional comparisons. This approach is not intended to limit question-driven research which will require the development of appropriate replication and sampling design following pilot studies (see Chapter 7).

In conclusion, it should be understood that there are a variety of more expensive, but useful technologies available which may be utilised in monitoring programs such as underwater video cameras. As the technologies develop video transects are becoming a reliable method for the collection of data describing the distribution and abundance of reef benthic communities. The equipment required is relatively expensive to purchase and maintain, however, where available it can substitute for the Line Intercept Transect Method described in this chapter. Appendix II contains a description of a method for sampling sessile benthos using video.

2.1 Measurement of Ambient Environmental Parameters

Abstract

All surveys of living resources of coral reefs should include environmental parameters which characterise the conditions at the site when the data were collected. The parameters to be included with the survey methods described in this manual have been selected because they are important to the 'health' of the reef and they do not require expensive, sophisticated equipment. The environmental parameters that should be measured are: temperature, salinity, turbidity, light penetration, cloud cover and wind. These parameters, together with data on the benthos and fishes, characterise a particular reef site/zone. The recommended equipment is easily obtained and will provide standardised measures in all countries.

Logistics

Equipment

❏ Mercury thermometer enclosed in a protective casing - used to measure temperature with an accuracy of ±0.5 degrees Celsius.

❏ Refractometer - used to determine salinity (Fig. 2.1).

❏ 10 millilitre plastic vials/bottles (tight-sealing) - used to collect water samples for salinity measurements.

❏ Secchi disc - used to determine turbidity in the study area. The disc is 30 centimetres in diameter and divided into 4 quarters alternating black and white in colour (Fig. 2.2).

❏ A portable light meter - used to determine the turbidity and light penetration of water in the study area (Fig. 2.3). A model widely used for surveys conducted as part of the ASEAN-Australia project is the LI-COR® 1000 quantum meter with an underwater quantum sensor.

Maintenance

❏ Rinse all equipment with freshwater after use.

❏ Pay special attention to the photocell of the light meter to ensure that saltwater does not splash onto the main console. Care should also be taken to avoid scratching the surface of the cell.

❏ The glass cell and cover of the refractometer should be rinsed carefully after use (with distilled water if possible) and then wiped dry with tissue paper.

❏ Store the refractometer in its protective box/bag when not in use.

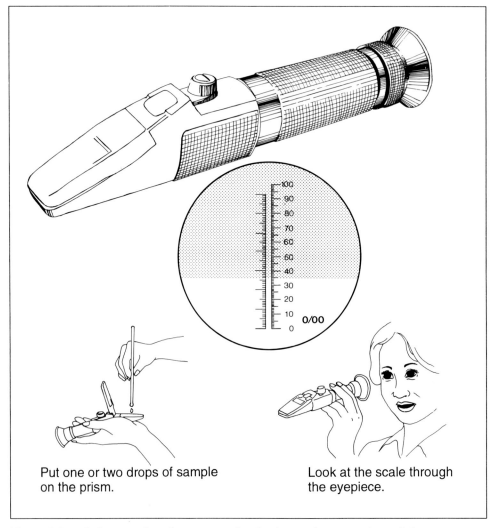

Put one or two drops of sample on the prism.

Look at the scale through the eyepiece.

Figure 2.1   A diagram of a refractometer showing its use for measuring salinity.

General procedure

Temperature
❑ Take the readings before commencing surveys.

❑ Read the thermometer in the water just below the surface (30 centimetres) and at the depth of the transects ('transect depth').

❑ When thermoclines are encountered take a series of measurements, recording the depth and the temperature.

Salinity

❏ Obtain water samples 30 centimetres below the surface and at 'transect depth' using small plastic vials. These samples are taken back to the shore for measurement using a refractometer. Put a small sample of water under the cover of the refractometer. Hold the cover down, and looking through the eyepiece, face the instrument to the light so that the salinity can be read (Fig. 2.1).

❏ A series of salinity measurements should be made at sites near freshwater discharge to determine the extent of any gradient in salinity caused by the freshwater input.

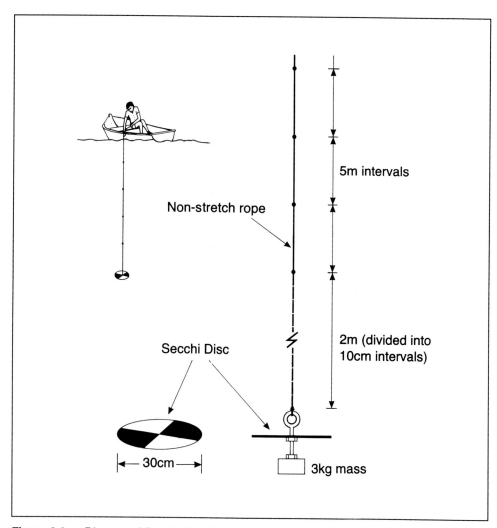

Figure 2.2. Diagram of Secchi disc showing its use.

Turbidity

❏ Use the Secchi disc to measure vertical visibility in deeper water. The disc is attached to a weighted rope which is marked at intervals along its length. Lower the disc until you can no longer see it, then pull it slowly back toward the surface until it is just visible. Record the distance to the disc from the marks on the rope (Fig. 2.2).

❏ Make the measurements with the Secchi disc on a clear day, within 2 hours before or after noon. If cloud cover does not allow measurement, then the cloud should be recorded in oktas.

❏ A light meter should be used to determine the amount of light penetration (at the depth of the transect) in situations when the Secchi disc is not appropriate, i.e. the water is shallow or very clear. An underwater sensor is taken to the transect depth and the light level is read from the meter, which is in the boat (Fig. 2.3).

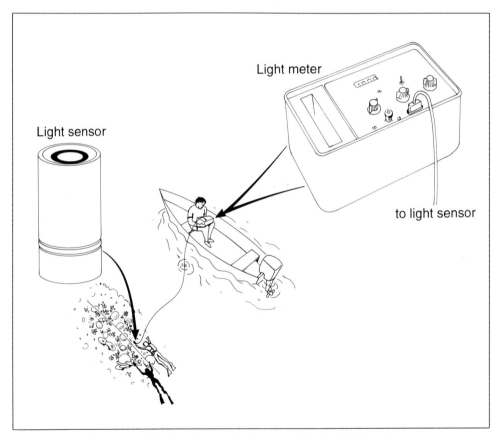

Figure 2.3   The sensor is held at the required depth while the light level measurements are recorded from the meter on the boat.

Coral Reefs

Cloud Cover

❏ The amount of cloud is estimated according to the number of eighths of sky (celestial dome) that is covered by cloud (Fig. 2.4). The unit of measure is the okta.

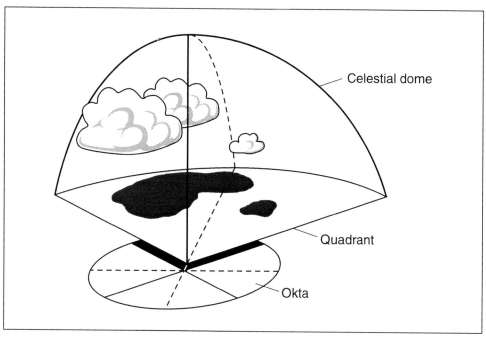

Figure 2.4   Estimation of cloud cover using oktas.

❏ Observation should be made from a position where the entire sky can be seen. Commence by subdividing the sky into quadrants (1 quadrant = 2 oktas), and estimate the amount of cloud in each quadrant.

❏ Combine the quadrant estimates to give the total amount. If the sky is completely free of cloud it is recorded as "0". If there is only a small amount of cloud it is recorded as "1". See Table 2.1 for cloud categories.

Wind and Sea State

❏ Wind and sea state are described in the "Beaufort Wind Scale and Sea Disturbance Table". A modified extract, using 5 categories, is presented in Table 2.2.

Table 2.1 Categories used to record cloud cover. See Figure 2.4 for a description of oktas.

Category	Amount of Cloud
0	cloudless
1	1 okta or less, but > 0
2	2 oktas
3	3 oktas
4	4 oktas
5	5 oktas
6	6 oktas
7	7 oktas
8	8 oktas

Table 2.2 Five categories used to describe wind and sea state criteria (modified from the Beaufort scale).

Wind Force	Wind (knots)	Sea State	Wind	Sea Criteria
1	0 - 5	calm	light air	mirror-like, to small ripples
2	6 - 10	smooth	gentle breeze	large wavelets, crests begin to break
3	11 - 15	slight	moderate breeze	small waves becoming longer
4	16 - 20	moderate	fresh breeze	many white caps forming
5	21 - 25	rough	strong breeze	large waves, extensive white caps

Data recording

❑ Ambient environmental parameters are measured for each set of manta tows and for each set of transects, quadrats etc. The environmental parameters measured in conjunction with each of these survey methods may differ.

Data processing

❏ At the end of each day the data should be entered into the database using the structure described at the end of this chapter (Section 2.9).

❏ The sample table (XXCRSAMP) contains a description of the data collected in each sample and indicates the type of data collected in that sample. Ambient data are denoted by a DATA_TYPE of "A".

❏ Every sample taken has a unique sample identifier (SAMPLE_ID).

❏ The ambient data are entered into the data table (XXCRADAT) using the sample identification allocated in the sample table.

☞ *While the ambient environmental parameters are collected in conjunction with survey methodologies, such as manta tow, the ambient table is not linked to that data in the relational design. Ambient data has its own sample_id and is connected to the survey data (e.g. manta tow) by common values for location, reef name, date, latitude and longitude.*

☞ *The database does not cater for multiple temperature readings which may be taken at a thermocline. If temperature is sampled by taking multiple readings at multiple depths then design a database to accomodate this information.*

❏ **Always check and verify data after entry.**

❏ Always backup data regularly.

Suggested reading

UNEP/IAEA/IOC 1991. Standard chemical methods for marine environmental monitoring. Reference Methods for Marine Pollution Studies No. 50. UNEP, Nairobi.

Coral Reefs

2.2 Manta Tow Survey

Abstract

The manta tow technique is used to assess broad changes in the benthic communities of coral reefs where the unit of interest is often an entire reef, or large portion thereof. It enables visual assessment of large areas of reef within a short time and is highly recommended for determining the effects of large-scale disturbances such as those caused by cyclonic storms, coral bleaching and outbreaks of *Acanthaster* (crown-of-thorns starfish). The technique is also useful for selecting sites that are representative of large areas of reef.

The technique involves towing an observer, using a rope and manta board, behind a small boat powered by an outboard motor. Tows are carried out at a constant speed around the perimeter of a reef and are broken into units of 2 minutes duration. During each 2-minute tow, observations are made on several variables (e.g. percent cover of live coral, dead coral and soft coral). These are recorded onto data sheets as categories. Additional information may be collected, dependent on the survey objectives, e.g. percent cover of sand and rubble, and numbers of *Acanthaster*, *Diadema* or Tridacnid clams. However, Fernandes (1989), cautions against recording data on too many variables, and the technique is not recommended for fish counts.

The method described in this manual is not only useful for assessing the distribution and abundance of corals, but is also widely used for the study of *Acanthaster*. Details of the *Acanthaster* assessment have been included because of the extensive destruction to many reefs in the Indo-Pacific which has been caused by these starfish. The technique may also be used to assess other organisms of particular interest to a survey region. However, it should be noted that estimates of the accuracy and precision of the technique have only been made in relation to coral cover and *Acanthaster* (Fernandes 1989, 1990; Fernandes *et al.* 1990, 1993; Kenchington and Morton 1976; Miller and De'ath 1996; Miller and Muller in press; Moran and De'ath 1992).

Background

In general, the manta tow technique has been used to investigate issues at a broad level (Kenchington 1978). Since Chesher's study (1969) to assess the effects of *Acanthaster* on coral reefs in Micronesia, similar surveys have been conducted on reefs within the Red Sea (Roads and Ormond 1971) and the Great Barrier Reef (GBR) (Endean and Stablum 1973; Moran *et al.* 1988). The technique has also been used for more general, broadscale surveys of coral reef systems (Done *et al.* 1982; Kenchington 1984).

While manta tow techniques have been used extensively since the early 1970's, the details of the method have varied between the different studies (Kenchington 1975; Kenchington and Morton 1976; Done *et al*. 1982; Nash and Zell 1982; Kenchington 1984). Work by Moran *et al*. (1988, 1989) to assess the broadscale distribution and abundance of *Acanthaster* and their effect on the GBR has greatly refined the technique.

More recently, studies have focussed on the precision of the manta tow technique for estimating coral cover and *Acanthaster* abundance (Fernandes 1989, 1990; Fernandes *et al*. 1990, 1993; Moran and De'ath 1992). These studies have shown the technique to be particularly useful for assessing broad changes in the distribution and abundance of coral cover (especially live coral) and *Acanthaster*. For example, a typical manta tow survey (of approximately 50-60 tows) is capable of detecting a 20% change in the abundance of an outbreaking population of *Acanthaster* (Moran and De'ath 1992). The studies also show that, despite underestimating the number of *Acanthaster*, manta tow counts can be calibrated to predict estimates obtained from SCUBA swim surveys. Over the same sized area the latter are more accurate, however, the manta tow technique surveys a far greater area than that possible by SCUBA swims. Hence, the combined information from a relatively large number of tows can give more accurate estimates of abundance when the spatial distribution of the target organism is highly variable (e.g. *Acanthaster*), and the unit of interest is the whole reef.

Advantages

❑ Large areas of a reef can be surveyed in a relatively short time. This reduces the possibility of overlooking population changes or disturbances which can be variable in space and time (e.g. dynamite fishing, *Acanthaster*, bleaching, storm damage).

❑ It is relatively simple to perform after some training.

❑ It does not use expensive or specialised equipment which would require the observer to have special qualifications (e.g. SCUBA).

❑ It can be performed in remote locations with minimal support.

❑ The observer can cover great distances with little fatigue.

Disadvantages

❑ The survey may be conducted over inappropriate sections of the reef (e.g. large areas of sand or deep water) because the tow path is controlled by the driver who views the reef from above the water.

❑ If the animals are not obvious they may be overlooked.

❑ The observer may have too much information to remember, particularly if many variables are being recorded.

Coral Reefs

❏ The method is not suitable for areas with poor visibility (less than 6 metres).

Logistics

Personnel

❏ Manta tow surveys are conducted by teams of one or more pairs of trained personnel. The duties of the team are divided between the boat driver and the observer. See notes in the "Standardisation" section for details of training.

❏ Each series of manta tows is coordinated by a leader who is responsible for the safety of personnel and for ensuring that the technique is conducted in a standardised way, and for determining when conditions are appropriate for surveying.

Equipment

❏ A small boat with an outboard motor and safety equipment is used for towing observers. The boat should be fitted with a towing bridle.

❏ A 17 metre tow rope connects the manta board to the boat (Figs. 2.5 and 2.6). The rope should be braided and approximately 10 mm in diameter (polyethylene ski-rope is recommended). Two buoys are placed on the rope, one at 6 metres from the manta board, and the other at 12 metres. These buoys allow the observer to estimate visibility in a standard manner.

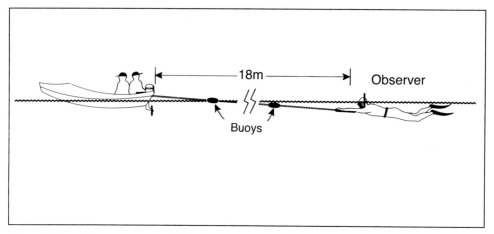

Figure 2.5   The manta tow technique showing the observer being towed along the surface of the water behind a small boat.

❏ The dimensions of the manta board (Fig. 2.6) are 40 x 60 x 2 cm (length x breadth x thickness). It is recommended that the board be made from marine ply and painted white. Two indented handgrips are positioned towards each corner of the front of the board. A single handhold is located centrally at the back of the board.

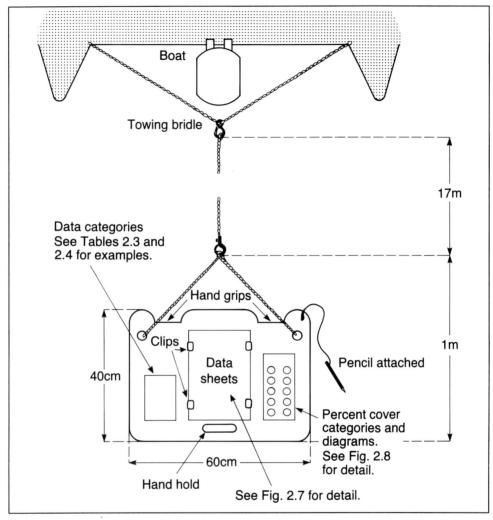

Figure 2.6   Detail of the manta board and associated equipment. Summaries of the categories are attached to the board for easy reference by the observer.

❑ A data sheet (A4 underwater paper is recommended) is held in position within a recess on the centre of the board. The data sheets should be preprinted to assist the observer record a set of biological variables and other significant observations (Fig. 2.7).

❑ Schematic representations of coral cover categories (Fig. 2.8) are attached to the board for observer reference. Any other list which may assist the observer may also be attached, e.g. if survey will include *Acanthaster*, then categories used to record feeding scars and *Acanthaster* size (Tables 2.3 and 2.4) should be provided.

MANTA TOW SURVEY

Location .... Sample ID ....

Reef name .... Reef zone .... Latitude ....

Date .... Time .... Wind .... Cloud .... Longitude ....

Remarks .... Collector ....

Tow No.	Coral Cover			Vis.	COT				Notes
	Live	Dead	Soft		No.	Scars	Size		
1									
2									
3									
4									
5									
6									
7									
8									
9									
10									
11									
12									
13									
14									
15									
16									
17									
18									
19									
20									
21									
22									
23									
24									
25									
26									
27									

Figure 2.7 Example of a printed sheet used by observers to record data. The column headed "Notes" is used for general comments (to record items of interest, e.g. a large concentration of *Porites* colonies). The columns headed "COT" are only required when crown-of-thorns starfish (*Acanthaster*) are to be surveyed. The blank column can be used for additional variables.

Coral Reefs

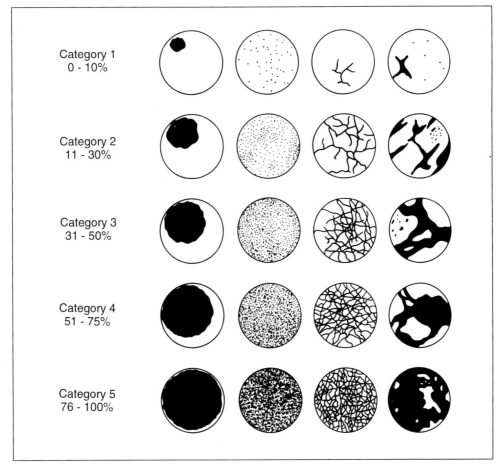

Figure 2.8 Schematic representations of percent cover. These categories can be used to estimate cover of selected benthic variables e.g. live and dead coral, soft coral and sand/rubble (after Dahl 1981).

❑ A pencil(s) is attached with light twine to the board.

❑ The observer wears snorkelling equipment (mask, snorkel and fins) and preferably a full-length dive suit or nylon ('stinger') suit.

❑ The driver should be protected from the sun, and should have the following equipment in the boat:

　》 Waterproof watch for timing the duration of tows.

　》 An image of the reef sealed in plastic and attached with rubber bands to a plastic board. An aerial photograph of the reef is recommended (Fig. 2.9), however, a map or photocopy can be substituted if this is not available.

　》 A waterproof pen for marking the position of the tows.

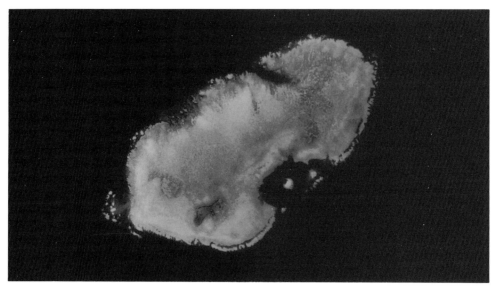

Figure 2.9   An aerial photograph of the reef is used by the driver to record the location of the manta tows.

Site selection

❏ Whole (unbroken) reef perimeters are surveyed where possible. Shoals and ill-defined areas of reef, separated by deeper water, are not usually surveyed.

❏ Tows are begun from an easily identifiable point on the reef. This is particularly important when resurvey of the reef is intended. A GPS (Global Positioning System), if available, can be very useful for relocating the starting point of a series of tows.

❏ For long sections of coastline with fringing reefs, allocate a section of the length as a reef, e.g. headland to headland.

❏ If there are 2 teams conducting the survey, the teams should start from the same point and then proceed in opposite directions. Tows are continued until the boats meet again. In situations where the reef is not circular, teams should start at opposite ends of the reef and proceed toward one another, repeating the tows until the boats meet. Hence, each reef will consist of a set of consecutive tows which will vary in number according to the size of the reef to be surveyed.

❏ If it is not possible to complete a survey in a single set of consecutive tows, marker buoys are left to denote where the next set of tows will begin.

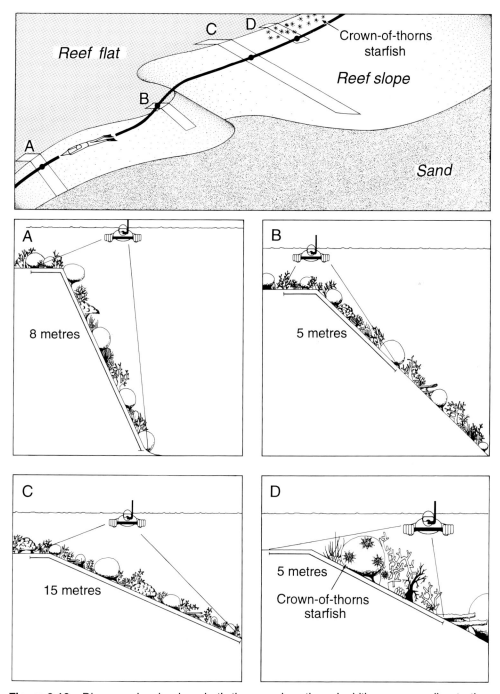

Figure 2.10   Diagram showing how both the search path and width vary according to the angle of the slope, the position of the observer relative to the perimeter and the presence of starfish (taken from Moran and De'ath 1992). The solid line indicates the tow path and the rectangular boxes indicate the search path and width.

General procedure

❏ The survey of the reef is broken into manta tows of 2 minutes duration. At the end of each 2-minute tow, the boat is stopped to allow the observer to record the data on the printed sheet attached to the manta board. At this time, the driver marks the tow number and position of the boat on the aerial photograph. When the observer is ready to continue, he/she signals the driver to start another 2-minute tow. This procedure is repeated until the entire perimeter, or length, of the reef has been surveyed.

❏ The observer is towed parallel to the reef crest so that the maximum amount of slope can be seen, i.e. the tow path should be close to the crest. The tow speed should be constant. During calm weather the speed should be between 3 to 5 km per hour (1 to 1.5 knots, or the equivalent to a slow walk). Factors such as currents and sea conditions may vary the tow speed.

❏ Since the boat driver may not be able to position the boat on an ideal tow path, the observer may have to vary the search relative to their position on the reef slope (Fig. 2.10). The width of search is variable, but a scan of a 10 to 12 metre strip of the reef is recommended. The search path and width will also vary according to visibility, reef gradient, distance from the substratum, and the distribution and density of the organisms being counted.

❏ The direction for surveying the reef is determined by factors such as wind, currents and angle of sun. When weather conditions allow, it is advised to standardise the direction in which tows are conducted (e.g. clockwise on a circular reef; north to south, or east to west, along a length of fringing reef) so that comparison of resurveyed reefs requires less correction.

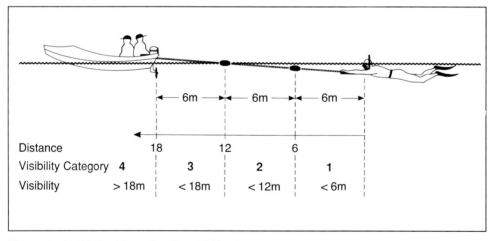

Figure 2.11 Method for estimating visibility during manta tow survey. Categories for recording data are indicated.

Figure 2.12 Hand signals used between observers and drivers.

Coral Reefs

❑ Observations should be discontinued where visibility is less than 6 metres (category 1). This distance is determined using the buoys located along the tow rope (Fig. 2.11). If the back of the boat can be seen, the visibility is judged to be greater than 18 metres.

❑ Standard hand signals should be used between the observer and the driver to allow effective communication (Fig. 2.12). For instance, observers should signal the driver to move closer to the reef when being towed over deep water.

❑ The maximum number of consecutive tows conducted by an observer is normally 15. Once a series of 15 tows have been completed, the observer and the driver (or a fresh observer) exchange roles. During this changeover a debriefing should occur. This includes discussion about general conditions, state of the reef, number of *Acanthaster*, and anything else of note seen by the observer during the tows.

❑ Observations are generally made from the surface. Manta towing below the surface may be necessary when the substratum is not clearly visible or closer inspection is required. Prolonged diving should be avoided.

Data recording

❑ Before the observer enters the water ambient or environmental variables should be recorded at the top of the data sheet (Fig. 2.7). See Section 2.1 for a description of the variables measured.

❑ At the beginning of a series of tows, the boat driver should mark the starting point (denoted as **zero**) on an aerial photograph and record the direction of the tows. The starting position should be near a prominent feature (Fig. 2.13).

❑ At the end of each 2-minute tow:

» The observer records the percent cover of live and dead coral, and soft corals (Fig. 2.8). Other features such as recent storm damage, *Acanthaster*, clams etc. can be included in the "others" column.

» The boat driver marks, on the aerial photograph the boat position at the end of each tow, taking note of any prominent features. The starting position is marked as zero. The end of the first tow is then marked by 1, the end of the second tow marked by 2, and so on, until the survey is complete (Fig. 2.13). If unable to mark every tow, keep count and mark when your position is known.

❑ Visibility should be recorded for every tow, or whenever a change is observed (Fernandes 1989). It is estimated using buoys along the tow rope and is recorded as one of 4 categories (Fig. 2.11).

❑ It must be emphasised that the percent cover of live and dead coral are the minimum requirements for the manta tow survey data.

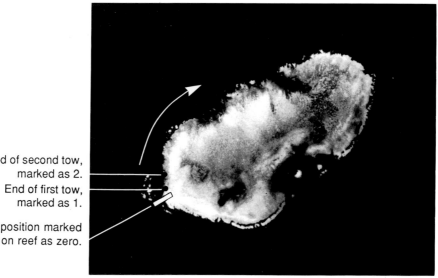

Coral Reefs

End of second tow,
marked as 2.
End of first tow,
marked as 1.

Starting position marked
on reef as zero.

Figure 2.13 The boat driver marks, on the aerial photograph, the direction of tows, the starting position and the position at the end of each tow.

❏ Data describing the distribution and abundance of *Acanthaster* (crown-of-thorns starfish) can also be recorded using the manta tow technique. Where surveys are to include estimates of *Acanthaster* abundance, the observer should use the data categories that have been tested in studies of the starfish on the Great Barrier Reef to allow comparisons of data between researchers. The variables recorded include:

> » The number of feeding scars (see Table 2.3).

> » The number of *Acanthaster* - observations are given as integer values, or where values are greater than this, as 100.

> » The average size of the *Acanthaster* (see Table 2.4).

❏ Other variables may be included which are specific to the survey aims (e.g. *Diadema* or clams), but accuracy and precision of the counts should be verified.

Table 2.3 Categories used to record *Acanthaster* feeding scars.

Category	Number of Scars
Absent (**A**)	0
Present (**P**)	1 - 10
Common (**C**)	> 10

Table 2.4 Categories used to record the size of *Acanthaster* starfish.

Category	Average Size
Small	1 - 15 cm
Large	> 15 cm

Standardisation

❏ All personnel should be trained in the manta tow method. This is done by repeatedly towing observers over the same area of a reef until all team members have developed consistency in all aspects of the methodology (e.g. tow speed, observer recording). Retraining in the field should be conducted regularly (twice a year) (Miller and Muller in press) and may be supplemented by laboratory-based training using video footage and colour transparencies (slides). A useful piece of equipment for training is a manta board that can accommodate more than one observer (Miller and De'ath 1996).

❏ The variability in recording between observers should be checked at the beginning of each survey trip by towing each observer over the same section of reef and comparing the data collected. Surveys of this section of reef should be repeated until comparable data are recorded by all observers. It is particularly important to test inexperienced observers against experienced team members.

❏ The minimum requirements must always be met to ensure that the exchange of data is possible.

Data processing

❏ The starting point for each survey should be checked and tow numbering corrected so that each consecutive tow follows the previous one in a **clockwise** direction around the reef perimeter. For fringing reefs, the team must set their sampling protocol (e.g. east to west), and then follow that protocol for all data collected for that reef. The standardisation of starting point and tow direction is essential for temporal comparison of data collected during the manta tows. Correction of data ensures that the same sections of reef can be identified from resurvey datasets. Examples of the types of corrections that may be required are given in the worked example at the end of this section.

❏ At the end of each day the data should be corrected and then entered into the database using the structure described at the end of this chapter (Section 2.9).

❏ Information about the sample is entered into the sample table (XXCRSAMP) and a unique sample identifier (SAMPLE_ID) is allocated. The type of data collected in the sample is described by the DATA_TYPE field, which for manta tow data is denoted by the letter "M".

❏ The manta tow data are entered into the data table (XXCRMDAT) using the sample identification allocated in the sample table. The manta table has one row, or record, for each 2-minute tow (TOW_NO). Hence, the set of tows which make up the reef perimeter have the same SAMPLE_ID.

❏ An entry is made into the sample table (XXCRSAMP) to describe the ambient data collected in conjunction with the manta tow survey, i.e. DATA_TYPE is "A". The ambient data are entered into the ambient table (XXCRADAT) using the sample identification allocated in the sample table.

☞ *The manta tow data and ambient data will have different sample identification numbers but are connected through common values for fields in the sample table e.g. location, reef name, date, latitude and longitude.*

❏ A diagram of the survey area with the starting point of the survey, and the position, clearly marked, of the end of each tow should be stored with the raw data for future reference.

❏ The distance covered by a 2-minute tow will vary with tow speed and currents. Therefore, comparisons between surveys are only approximate. Resurveyed reefs can be compared in sections (groups of tows) if accurate records are kept on the location of tows against prominent features on the reef.

❏ **Always check and verify data after entry.**

❏ Always backup data regularly.

Analysis

❏ The database file allows the retrieval of information about general conditions of the reef slope in relation to percent cover of live coral, dead coral and soft coral. Information on the conditions of the reef slope in relation to different locations of the reef is readily obtained when cross-referenced with the map showing the position of individual tows (e.g. Bass *et al.* 1989; Bainbridge *et al.* 1994).

❏ Median values of biological variables give an indication of the state of the whole reef (see summary sheet in the worked example). These values are readily calculated using statistical software packages.

❏ If estimates of abundance are required for organisms other than those included in this handbook (e.g. *Tridacna*), then detailed analysis of data will be required to measure the precision of the technique for that organism.

Worked example

❏ Resurvey of reefs is an essential part of any monitoring program. It is therefore important that data entry of manta tow information follows a strict protocol.

❏ All tow data should be entered from a fixed starting point, following a set direction (clockwise) along the reef.

❏ Store an outline of the reef with the data, marking the starting point, tow direction and tow numbers for each set of data. This will allow the identification of sections of reef for comparison through time.

❏ If circumstances arise which prevent the collection of data in the preferred format (e.g. weather conditions, availability of more than one team) the data must be corrected before entry into the database.

❏ Examples are given using data collected as part of the crown-of-thorns starfish surveys on the GBR (Bass *et al.* 1989). A variety of sampling situations are presented:

  » Tows conducted clockwise around the reef - no adjustment to data necessary (Fig. 2.14).

  » Tows conducted anticlockwise around the reef - the data must be adjusted so that the tow data are entered in a clockwise direction (Fig. 2.15).

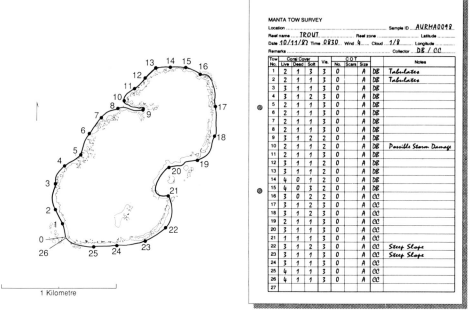

MANTA TOW SURVEY

Location .... Sample ID ...AURMA0098..
Reef name .....TROUT........................... Reef zone .... Latitude ....
Date .10/11/87. Time .0830.. Wind .4..... Cloud ...1/8........ Longitude ....
Remarks .... Collector ..DB / CC..

Tow No.	Coral Cover Live	Dead	Soft	Vis.	COT No.	Scars	Size		Notes
1	2	1	3	3	0		A	DE	Tabulates
2	2	1	1	3	0		A	DE	Tabulates
3	3	1	1	3	0		A	DE	
4	3	1	2	3	0		A	DE	
5	2	1	1	3	0		A	DE	
6	2	1	1	3	0		A	DE	
7	2	1	1	3	0		A	DE	
8	2	1	1	3	0		A	DE	
9	3	1	2	2	0		A	DE	
10	2	1	1	2	0		A	DE	Possible Storm Damage
11	2	1	1	3	0		A	DE	
12	3	1	1	2	0		A	DE	
13	3	1	1	2	0		A	DE	
14	4	0	1	2	0		A	DE	
15	4	0	3	2	0		A	DE	
16	3	0	2	2	0		A	CC	
17	3	1	2	3	0		A	CC	
18	3	1	2	3	0		A	CC	
19	2	1	1	3	0		A	CC	
20	3	1	1	3	0		A	CC	
21	1	1	1	3	0		A	CC	
22	3	1	2	3	0		A	CC	Steep Slope
23	3	1	1	3	0		A	CC	Steep Slope
24	3	1	1	3	0		A	CC	
25	4	1	1	3	0		A	CC	
26	4	1	1	3	0		A	CC	
27									

1 Kilometre

Figure 2.14 Tows conducted in a clockwise direction around the reef. A prominent starting point should be selected which is then the reference point for all resurvey data. Outline of the reef locates the relative position of the tows.

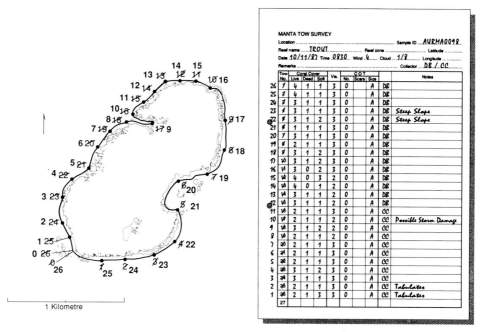

Figure 2.15 Tows were conducted in an anticlockwise direction. Data are then corrected so that the tows are entered into the database in a clockwise direction.

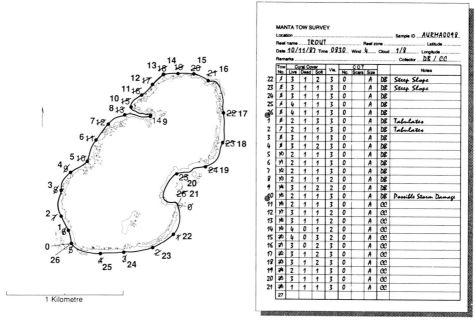

Figure 2.16 Tows were begun from a different starting point to previous survey(s). Data are adjusted so that tow numbers begin from the same position.

» Different starting point from a previous survey - the data must be adjusted so that tows start from the same point. This will ensure that tow data are from the same sections of reef (Fig. 2.16).

» Two boats surveying the same reef - data must be combined to single clockwise dataset around the reef (Fig. 2.17).

❏ Data from a reef may be summarised as median values (see below). In this data Crown-of-Thorns Starfish (COTS) have also been counted.

Reef	Date	SAMPLE_ID	No. tows	Median live coral	Median dead coral	Median soft coral	No. COTS
Trout Trout	10/11/87 .	AURMA0098 .	26 .	3 .	1 .	1 .	0 .
. .	. .	. .	. .	. .	. .	. .	. .

❏ Data summaries allow quick comparison of data collected from reefs. See Figure 2.18 for an example summary sheet.

References

Bainbridge, S.J., D.K. Bass and I.R. Miller (1994). Broadscale surveys of crown-of-thorns starfish on the Great Barrier Reef, 1992 to 1993. Long-term Monitoring of Great Barrier Reef. COTS Report Number 1. Australian Institute of Marine Science, Townsville. 131pp.

Bass, D.K., J. Davidson, D.B. Johnson, B.A. Miller-Smith and C.N. Mundy (1989). Broadscale surveys of crown-of-thorns starfish on the Great Barrier Reef, 1987 to 1988. The Crown-of-thorns Study. Australian Institute of Marine Science, Townsville. 172pp.

Chesher, R.H. (1969). *Acanthaster planci*: impact on Pacific coral reefs; final report to United States Department of the Interior, October 15, 1969. Pittsburgh, Pennsylvania: Westinghouse Electric Corporation Research Laboratories. 151pp.

Dahl, A.L. (1981). Coral reef monitoring handbook. South Pacific Commission Noumea, New Caledonia. 22pp.

Done, T.J., R.A. Kenchington and L.D. Zell (1982). Rapid, large area, reef resource surveys using a manta board. Proceedings of the Fourth International Coral Reef Symposium, Manila, 2: 597-600.

Endean, R. and W. Stablum (1973). A study of some aspects of the crown-of-thorns starfish (*Acanthaster planci*) infestations of reefs of Australia's Great Barrier Reef. Atoll Research Bulletin, 167: 1-62.

A

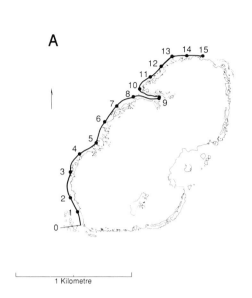

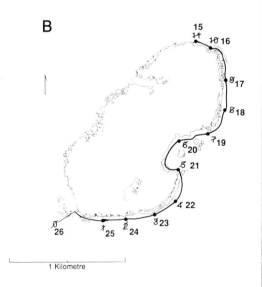

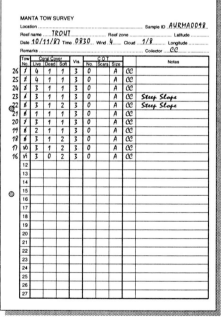

MANTA TOW SURVEY

Location .... Sample ID *AURMA0098*
Reef name ...*TROUT*............................ Reef zone .... Latitude ....
Date *10/11/87* Time *0830* Wind *4* Cloud *1/8* Longitude ....
Remarks .... Collector *DB*

Tow No.	Coral Cover Live	Dead	Soft	Vis.	C.O.T No.	Scars	Size		Notes
1	2	1	3	3	0		A	DB	Tabulates
2	2	1	1	3	0		A	DB	Tabulates
3	3	1	1	3	0		A	DB	
4	3	1	2	3	0		A	DB	
5	2	1	1	3	0		A	DB	
6	2	1	1	3	0		A	DB	
7	2	1	1	3	0		A	DB	
8	2	1	1	2	0		A	DB	
9	3	1	2	2	0		A	DB	
10	2	1	1	2	0		A	DB	Possible Storm Damage
11	2	1	1	3	0		A	DB	
12	3	1	1	2	0		A	DB	
13	3	1	1	2	0		A	DB	
14	4	0	1	2	0		A	DB	
15	4	0	3	2	0		A	DB	
16									
17									
18									
19									
20									
21									
22									
23									
24									
25									
26									
27									

1 Kilometre

B

MANTA TOW SURVEY

Location .... Sample ID *AURMA0098*
Reef name ...*TROUT*............................ Reef zone .... Latitude ....
Date *10/11/87* Time *0830* Wind *4* Cloud *1/8* Longitude ....
Remarks .... Collector *CC*

Tow No.		Coral Cover Live	Dead	Soft	Vis.	C.O.T No.	Scars	Size		Notes
26	1	4	1	1	3	0		A	CC	
25	2	4	1	1	3	0		A	CC	
24	3	3	1	1	3	0		A	CC	
23	4	3	1	1	3	0		A	CC	Steep Slope
22	5	3	1	2	3	0		A	CC	Steep Slope
21	6	1	1	1	3	0		A	CC	
20	7	3	1	1	3	0		A	CC	
19	8	2	1	1	3	0		A	CC	
18	9	3	1	2	3	0		A	CC	
17	10	3	1	2	3	0		A	CC	
16	11	3	0	2	3	0		A	CC	
12										
13										
14										
15										
16										
17										
18										
19										
20										
21										
22										
23										
24										
25										
26										
27										

1 Kilometre

Figure 2.17 Survey of the reef was conducted by 2 teams (A and B). Data are combined to reflect the agreed starting point and the clockwise direction of tows.

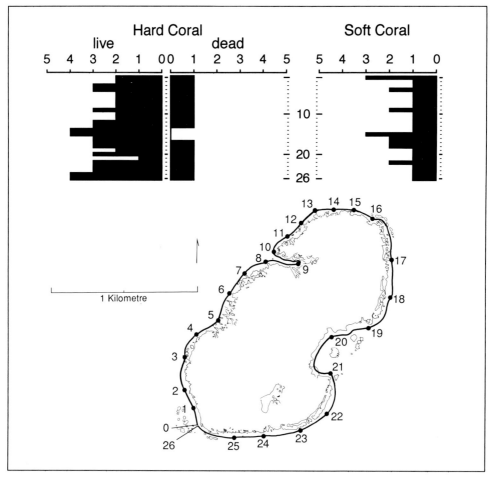

Figure 2.18 Example of a summary data sheet showing percent cover data collected using manta tow survey of Trout Reef, Great Barrier Reef (Bass *et al.* 1989).

Fernandes, L. (1989). Biases associated with the use of the manta tow, a rapid reef surveillance technique, with particular application to the crown-of-thorns starfish (*Acanthaster planci*). M.Sc. Dissertation, James Cook University of North Queensland, Townsville. 128pp.

Fernandes, L. (1990). Effect of the distribution and density of benthic target organisms on manta tow estimates of their abundance. Coral Reefs, **9**: 161-165.

Fernandes, L., H. Marsh, P.J. Moran and D. Sinclair (1990). Bias in manta tow surveys of *Acanthaster planci*. Coral Reefs, **9**: 155-160.

Fernandes, L., P.J. Moran and H. Marsh (1993). A system for classifying outbreaks of crown-of-thorns starfish as a basis for management. Abstract. Proceedings of the Seventh International Coral Reef Symposium, Guam, **2**: 803-804

Kenchington, R.A. (1975). A survey of the crown-of-thorns starfish *Acanthaster planci* (Linne) over a section of the Great Barrier Reef. pp. 1-7. In: "Crown-of-thorns starfish seminar proceedings, Brisbane, 6 September 1974". Australian Government Publishing Service, Canberra.

Kenchington, R.A. (1978). Visual surveys of large areas of coral reefs. pp. 149-162. In: Stoddart, D.R. and R.E. Johannes (editors) "Coral Reefs: research methods". UNESCO, Paris.

Kenchington, R.A. (1984). Large area surveys of coral reefs. UNESCO Reports in Marine Science, **21**: 92-103.

Kenchington, R.A. and B. Morton (1976). Two surveys of the crown-of-thorns starfish over a section of the Great Barrier Reef: report of the Steering Committee for the crown-of-thorns survey, March 1976. Australian Government Publishing Service, Canberra. 186pp.

Miller, I.R. and G. De'ath (1996). Effects of training on observer performance in assessing benthic cover by means of the manta tow technique. Marine and Freshwater Research, **47**: 19-26.

Miller, I.R. and R. Muller (in press). A quality control procedure for observer agreement of manta tow cover estimates. Proceeedings of the Eighth International Coral Reef Symposium, Panama.

Moran, P.J., R.H. Bradbury and R.E. Reichelt (1988). Distribution of recent outbreaks of the crown-of-thorns starfish (*Acanthaster planci*) along the Great Barrier Reef: 1985-1986. Coral Reefs, **7**: 125-137.

Moran, P.J. and G. De'ath (1992). Suitability of the manta tow method for estimating the relative and absolute abundance of crown-of-thorns starfish and corals. Australian Journal of Marine and Freshwater Research, **43**: 357-378.

Moran, P.J., D.B. Johnson, B.A. Miller-Smith, C.N. Mundy, D.K. Bass, J. Davidson, I.R. Miller and A.A. Thompson (1989). A guide to the AIMS manta tow technique. The Crown-of-thorns Study. Australian Institute of Marine Science, Townsville. 20pp.

Nash, W. and L. Zell (1982). *Acanthaster* on the Great Barrier Reef: distribution on five transects between 14°S and 18°S. Proceedings of the Fourth International Coral Reef Symposium, Manila, **2**: 601-605.

Roads, C.H. and R.F.G. Ormond (eds.) (1971). New studies on the crown-of-thorns starfish, (*Acanthaster planci*) from investigations in the Red Sea: Report of the Third Cambridge Red Sea Expedition, 1970. Cambridge Coral Starfish Research Group, Cambridge. 124pp.

Coral Reefs

2.3 Line Intercept Transect

Abstract

Line intercept transects are used to assess the sessile benthic community of coral reefs. The community is characterised using lifeform categories which provide a morphological description of the reef community. These categories are recorded on data sheets by divers who swim along lines which are placed roughly parallel to the reef crest at depths of 3 metres and 10 metres at each site. For future monitoring, the location of each site is recorded and marked on the reef. If the expertise of the observer allows the identification of coral species, this methodology may be expanded to include taxonomic data in addition to the lifeform categories. Where possible, monitoring should be repeated each year, or at least every 2 years. If equipment is available video transects may be used, following the protocols described in Appendix II.

Background

The Line Intercept Transect (LIT) technique was developed in terrestrial plant ecology, and subsequently was adopted by coral reef ecologists (Loya 1978; Marsh *et al.* 1984). The procedure fuses a classification system based on structural attributes of lifeforms rather than species level data (De Vantier 1986). The LIT is used to estimate the cover of an object or group of objects within a specified area (Gates 1979) by calculating the fraction of the length of the line that is intercepted by the object. This measure of cover, usually expressed as a percentage, is considered to be an unbiased estimate of the proportion of the total area covered by that object if the following assumptions apply: that the size of the object is small relative to the length of the line; and that the length of the line is small relative to the area of interest. For a discussion of the technique see McIntyre (1953), Lucas and Seber (1977), and Mundy (1991).

The LIT has been used for objectives ranging from large-scale spatial problems (Benayahu and Loya 1977; 1981), to morphological comparisons of coral communities (Bradbury *et al.* 1986; Reichelt *et al.* 1986), and studies assessing the impact of natural and anthropogenic disturbances (Moran *et al.* 1986; Mapstone *et al.* 1989). Most studies using this method have used similar techniques (a plastic fibre tape, placed on the substratum parallel with the reef crest) with the following variations: Bouchon (1981) used tape tensioned between two pegs; Rylaarsdam (1983) used 3.75 metre metal chains with 2 centimetre links; Hughes and Jackson (1985) used 10 metre chains (the size of the links was not stated).

Advantages

❏ The lifeform categories allow the collection of useful information by persons with limited experience in the identification of coral reef benthic communities.

❏ LIT is a reliable and efficient sampling method for obtaining quantitative percent cover data.

❏ LIT can provide detailed information on spatial pattern.

❏ If LIT is repeated through time with sufficient replication (see Chapter 7) it can provide information on temporal change. Meaningful temporal data requires regular comparisons between observers to overcome observer differences.

❏ LIT requires little equipment and is relatively simple.

Disadvantages

❏ It is difficult to standardise some of the lifeform categories.

❏ Objectives are limited to questions concerning percent cover data or relative abundance.

❏ It is inappropriate for assessing demographic questions concerning growth, recruitment or mortality. If the objectives of a study specifically address these questions, then photo-quadrat techniques should be used in addition to LIT.

Logistics

Personnel

❏ A team of at least 3 personnel is required - 2 divers and a person in the boat.

❏ All observers should be familiar with the definitions of each lifeform (Fig. 2.19 a,b,c; Table 2.5). Branching forms are defined as those with at least secondary branching (see inset, Fig. 2.19a). Training should be carried out in the field, but may include the use of slides and/or photographs in the laboratory.

❏ Standardisation between observers, and continuity of observers throughout the project is very important, as observer variability may obscure or complicate any real spatial patterns.

❏ Observers should spend 30 - 45 minutes in the water at the beginning of each field trip, comparing and standardising their interpretations of the various lifeforms. Particular attention should be given to the following lifeforms: CE, CS, CM, ACB, ACS, ACD, and the algae (see Table 2.5 for abbreviations).

Equipment

❏ Small boat/s, with outboard motors and safety equipment.

❏ SCUBA equipment.

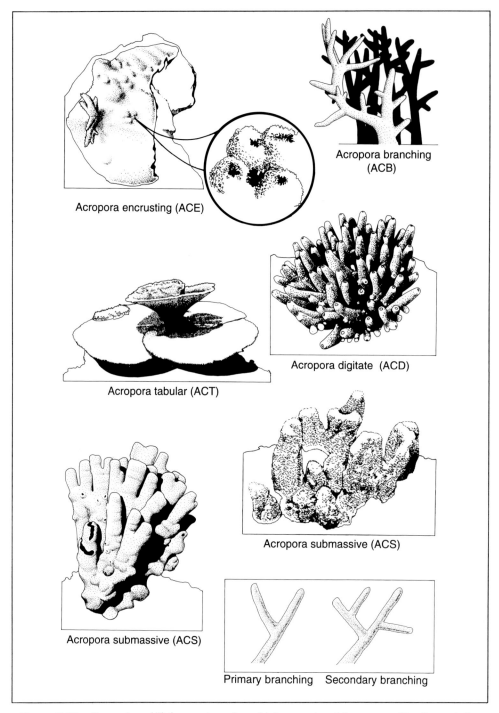

Figure 2.19a Examples of lifeform categories which group benthic communities through the use of morphological characteristics. Inset shows primary and secondary branching.

Coral Reefs

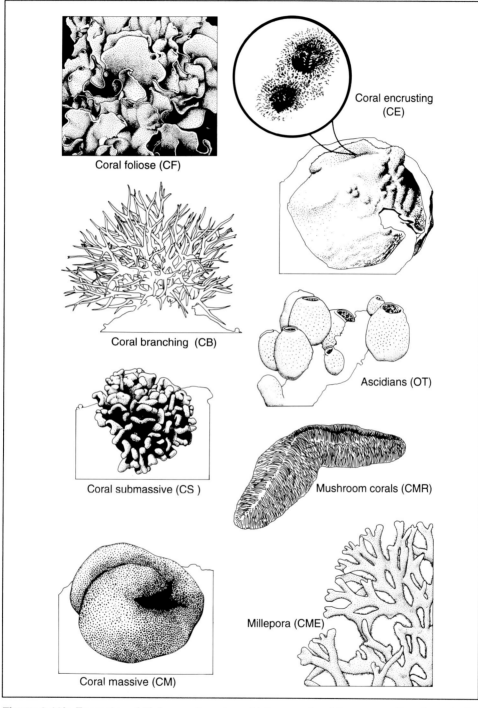

Coral foliose (CF)

Coral encrusting (CE)

Coral branching (CB)

Ascidians (OT)

Coral submassive (CS)

Mushroom corals (CMR)

Coral massive (CM)

Millepora (CME)

Figure 2.19b Examples of lifeform categories which group benthic communities through the use of morphological characteristics.

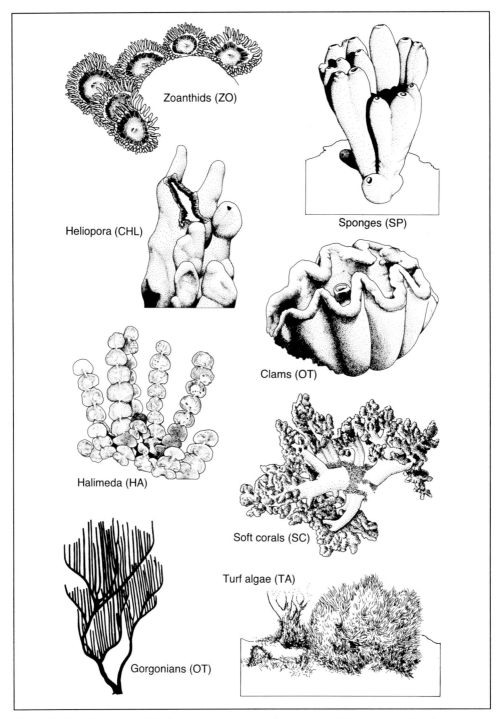

Figure 2.19c Examples of lifeform categories which group benthic communities through the use of morphological characteristics.

ACT *Acropora* tabular

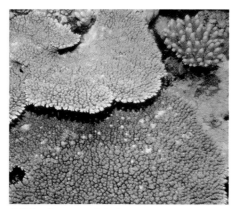

ACT *Acropora* tabular

ACE *Acropora* encrusting (*A. palifera*)

ACD *Acropora* digitate

ACS *Acropora* submassive (*A. palifera*)

ACS *Acropora* submassive (*A. palifera*)

ACB *Acropora* branching. Note axial corallites on branch tips

CB Coral branching (*Seriatopora hystrix*)

CB Coral branching (*Porites cylindrica*)

CB Coral branching (*Hydnophora rigida*)

CM Coral massive *(Leptoria phrygia)*

CM Coral massive (*Symphyllia* sp.). Note dead surface

CE   Coral encrusting (*Goniastrea* sp.) - centre. Note coralline algae (pink)

CE   Coral encrusting (pink). Other forms in left of frame are ACD and CM

CS & CE   Coral submassive and encrusting (*Montipora* sp.)

CS   Coral submassive (*Stylophora pistillata*)

CF   Coral foliose (*Turbinaria* sp.)

CMR   Mushroom coral (*Fungia* sp.)

CHL   Blue coral (*Heliopora coerulea*)

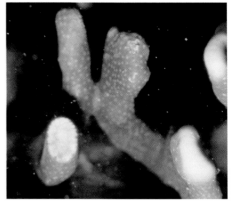

CHL   Blue coral (*Heliopora coerulea*)

CTU   Organ-pipe coral (*Tubipora musica*)

OT   Other (Gorgonian)

CME   Fire Coral (*Millepora* sp.)

CME   Fire Coral (*Millepora* sp.)

OT   Other (Hydroid - *Aeglophenia* sp.)

OT   Other (Ascidian)

OT   Other (Ascidian)

SP   Sponge

SP   Sponge

SP   Sponge

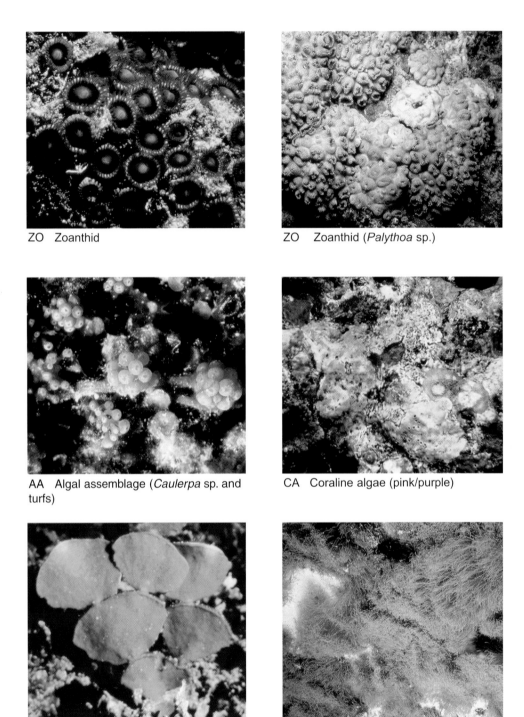

ZO   Zoanthid

ZO   Zoanthid (*Palythoa* sp.)

AA   Algal assemblage (*Caulerpa* sp. and turfs)

CA   Coraline algae (pink/purple)

HA   Halimeda

MA   Macroalgae
Turtleweed (*Chlorodesmis* sp.)

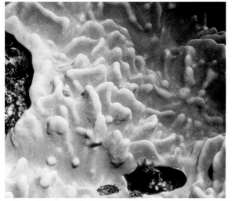

SC   Soft coral (*Sinularia* sp.)

SC   Soft coral (*Nepthea* sp.)

SC   Soft coral (*Efflatounaria* sp.).
Note pinnate tentacles

SC   Soft coral (*Xenia sp.*)

SC   Soft coral (*Sarcophyton* sp.)

SC   Soft Coral (*Lobophytum* sp.)

DC   Dead coral (*Acropora* sp.)

DC   Dead coral. *Acropora* sp. with
Crown-of-thorns starfish

DCA   Dead coral with algae

DCA/CM   DCA patches on coral massive
(CM - *Platygyra* sp.)

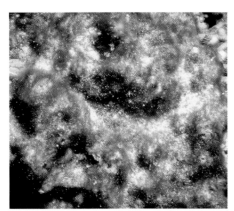

TA   Turf algae

R   Rubble

Table 2.5. Lifeform categories and codes. See Figure 19 (a, b and c) and colour insert for examples.

CATEGORIES		CODE	NOTES / REMARKS
Hard Coral:			
Dead Coral		DC	recently dead, white to dirty white
Dead Coral with Algae		DCA	this coral is standing, skeletal structure can still be seen
Acropora	Branching	ACB	at least 2° branching, e.g. *Acropora palmata, A. formosa*
	Encrusting	ACE	usually the base-plate of immature *Acropora* forms, e.g. *A. palifera* and *A. cuneata*
	Submassive	ACS	robust with knob or wedge-like form e.g. *A. palifera*
	Digitate	ACD	no 2° branching, typically includes *A. humilis, A. digitifera and A. gemmifera*
	Tabular	ACT	horizontal flattened plates e.g. *A. hyacinthus*
Non-*Acropora*	Branching	CB	at least 2° branching e.g. *Seriatopora hystrix*
	Encrusting	CE	major portion attached to substratum as a laminar plate e.g. *Porites vaughani, Montipora undata*
	Foliose	CF	coral attached at one or more points, leaf-like, or plate-like appearance e.g. *Merulina ampliata, Montipora aequituberculata*
	Massive	CM	solid boulder or mound e.g. *Platygyra daedalea*
	Submassive	CS	tends to form small columns, knobs, or wedges e.g. *Porites lichen, Psammocora digitata*
	Mushroom	CMR	solitary, free-living corals of the *Fungia*
	Heliopora	CHL	blue coral
	Millepora	CME	fire coral
	Tubipora	CTU	organ-pipe coral, *Tubipora musica*

Coral Reefs

Table 2.5 (continued)

CATEGORIES		CODE	NOTES / REMARKS
Other Fauna:			
Soft Coral		SC	soft bodied corals
Sponges		SP	
Zoanthids		ZO	examples are *Platythoa*, *Protopalythoa*
Others		OT	Ascidians, anenomes, gorgonians, giant clams etc.
Algae	Algal Assemblage	AA	consists of more than one species
	Coralline Algae	CA	
	Halimeda	HA	
	Macroalgae	MA	weedy/fleshy browns, reds, etc.
	Turf Algae	TA	lush filamentous algae, often found inside damselfish territories
Abiotic	Sand	S	
	Rubble	R	unconsolidated coral fragments
	Silt	SI	
	Water	WA	fissures deeper than 50 cm
	Rock	RCK	
Other		DDD	Missing data

❑ 5 fibreglass measuring tapes - 50 metres in length with hooks attached to the end of the tape and to the casing (Fig. 2.20). This tape length is recommended when visual fish censuses are conducted in conjunction with the LIT, otherwise a shorter tape length could be used.

❑ Slates, data sheets (A4 underwater paper is recommended), and pencils. Printed data sheets will assist the observer to record the intercept data (Fig. 2.21).

❑ Float or other material (e.g. plastic bottles) to mark site.

Maintenance

❑ Wash equipment in freshwater after use (especially tapes).

❑ Develop a routine of maintenance which is adhered to before and after each trip.

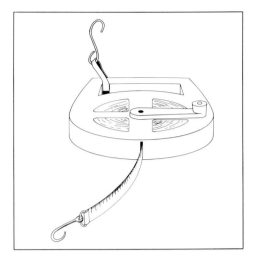

Figure 2.20   Hooks attached to the tape anu casiriy rieip secure tne tape during surveys.

Site selection

❑ Conduct a general survey of the reef to select suitable sites on the reef slope which are representative of that reef. Manta towing is a useful technique for site selection.

❑ At least 2 sites should be selected. If distinct windward (front-reef) and leeward (back-reef) zones exist, sites should be selected in each habitat.

❑ The precise location of sites should be recorded while at the site, noting landforms or unique reef features such as bays or indentations, points or channels, which may be useful for relocating the site. A GPS (Global Positioning System) and an aerial photo or chart of the area is extremely useful for positioning and relocating sites.

❑ Mark the position of the transect. Metal stakes, such as angle iron or star-pickets, should be hammered deep into the substratum (at least 0.5 metres). Attachment of subsurface buoys may help reduce loss of site markers.

General procedure

❑ At each site on a reef, lay at least 5 (replicate) transects of 20 metres length at each of two depths, identifying shallow (3 metres) and deep (9 - 10 metres) coral communities.

❑ The replicate transects are located haphazardly at each depth and should not overlap.

❑ The transect lines should be stretched tightly and follow the depth contour.

☞ *If permanent quadrats are monitored in the area, care should be taken to lay transects away from these quadrats in order to avoid damage.*

LINE INTERCEPT DATA

Location .... Sample ID ....

Reef name .... Reef zone .... Latitude ....

Date .... Time .... Wind .... Cloud .... Longitude ....

Turbidity .... Light .... Top .... Top ....

Depth .... Sea .... Tide .... Temp. Bot. .... Salinity Bot. ....

Replicate .... Site Nº .... Collector ....

Remarks ....

Benthos	Transition	Occurrence		Field code	Notes

Figure 2.21   Example of printed sheet used by observers to record line intercept data. The column headed "Field code" is only used if the observer has expertise in coral taxonomy.

❏ If a typical reef flat, crest, and slope is present, the shallow transects will be located on the reef slope, approximately 3 metres **below the crest**. The deeper transects will be located approximately 9-10 metres **below the crest**. If the site is on a reef without a well-defined crest, then transect depth should be approximated to a depth below mean low water.

☞ *If there is little or no coral at 10 metres then transects should be laid at 6-8 metres below the crest and the difference should be noted.*

❏ The number of observers recording data should be kept to a minimum. These observers should collect data at all sites and, where possible, during repeat surveys.

❏ If personnel are available, it is more efficient if there are two observers recording data from the transects and a third diver rolling out, and rolling up the tapes.

❏ Each individual 20 metre transect should be completed by a single observer.

❏ The diver responsible for the tape should firmly attach the hook on the beginning of the tape (Fig. 2.20), to coral or other suitable 'anchor' and then roll the tape out parallel to the crest, following a constant depth contour (use depth gauge).

❏ The tape must remain close to the substratum (0-15 cm) at all times and should be securely attached to prevent excessive movement. This can be achieved by using the coral as a natural hook, e.g. by pushing the tape between branches. Do not wrap the tape around coral heads/branches or other lifeforms as this will affect intercept measurements. Care should be taken to minimise areas where the tape is suspended more than 50 cm above the substratum, i.e. the water category (WA).

☞ *When dive teams are limited and individuals must complete a number of transects on any one day, they must be aware of decompression safety. Divers must start with the deeper transects. When these are completed they can proceed to the transects at 3 metres depth.*

Figure 2.22 Diver recording lifeform categories encountered under the transect tape.

❏ After transects have been completed, divers should mark the study site by stakes or subsurface buoys. A GPS (Global Positioning System) can be very useful for relocating sites.

Data recording

❏ Before entering the water record the precise location of the site and any ambient parameters onto the datasheet.

❏ While the transect is being laid out the observer should record details of the site, depth etc. onto the datasheet. Detailed comments about the condition of the site at the time of survey should be included.

❏ Once the transect has been laid out, the observer moves slowly along the transect recording onto the data sheet the lifeforms encountered under the tape (Fig. 2.22). At each point where the benthic lifeform changes, the observer records the transition point in centimetres and the code of the lifeform. Hence, along the length of a transect (XY) a number of transition points (T) are recorded for each of the lifeforms (Fig. 2.23). The length of each lifeform encountered under the transect (L) is the difference between the transition points recorded for each lifeform.

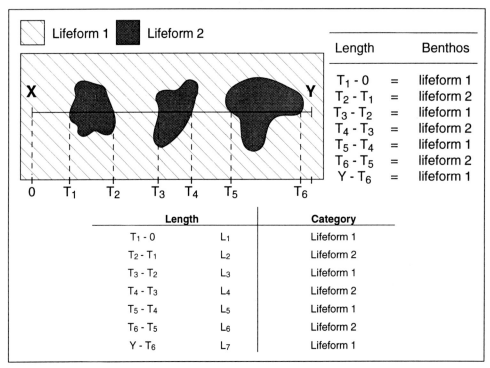

Figure 2.23 Schematic diagram of a transect (XY) showing the transition points (T) for each lifeform crossed by the transect. The difference between consecutive transition points is the "length" of the lifeform.

❑ To facilitate accurate calculation of the number of occurrences of each lifeform, observers should note instances when the tape intercepts a single lifeform or colony more than once. For example, when a massive *Porites* colony (CM) includes both living tissue, dead patches with algal growth (DCA) and other fauna (OT), each intercept with living tissue should be recorded as belonging to the same colony (Fig. 2.24). The numbers in brackets identify that the transition points of CM (Coral massive - *Porites*) belong to the same colony.

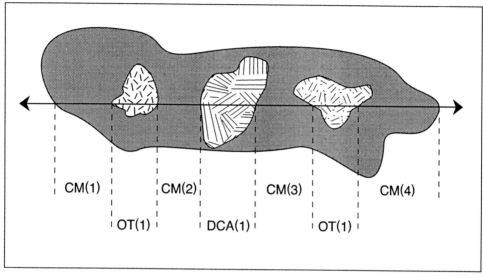

Figure 2.24   Diagram showing a transect crossing a single colony more than once. The number in parentheses indicates that it is the same occurrence of a colony.

❑ Some colonies may be encountered which could be recorded as either of 2 lifeform categories, depending on where the colony is intercepted by the tape. Such colonies should be recorded by their dominant lifeform (i.e. the lifeform displayed by more than 50% of the colony). For example, large digitate *Acropora* species (*A. digitifera, A. humilis*) may have secondary and tertiary branching at the ends of some of their branches. However, the proportion of the colony which displays these characteristics relative to the digitate form is small and hence the colony would be recorded as ACD.

❑ More specific taxonomic identification may be included in addition to the lifeform category, dependent on the observer's knowledge. Veron (1993) is a recommended reference book for identification of scleractinian corals in the Indo-Pacific. Further references for regional coral identification are included at the end of this method (Suggested Reading).

❑ A list of coral species codes is included at the end of this chapter. This list should be updated if required, but ensure that codes are compatible with other survey teams to guarantee future compatibility of data collected.

❏ It must be emphasised that the lifeform categories specified are the **minimum** requirements for a regional database. If there is a need to add new categories for specific purposes, the category must allow retrieval of the minimum information (i.e. the new list of categories can readily be collapsed into the old one). For example, if the SC (soft corals) group is divided to note its growth form, provision must be made to allow the combination of the new categories back into SC for purposes of data exchange. Similarly, species data for corals should always include lifeform categories to allow comparison with other data sets.

Standardisation

❏ Observers must be as consistent as possible when recording benthic lifeforms. The same people should collect data at all sites and, where possible, during repeat surveys.

❏ Regular training and discussion of lifeforms should be undertaken in the field to ensure that interpretation of lifeform categories is the same for all observers, and that it does not change over time (i.e. data are comparable).

❏ The use of samples and photographs or slides in the laboratory is a useful training tool.

❏ The minimum requirements must always be met to ensure that the exchange of data is possible.

Data processing

❏ At the end of each day the data should be entered into the database using the structure described at the end of this chapter (Section 2.9).

❏ Information about the sample is entered into the sample table (XXCRSAMP) and a unique sample identifier (SAMPLE_ID) is allocated. The type of data collected in the sample is described by the DATA_TYPE field, which for line intercept data, is denoted by the letter "T".

❏ Enter the line intercept data into the data table (XXCRTDAT) using the sample identification allocated in the sample table. The data table has one row or record for each intercept recorded along the transect. Replicate transects have the same SAMPLE_ID but have a unique replicate number.

❏ Each record in the data table should include a sample identifier (SAMPLE_ID), the replicate number, the lifeform, the transition point (as read from the tape) and any other information such as the taxonomic code. Each transition along the one transect must have the same sample identifier and the same replicate number. In this way all the records belonging to the same transect can be identified in the database and these in turn can be linked to the information in the sample table.

❏ An entry is made into the sample table (XXCRSAMP) to describe the ambient data collected in conjunction with the line intercept transect, i.e. DATA_TYPE is "A". The ambient data, e.g. temperature, salinity and turbidity, are entered into the ambient table (XXCRADAT) using the sample identification allocated in the sample table.

☞ *The LIT data and ambient data will have different sample identification numbers but are connected through common values in fields in the sample table, e.g. location, reef name, date, latitude and longitude.*

❏ Relatively large amounts of data will be collected, therefore adequate space for data storage and manipulation must be available.

❏ **Always check and verify data after entry.**

❏ Always backup data regularly.

Analysis

❏ Summary data showing percent cover and number of occurrences of each lifeform may be calculated using the line intercept data. After calculating the intercept (length) from the transition points recorded along the transect (see Fig. 2.23), the percent cover of a lifeform category is calculated.

$$Percent\ cover = \frac{Total\ length\ of\ category}{Length\ of\ transect} \times 100 \qquad (2\text{-}1)$$

Hence, for the lifeforms shown in Figure 2.23

$$Percent\ cover\ Lifeform\ 1 = \frac{L_1 + L_3 + L_5 + L_7}{Y} \times 100$$

$$Percent\ cover\ Lifeform\ 2 = \frac{L_2 + L_4 + L_6}{Y} \times 100$$

❏ These analyses will provide quantitative information on the community structure of the sample sites. Successive samples can also be compared when the sites have been sampled repeatedly over time.

❏ If reefs have been selected to represent both disturbed and pristine sites, then comparison of change detected in these sites may allow recognition of change due to disturbance from natural and human-induced pressures. This provides a predictive tool in reef management.

❏ Where rigorous statistical comparisons of reef community structures within and between sites are needed, greater replication of transects at each sampling site will be required. This should be identified in a pilot study (see Chapter 7).

Comments

❏ Standardisation between observers and continuity of observers throughout the project is very important, as observer variability may obscure or complicate real spatial patterns.

❏ LIT should not be considered for obtaining quantitative assessments of percent cover or abundance of rare and small species.

Worked example

❏ Figure 2.25 shows a section of a line intercept transect and the data collected from that section of transect tape. The transition and category data would be recorded onto a data sheet similar to that shown in Figure 2.21. The species name (FIELDCODE) is only recorded if taxonomic expertise is available. It is then collected in addition to the lifeform data.

❏ Calculations of percent cover for Coral Foliose lifeform (CF) and Coral Massive lifeform (CM) present in Figure 2.25 are presented here.

　» The length of the transect shown in Figure 2.25 is 272 centimetres.

　» The total length of CF is the sum of its intercept lengths:

$$\text{Total length} = 57 + 20 = 77$$

　» Therefore, using equation 2-1:

$$\% \text{ cover CF} = \frac{77}{272} \times 100 = 28.3\%$$

　» Similarly, for CM:

$$\text{Total length} = 11 + 2 + 25 + 7 = 45$$

$$\% \text{ cover CM} = \frac{45}{272} \times 100 = 16.5\%$$

❏ To determine the number of individual colonies of each of the lifeforms CF and CM in Figure 2.25 count only those colonies which have an occurrence value of "1" (see Fig. 2.24). Hence, the number of colonies for the two lifeforms used in this example are:

　Coral Foliose = 2; and

　Coral Massive = 4.

Coral Reefs

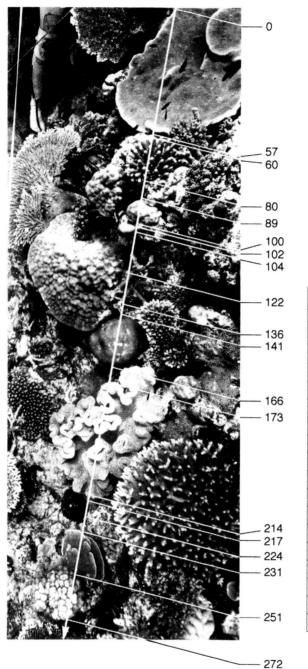

Benthos	Transition	Occurrenc:
CF	57	1
AA	60	1
ACD	80	1
AA	89	1
CM	100	1
AA	102	1
CM	104	1
A	122	1
ACB	136	1
AA	141	1
CM	166	1
AA	173	1
SC	214	1
AA	217	1
CM	224	1
AA	231	1
CF	251	1
CS	272	1

Figure 2.25 A section of a length of transect showing points at which the lifeforms change -
the transition points. The code for the lifeform and transition points are recorded
onto the datasheet. The field code is only recorded if the observer has the
appropriate expertise.

References

Benayahu, Y. and Y. Loya (1977). Space partitioning by stony corals, soft corals and benthic algae on the coral reefs of the northern Gulf of Eilat (Red Sea). Helgolander wiss. Meeresunters, **30**: 362-382.

Benayahu, Y. and Y. Loya (1981). Competition for space among coral-reef sessile organisms at Eilat, Red Sea. Bulletin of Marine Science, **31**: 514-522.

Bouchon, C. (1981). Quantitative study of the Scleractinian coral communities of a fringing reef of Reunion Island (Indian Ocean). Marine Ecology Progress Series, **4**: 273-288.

Bradbury, R.H., Y. Loya, R.E. Reichelt and W.T. Williams (1986). Patterns in the structural typology of benthic communities on two coral reefs of the central Great Barrier Reef. Coral Reefs, **4**: 161-167.

De Vantier, L.M. (1986). Studies in the assessmant of coral reef ecosystems. In: Brown, B.E. (editor) "Human Induced Damage To Coral Reefs". Unesco Reports in Marine Science, **40**: 99-111.

Gates, C.E. (1979). Line transect and related issues. In: Cormack, R.M., G.P. Patil and D.S. Robson (editors). "Sampling Biological Populations". International Co-operative Publishing House, Fairland, Maryland.

Hughes, T.P. and J.B.C. Jackson (1985). Population dynamics and life histories of foliaceous corals. Ecological Monographs, **55**: 141-166.

Loya, Y. (1978). Plotless and transect methods. pp. 197-217. In: Stoddart, D.R. and R.F. Johannes (editors). "Coral Reefs: Research Methods". UNESCO, Paris.

Lucas, H.A. and G.A.F. Seber (1977). Estimating coverage and particle density using the Line Intercept Method. Biometrika, **64**: 618-622.

McIntyre, G.A. (1953). Estimation of plant density using line transects. Journal of Ecology, **41**: 319-330.

Mapstone, B.D., J.H. Choat, R.L. Cumming and W.G. Oxley (1989). The fringing reefs of Magnetic Island: benthic biota and sedimentation. A baseline study. A report to the Great Barrier Reef Marine Park Authority. March 1989. 88pp.

Marsh, L.M., R.H. Bradbury and R.E. Reichelt (1984). Determination of the physical parameters of coral distributions using line transect data. Coral Reefs, **2**: 175-180.

Moran, P.J., R.H. Bradbury and R.E. Reichelt (1986). Mesoscale studies of the crown-of-thorns/coral interaction: a case history from the Great Barrier Reef. In: Proceedings of the Fifth International Coral Reef Symposium, Tahiti, **5**: 321-326.

Coral Reefs

Mundy, C.N. (1991). A critical evaluation of the line intercept transect methodology for surveying sessile coral reef benthos. MSc. Thesis, James Cook University. 127pp.

Reichelt, R.E., Y. Loya and R.H. Bradbury (1986). Patterns in the use of space by benthic communities on two coral reefs of the Great Barrier Reef. Coral Reefs, **5**: 73-79.

Rylaarsdam, K.W. (1983). Life histories and abundance patterns of colonial corals on Jamaican reefs. Marine Ecology Progress Series, **13**: 246-260.

Veron, J.E.N. (1993). "Corals of Australia and the Indo-Pacific". University of Hawaii Press. 644pp.

Suggested reading

Allen, G.R. and R. Steene (1994). "Indo-Pacific Coral Reef Field Guide". Tropical Reef Research Singapore. 378pp.

Bright,T.J., G.P. Kraemer, G.A. Minnery and S.T. Viada (1984). Hermatypes of the flower garden banks, Northwestern Gulf of Mexico: A comparison to other western Atlantic Reefs. Bulletin of Marine Science, **34**(3): 461-476.

Cairns, S.D. (1982). Stony corals (Cnidaria: Hydrozoa, Scleractinia) of Carrie Bow Cay, Belize. Smithson. Contributions to Marine Science, **12**: 271-302.

Colin, P.L. and C. Arneson (1995). "Tropical Pacific Invertebrates. A Field Guide to the Marine Invertebrates Occurring on Tropical Pacific Coral Reefs, Seagrass Beds and Mangroves". Coral Reef Press California. 296pp.

Sheppard, C.R.C. and A.L.S. Sheppard (1991). Corals and coral communities of Arabia. Fauna of Saudi Arabia, **12**: 1-170.

Veron, J.E.N. (1992a). Hermatypic corals of Japan. Australian Institute of Marine Science Monograph Series, **9**: 1-244.

Veron, J.E.N. (1992b). A biogeographic database of hermatypic corals: species of the central Indo-Pacific, genera of the world. Australian Institute of Marine Science Monograph Series, **10**: 1-430.

Walton Smith, F.G. (1971). Atlantic Reef Corals: A Handbook of the Common Reef and Shallow water corals of Bermuda, the Bahamas, Florida, the West-Indies, and Brazil. University of Miami Press.

2.4 Permanent Quadrat Method

Abstract

The permanent quadrat method is designed to monitor change in the macrobenthos community through time. The technique involves monitoring the biological condition, growth, mortality and recruitment of corals in a permanently marked (fixed) quadrat located at 3 metres depth on the reef slope. It complements the Line Intercept Transect method (Section 2.3) by providing a detailed record of changes in individual corals and recruitment to a mapped area. A series of photographs are taken periodically of the quadrat using an underwater camera, which is mounted on a specially designed frame. These photographs are combined to form a photocomposite of the quadrat. Sediment traps should be placed near the permanent quadrat to measure the sediment load at the site.

Background

Many subtidal communities have been examined using photo-quadrat methods (see Hanisak *et al.* 1989 for examples). The use of photographs to monitor recruitment, growth and mortality of individual coral colonies within quadrats, over several years, was begun by Connell (1973, 1976), and has been used in many other studies of coral reef communities (Endean and Stablum 1973, Pearson 1981, Hughes 1989). The technique is still widely used to monitor the growth of corals (Done 1981, 1992; Porter and Meier 1992, Witman 1992). The photographs not only allow speedy collection of data in the field, but also provide a permanent record of the quadrat, which is useful for long-term monitoring of growth, mortality and recruitment (Gittings *et al.* 1990). Monitoring of coral colonies over time using successive observation and photography can also be a useful technique for detecting sediment smothering (Rogers 1990).

Sedimentation resulting from land clearing, construction, mining, dredging and drilling activities poses a major threat to corals (reviews - Hatcher *et al.* 1989, Rogers 1990). While some coral species are able to tolerate varying periods of exposure to high levels of suspended sediment (Rice and Hunter 1992), heavy sedimentation adversely affects many aspects of coral survival, including coral growth and recruitment, which can result in fewer coral species, less live coral, lower coral growth rates, greater abundance of branching forms and decreased net productivity (Rogers 1990).

Sediment traps yield time-integrated samples of material settling from the water column (Boyce *et al.* 1990). The design of sediment traps is important to their overall efficiency, for example, traps with small mouths and wide bodies appear to overtrap and are not consistent. Gardner (1980) found the most important factor controlling trap efficiency of a cylindrical settling tube to be its height (H) to width (W) ratio; a H/W ratio between 2 and 3 giving the most accurate yield of vertical flux in currents up to 15 centimetres per second. Taller traps are the best choice for higher water velocity regimes. In addition, baffles, placed in the top of the trap reduce resuspension in the trap and help exclude animals which might otherwise live or feed in a trap. The cells of a baffle should have a height to width ratio greater than 2, but less than 6 (Gardner 1980).

Advantages

❑ Sampling is nondestructive.

❑ Detailed and careful observation, photography, and mapping of such a fixed area provides a good record of what takes place in the area.

❑ Can be a good source of information on population estimates for growth rates, partial mortality, mortality and recruitment, if sufficiently replicated.

❑ Provides a permanent record of the site.

Disadvantages

❑ The method is slow.

❑ The equipment is somewhat cumbersome, especially in strong currents.

❑ The photography requires a relatively flat area.

❑ The method only examines a small area.

❑ Curved images between photo-quadrats make joining of the photographs into a photocomposite of the entire quadrat difficult.

❑ Sediment traps cannot be left for long periods.

❑ Sediment traps do not sample effectively in currents where the water velocity is above 20 centimetres per second (White 1990).

Logistics

Personnel
❑ A team of at least 3 personnel is required for these studies - 2 divers and a person in the boat.

Equipment
❑ Small boat with outboard motors and safety equipment.

❑ SCUBA equipment.

Coral Reefs

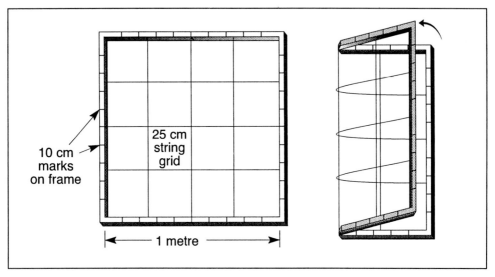

Figure 2.26 A portable quadrat subdivided with string and marked at 10 centimetre intervals along the side. This quadrat is collapsible.

❏ Markers which permanently mark the quadrat to allow relocation, e.g. steel rods, angle iron, star pickets.

❏ A portable quadrat, 1 metre x 1 metre, subdivided with string into 16 equal parts. Mark the sides of the quadrat with scale marks at 10 centimetre intervals (Fig. 2.26). The quadrat may be rigid or collapsible.

❏ Flexible architect's ruler and large, plastic calipers (Fig. 2.27).

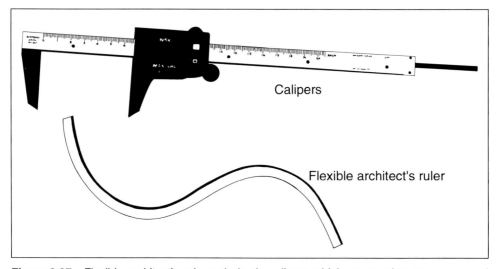

Figure 2.27 Flexible architect's rule and plastic calipers which are used to measure coral growth *in situ*.

❏ Underwater Nikonos camera with 15 mm lens and flash/strobe.

❏ A stable tetrapod stand to hold a camera a fixed distance from the substratum for vertical-plane photographs. The base of the frame should be 1 metre x 1 metre and the plate for attachment of the camera should be 0.8 metres high (Fig. 2.28).

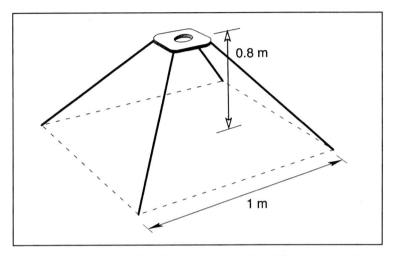

0.8 m

1 m

Figure 2.28 Tetrapod stand which holds the camera a fixed distance from the substratum.

☞ *The dimensions and lens size given above may not be suitable in areas with very poor visibility. In these circumstances it may be necessary to position the camera closer to the substratum. Hence, in turbid waters a frame with a base of 0.5 metre x 0.5 metre should be used (see Table 2.6).*

❏ Slates, data sheets (A4 underwater paper is recommended), and pencils. Printed data sheets will assist the observer record the data.

❏ Tags made of plastic or aluminium with numbers or some other identifying mark stamped onto the surface.

❏ Cable ties or stainless steel wire to attach tags to the coral colonies.

❏ Sediment traps constructed from 5 centimetre internal diameter PVC pipe, 11.5 cm long and sealed at one end (Fig. 2.29). Baffles should be placed in the top of the pipe. The cells of a baffle should have a height to width ratio greater than 2 but less than 6 (Gardner 1980). A lid is necessary to seal each trap before removal.

❏ Drying oven - to dry samples at 60° C.

❏ Balance - to measure to the nearest milligram.

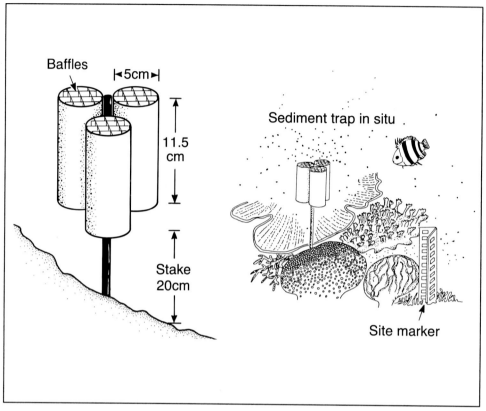

Figure 2.29 Sediment traps showing baffles which are used to deter settlement by fishes.

Maintenance

❏ Wash equipment in freshwater after use.

❏ Special care should be given to the camera to ensure all saltwater is removed from the casing, the lens is cleaned and protected, and all O-rings are greased.

❏ Traps should be thoroughly cleaned of encrusting organisms after use and painted with antifouling paint before reuse.

Site Selection

❏ The site should be established in conjunction with the Line Intercept Transects, on the reef slope at a depth of 3 metres below the crest (see LIT method, Section 3.2). A GPS (Global Positioning System) can be very useful for relocating sites.

❏ Permanent quadrats (2 metre x 2 metre) should be set up on reasonably flat substrata.

❏ Position the permanent quadrat(s) to avoid possible damage to coral within the quadrat from divers working on the line transects.

Coral Reefs

❑ Attach a float near the quadrat, to assist in its relocation. Do not attach floats too close to the sediment traps since algal growth on the mooring rope and float may contribute significantly to the trapped organic material.

❑ Place sediment traps 1 metre either side of the quadrat.

General procedure

❑ Mark the position of the 2 metre x 2 metre quadrat (the marked site) at each corner (steel rods, angle iron or any other available material). The markers must be hammered deep into the substratum to ensure that they are secure and to minimise 'human predation'.

❑ Divide the marked site into sectors (four 1 metre x 1 metre quadrats). Place the portable quadrat on each sector using the corners of the quadrat as a guide.

❑ Use cable ties or wire to tag a selection of colonies within each sector of the quadrat to allow individual identification for monitoring purposes. Select the colonies to give a good representation of the different growth forms, e.g. massive, branching, foliose, encrusting and submassive. The tags must be secured tightly to the coral.

❑ Draw a map of the area covered by the portable quadrat (sector) on underwater paper, showing type, position and size of the coral colonies within the sector. The grid made by the strings of the permanent quadrat provides a useful template (or guide) for positioning the corals and giving relative sizes. Record the positions of the tagged corals onto the map of the sector.

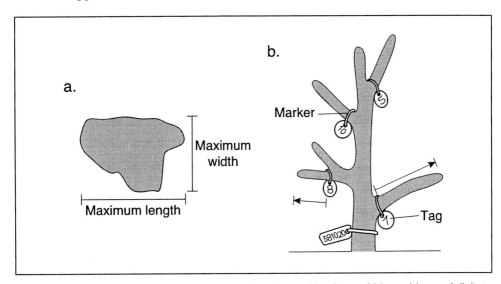

Figure 2.30 Measurement of coral growth. **a)** non-branching forms; **b)** branching and digitate forms are measured from a marker.

❏ Measure the coral colonies at least every 6 months using calipers and a flexible architect's ruler (Fig. 2.27).

❏ Measure the maximum length and the maximum width of non-branching corals (e.g. massive and encrusting corals) using calipers (Fig. 2.30a).

　》 The width measurement must be taken perpendicular to the length measurement (Fig. 2.30). The measurements are made in centimetres and are recorded onto preprinted data sheets (Fig. 2.31).

　》 Only live coral is measured. Any dead portions of the coral are not included.

❏ For branching and digitate forms, a 'marker' of coloured wire with number tag attached is tied to the colony and then individual branches are tagged.

　》 Tie a tag around the base of at least four branches within each colony. The longest length of the branch from the 'marker' to the apical tip is measured (Fig. 2.30b) using the flexible architect's ruler.

❏ Check tags during each survey and replace if necessary (tags may corrode or may be eaten by fish).

Photography

❏ Photograph quadrats at right angles to the reef substratum.

❏ Mount the camera on a tetrapod frame designed to hold the camera at the correct distance from the substratum. The base of the frame (tips of legs) provide the corners of the photo frame (Fig. 2.28).

❏ The dimensions of the frame may need adjustment in waters with poor visibility (Table 2.6). The 20 mm lens distorts the edges of the photograph hence images cannot be used for measurement.

Table 2.6 Camera and frame requirements for reefs with good or poor water visibility.

Visibility	Lens	Frame Height	Base Dimensions	No. of Exposures
Good	15 mm	0.8 m	1 m x 1 m	4
Good	28 mm	1.5 m	1 m x 1 m	4
Poor	15 mm	0.4 m	0.5 m x 0.5 m	16
Poor	20 mm	0.6 m	0.5 m x 0.5 m	16

CORAL GROWTH DATA

Location .... Sample ID ....

Reef name .... Reef zone .... Latitude ....

Date .... Quadrat N° .... Depth ....m Longitude ....

Collectors ....

Remarks ....

Tag N°	Measurement type*	Field code	Length	Width

* For example: branching, massive, encrusting

Figure 2.31 Datasheet for recording coral growth.

Coral Reefs

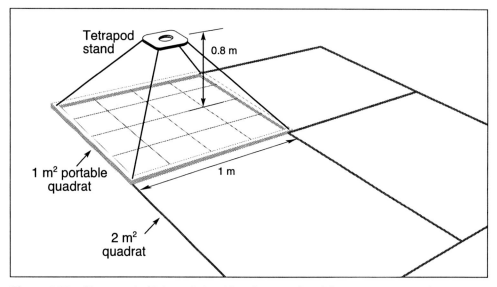

Figure 2.32 Placement of tetrapod stand for photography of the permanent quadrat.

❏ Divide the marked 2 metre x 2 metre quadrat(s) into sectors, and take photographs by placing the feet of the tetrapod at the corner of each sector (Fig. 2.32).

❏ The set of vertical-plane photographs which make up the photocomposite of the quadrat must be taken in a set sequence (Fig. 2.33) so that the photographs can be assigned to the correct section of the quadrat.

❏ Keep the portable quadrat in place while the photographs are taken.

☞ *Measurements of the colonies should be done in the field. It is possible to get measurements from photographs taken with suitable camera lenses. If poor visibility requires the use of 20 millimetre lens, measurements from the photographs will not be possible due to distortion.*

Sediment traps

❏ Hammer a steel rod deep into the substratum so that it is vertical, and firmly secured to the bottom.

❏ Attach 3 sediment traps (1 set) to the rod with electrical wire. The base of the traps should be 20 centimetres above the substratum (Fig. 2.29). The steel rod should not protrude above the opening of the pipes, otherwise results will be confounded by turbulence.

❏ Place 4 sets of sediment traps on the reef slope at a depth of 3 metres, 2 sets on either side of the permanent quadrat at 1 metre intervals.

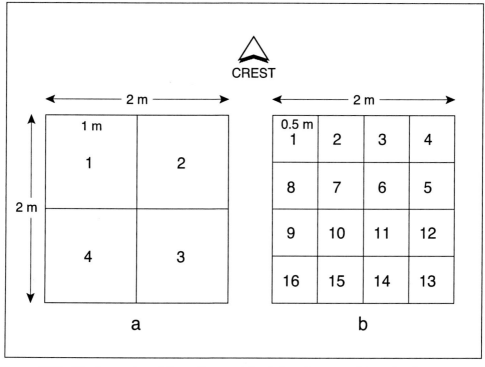

Figure 2.33 Photographs of the site must be taken in a predetermined sequence and using the same orientation to the crest: **a**) 1 metre x 1 metre sectors; **b**) 0.5 metre x 0.5 metre sectors.

❏ Seal traps before removing them from the rod to prevent loss of material while bringing the sample to the surface. The whole sample, including the seawater contained in the trap, is taken back to the laboratory for measurement.

❏ Collect traps at least once a month. Replace the traps immediately with a new set of cleaned traps.

☞ *Frequent collection is particularly important in areas of high sediment load; it also helps reduce the effects of fouling organisms and colonising fishes.*

❏ Open the sealed traps in the laboratory and filter off the sediment from the water contained in each tube.

❏ Dry the samples overnight in an oven at 60° C.

❏ Weigh the dried samples to the nearest milligram. The weight is recorded in grams e.g. 20·24 grams.

❏ Record data onto a data sheet. (Fig. 2.34)

❏ Sediment traps should be thoroughly cleaned of encrusting organisms before reuse.

SEDIMENT TRAP DATA

Location .... Sample ID ....

Reef name .... Reef zone ....

Site N° .... Depth ....m Latitude .... Longitude ....

Replicate .... Collectors ....

Remarks ....

Date set	Date collected	Trap N°	Tube N°	Dry weight (mg)

Figure 2.34 Datasheet for recording sediment collected in the traps.

Data recording

❏ Record the measurements (length and width) of each of the tagged corals onto preprinted data sheets (Fig. 2.31):

» Branching corals - measure at least 4 branches of each colony along the longest length of the branch from the 'marker' to the apical tip.

» Non-branching corals - measure the maximum length and width.

❏ Record the dry weight of sediment from each trap and the dates at which the traps were set (DATE_SET) and collected (DATE_COLL). From these dates the duration for which the trap was deployed is calculated. Note if a trap has unusually high or unusually low amounts of sediment as these may need special consideration, and may be discarded from final analysis.

❏ Combine the photographs of all the quadrat sectors to form a photocomposite of the 2 metre x 2 metre quadrat. In sites with good visibility this might mean 4 photographs were required to make up the photocomposite (see Table 2.6).

❏ Construct a detailed map of the quadrat (type, position and size) using the photocomposite, the map drawn in the field and the field measurements of the coral colonies.

☞ *Photographs of the quadrat may be mounted side by side, following the relationship in the field. This provides enough information to monitor individual corals without the necessity of the often difficult task of mounting the photographs into a photocomposite.*

Data processing

❏ Enter data into the database using the structure described at the end of this chapter (Section 2.9).

❏ Information about the sample is entered into the sample table (XXCRSAMP) and a unique sample identifier (SAMPLE_ID) is allocated. The type of data collected in the sample is described by the DATA_TYPE field, which for the quadrat data is denoted by the letter "Q".

❏ Enter data collected for the quadrat into the data table (XXCRQDAT) using the SAMPLE_ID allocated in the sample table.

❏ When ambient environmental parameters are measured at the site another entry is made into the sample table and a unique sample identifier is allocated. The ambient parameters are denoted in the sample table by the letter "A".

❏ After processing the sediment in the laboratory, enter into the sample table (XXCRSAMP) details of when and where data from the sediment traps were collected. A unique sample identifier (SAMPLE_ID) is allocated. The type of data

Coral Reefs

collected in the sample is described by the DATA_TYPE field, which for the sediment data is denoted by the letter "S".

❏ Data collected from the traps are entered into XXCRSDAT using the SAMPLE_ID allocated in the sample table.

❏ **Always check and verify data after entry.**

❏ Always backup data regularly.

Analysis

❏ Estimate growth rates of individual colonies in terms of area index (length x width). The calculation of the area of colonies depends on the shape of the coral (Fig. 2.35).

❏ Detailed mapping at intervals of 6 months, complemented with photography, will indicate recruitment into the quadrat area and changes in the community pattern of the macrobenthos within the quadrat.

❏ Photography and maps will also indicate reduction in coral cover and death rates of individual taxa.

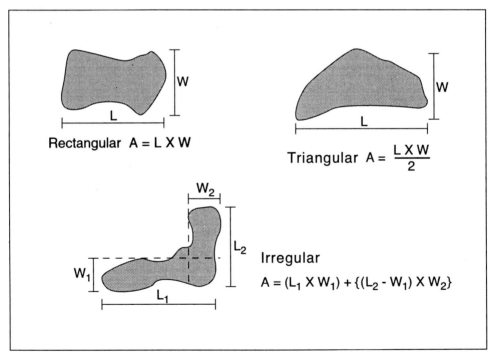

Figure 2.35 Calculation of the area of coral colonies must take into account the shape of the colony.

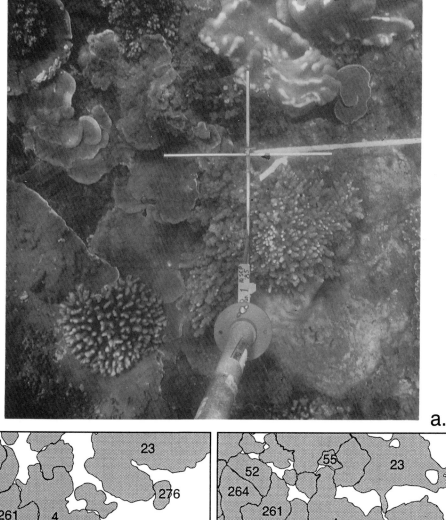

Coral Reefs

a.

b.

c.

Figure 2.36   Mapping of permanent quadrats. The photograph (**a**) is of a 1 x 1 metre quadrat at Pandora Reef in September 1985, the map (**b**) gives an outline of the colonies in the photograph, the second map (**c**) shows the colonies in November 1987. Comparison of the maps shows change in the community through time e.g #9 *Stylophora pistillata*.

Comments

❏ Detailed studies of growth and recruitment will require greater replication (see Chapter 7).

❏ A 28mm lens should be used if photogrammetry techniques (see Done 1981) are going to be used to measure growth.

Worked example

❏ Maps can be drawn *in situ*, or can be drawn from photographs (Fig. 2.36).

☞ *Photographs taken with a 20 millimetre lens will be distorted at the edges and would not be suitable for drawing corals in the quadrat. These images still provide a permanent record of change in the sites.*

❏ The maps and photocomposites can be used to graphically demonstrate change, or lack of change, in the quadrats (Fig. 2.36).

References

Boyce, F.M., P.F. Hamblin, D.G. Robertson and F. Chiocchio (1990). Evaluation of sediment traps in Lake St. Clair, Lake Ontario and Hamblin Harbour. Journal of Great Lakes Research, **16**(3): 366-379.

Connell, J.H. (1973). Population ecology of reef-building corals. pp. 205-245. In: O.A. Jones and R. Endean (editors). "Biology and Geology of Coral Reefs. Volume II: Biology 1". Academic Press, New York, 480pp.

Connell, J.H. (1976).Competitive interactions and the species diversity of corals. pp. 51-58. In: G.O. Mackie (editor). "Coelenterate Ecology and Behaviour". Plenum Press, New York, 744pp.

Done, T.J. (1981). Photogrammetry in coral ecology: a technique for the study of change in coral communities. Proceedings of the Fourth International Coral Reef Symposium, Manila, Vol. 2: 315-320.

Done, T.J. (1992). Constancy and change in some Great Barrier Reef communities: 1980-1990. American Zoologist, **32**: 655-662.

Endean, R. and W. Stablum (1973). The apparent extent of recovery of reefs of Australia's Great Barrier Reef devastated by the crown-of-thorns starfish (*Acanthaster planci*). Atoll Research Bulletin, **168**: 1-26.

Gittings, S.R., K.J.P. Deslarzes and B.S. Boland (1990). Ecological monitoring on the Flower Garden Banks: study design and field methods. Diving for Science, 1990, pp. 107-118.

Gardner, W.D. (1980). Field assessment of sediment traps. Journal of Marine Research, **38**: 41-52.

Hanisak, M.D., S.M. Blair and J.K. Reid (1989). Use of photogrammetric techniques to monitor coral reef recovery following a major ship grounding. Diving for Science, 1989, pp. 119-135.

Hatcher, B.G., R.E. Johannes and A.I. Robertson (1989). Review of research relevant to the conservation of shallow tropical marine ecosystems. Oceanography and Marine Biology an Annual Review, **27**: 337-414.

Hughes, T.P. (1989). Community structure and diversity of coral reefs: the role of history. Ecology, **70**: 275-279.

Pearson, R.G. (1981). Recovery and recolonization of coral reefs. Marine Ecology Progress Series, **4**: 105-122.

Porter, J.W. and O.W. Meier (1992). Quantification of loss and change in Floridian reef coral populations. American Zoologist, **32**:625-640.

Rice, S.A. and C.L. Hunter (1992). Effects of suspended sediment and burial on scleractinian corals from west central Florida patch reefs. Bulletin of Marine Science, **51**: 429-442.

Rogers, C.S. (1990). Responses of coral reefs and reef organisms to sedimentation. Marine Ecology Progress Series, **62**: 185-202.

White, J. (1990). The use of sediment traps in high-energy environments. Marine Geophysical Research, **12**: 145-152.

Witman, J.D. (1992). Physical disturbance and community structure of exposed and protected reefs: A case study from St. John, U.S. Virgin Islands. American Zoologist, **32**: 641-654.

Coral Reefs

2.5 Coral Reef Fish Visual Census

Abstract

Coral reef fish populations are assessed by visual census of the fishes along 50 metre transects. The transects are censused during daylight hours using SCUBA and should be done in conjunction with the Line Intercept Transect (LIT) method, also described in this chapter. The method used for the assessment and monitoring of fish is a combination of 2 techniques. The first detects differences in assemblages of reef fishes at different sites using abundance categories. It provides baseline data for zoning, management and monitoring of coral reefs. The second technique counts individual fish and estimates their total lengths in order to determine the standing stock and population size structure of specific species (those that are favoured by fishermen). The method is one of the most common quantitative and qualitative sampling methods used in coral reef surveys.

Background

Fish communities are a major resource of coral reefs. They play an important role in coral reef ecosystems (e.g. the role of grazers controlling algal growth), and are commercially important for both fisheries, and more recently, tourism.

The Great Barrier Reef Marine Park Authority (GBRMPA) developed 2 techniques of visual census during workshops on reef fish assessment and monitoring (GBRMPA 1978; 1979). The Australian Institute of Marine Science and GBRMPA have used these techniques to quantitatively assess coral reef fish along the entire length of the Great Barrier Reef (GBR) (Craik 1981; Williams 1982, 1991; Russ 1984a, 1984b). The first technique was used successfully to monitor the temporal change in reef fish assemblages in relation to outbreaks of crown-of-thorns starfish on the GBR (Williams 1986). These two techniques were combined, modified and used successfully to study the effects of fishing and protective management on Philippine coral reefs (Russ 1985; Russ and Alcala 1989). Visual census techniques have also been used in the Philippines to examine the influence of substrate structure on reef fish community structure (Carpenter et al. 1981, McManus et al. 1981, Gomez et al. 1988).

Advantages

❏ Visual census of fishes is one of the most common quantitative and qualitative sampling methods used in coral reef surveys.

❏ It is rapid, nondestructive and inexpensive.

❏ It utilises a minimum of personnel and specialised equipment.

❏ It can be used to resurvey the same area through time.

❏ It has the potential to produce large databases rapidly for management and stock assessment purposes.

Disadvantages

❏ Observers must be very well-trained and experienced.

❏ Fish may be attracted towards the divers, or actively swim away from the divers.

❏ Observer error and biases occur in estimating numbers and sizes.

❏ There is low statistical power to detect change in rare species.

❏ The use of abundance categories reduces the power to detect small changes.

❏ The techniques are restricted to shallow depths due to decompression constraints.

Logistics

Personnel
❏ The fish survey team consists of 2 or 3 divers, and a person in the boat. The observer (fish counter) must be able to identify the fish species of the area.

❏ One diver is designated as the observer to reduce bias.

❏ In areas of high fish abundance, the techniques could be divided among the 2 divers: one undertaking the census using abundance categories; while the other counts and estimates the length of specific 'target' species.

Equipment
❏ Small boat/s, with outboard motors and safety equipment.

❏ SCUBA equipment.

❏ Pencils and slates, with prepared data sheets (preprinted A4 underwater paper is recommended). Prepare data sheets after a list of the fish species from the area has been compiled.

❏ Fibreglass measuring tapes - one for each transect, each tape 50 metres in length (Fig. 2.20). The measuring tapes are also necessary to record benthic community data using Line Intercept Transects (Section 2.3) which are done in conjunction with the fish census.

❏ Fish models or 'fiddle sticks' to practise estimating total lengths of fishes while diving. See details of the method used for training in Section 2.8, later in this chapter.

Maintenance

❏ Wash equipment in freshwater after use.

Site selection

❏ Select the sites after a general survey of the reef slope so that sites are representative of that reef. All sites should be similar with respect to physical characteristics, slope and coral cover. Manta towing is useful for site selection.

❏ Where possible, the sites for visual censuses of fishes should include those selected for collection of benthic lifeform data using Line Intercept Transects (Section 2.3). This will provide the fish team with a detailed description of the reef area being censused.

❏ Select at least 2 replicate sites on the windward (front-reef) slope to estimate between site variability within the one habitat. Each site within the habitat (windward slope) must be similar to the other windward sites.

❏ If distinct windward and leeward (back-reef) habitats exist, select at least 1, preferably 2, sites in each habitat. In regions where reversing monsoon winds prevail, select sites from areas of the reef exposed to the different monsoons.

❏ The sites within habitats should be separated from each other by a reasonable distance (100 to 200 metres).

❏ Avoid variable sites such as spur formations, which are likely to include sand and fissures.

❏ Record the exact positions of all replicate sites. If available, a GPS (Global Positioning System) can be very useful for relocating the sites.

General procedure

Selection of species

❏ Reconnaissance dives at each site must be done to list dominant species for inclusion on prepared data sheets before the actual census begins. This minimises the time needed to write species names on the sheets, thereby improving the observer's ability to record fishes continually.

❏ Select species to be censused using the following criteria:

» The species should be visually and numerically dominant, without cryptic behaviour.

» They should be easily identified underwater.

» They must be associated with the reef slope.

❏ A core group of species appropriate for coral reef assessment should be made to:

» Quantitatively estimate abundance and size structure of species that are favoured **'targets'** of fishermen (e.g. serranids, siganids, acanthurids, lutjanids, lethrinids, haemulids).

» Quantitatively estimate the abundance of useful **'indicator'** species (e.g. chaetodontids).

» Semi-quantitatively estimate the relative abundance of other species belonging to major trophic categories (planktivores, algal grazers, fish and coral feeders) such as the pomacentrids, acanthurids, caesionids, scarids, siganids, labrids, mullids and other species that are **'visually obvious'**.

☞ *With experience, observers may be able to count each fish encountered along the transect. Where this is possible, actual counts should be done since they give greater statistical power to the data analysis.*

❏ Sample data sheets are shown for both abundance estimates (Fig. 2.37), and for density and size estimates (Fig. 2.38). The species listed on these sheets are from the ASEAN-Australia region. They should be replaced by species from the area being censused. These data sheets could be attached to either side of the slate, or where species numbers are not great, the data could be combined onto 1 data sheet.

Laying of the transect

❏ At each site on a reef, lay at least 3 transect lines of 50 metres length at each of the 2 depths (3-5 metres and 8-10 metres, see LIT method for discussion of depth).

❏ The transect lines should include the benthic lifeform transects (LIT) whenever both fish and benthic lifeforms are surveyed at the same reef.

☞ *The fish transect and LIT transect are different lengths but may use the same transect line (tape) - 50 metres is the length for an individual fish census, while for the LIT, a shorter transect length (20 metres) is used. Count the fish first if using the same transect.*

❏ The fish transect lines should be straight and follow the depth contour.

❏ The replicate transects (at least 3) at each depth are located haphazardly and should not overlap. Each transect should be separated by 10 to 20 metres.

❏ The basic unit of data collection for the fish visual census is 50 metres x 5 metres. Thus, 3 replicates provide a total census area of 750 m^2 at each depth.

☞ *For greater safety work from the deeper transects to the shallow.*

Census technique

❏ Wait for 5 to 15 minutes after laying the transect before counting, to allow fishes to resume normal behaviour (Carpenter *et al.* 1981).

FISH ABUNDANCE ESTIMATES

Location .... Sample ID ....

Reef name .... Reef zone .... Latitude ....

Date .... Time .... Depth .... Replicate .... Longitude ....

Remarks .... Collector ....

Abundance Counts	1	2-4	5-15	17-64	65-256	257-1024	1025-4096	4097-16384
I. SERRANIDAE (Groupers)								
Plectropomus leopardus								
Cephalopholis argus								
C. miniatus								
C. fasciatus								
Epinephelus merra								
E. coioides								
Anyperodon leucogrammicus								
Cromileptes altivelis								
Variola louti								
II. LUTJANIDAE (Snappers)								
Lutjanus biguttatus								
L. bohar								
L. carponotatus								
L. gibbus								
L. kasmira								
L. decussatus								
L. quinquelineatus								
Macolor niger								
III. LETHRINIDAE (Emperor Bream)								
Monotaxis grandoculis								
Lethrinus harak								
L. miniatus								
L. olivaceus								
IV. HAEMULIDAE (Sweetlips)								
Plectorhynchus chaetodontoides								
P. diagramma								
P. lineatus								
P. pictus								
V. CHAETODONTIDAE (Butterflyfishes)								
Chaetodon baronessa								
C. citrinellus								
C. ephippium								
C. kleini								
C. octofasciatus								
C. melannotus								
C. plebeius								
C. trifascialis								
Forcipiger longirostris								
Hemitaurichthys polylepis								

Abundance Counts	1	2-4	5-15	17-64	65-256	257-1024	1025-4096	4097-16384
VI. ACANTHURIDAE (Surgeonfishes)								
Acanthurus mata								
Naso lopezi								
VII. CAESIONIDAE (Fusiliers)								
Caesio cuning								
C. erythrogaster								
Pterocaesio pisang								
VIII. CARANGIDAE (Jacks)								
Carangoides sp.								
Caranx sexfasciatus								
IX. LABRIDAE (Wrasses)								
Choerodon fasciatus								
Gomphosus varius								
Labroides dimidiatus								
Thallasoma hardwicki								
T. lunare								
X. POMACENTRIDAE (Damsels)								
Chromis caerulea								
C. margaritifer								
Dascyllus aruanus								
Pomacentrus lepidogenys								
P. rhodonotus								
XI. SCARIDAE (Parrotfishes)								
Scarus niger								
XII. MULLIDAE (Goatfishes)								
Parupeneus bifasciatus								
XIII. SIGANIDAE (Rabbitfishes)								
Siganus corallinus								
XIV. POMACANTHIDAE (Angelfishes)								
Centropyge vrolickii								
Pygoplites diacanthus								

Figure 2.37 Preprinted data sheets for estimates of the abundance of reef fish. The species names listed are from the ASEAN-Australia region. Divers should make a list of the dominant species found in their study area before beginning sampling.

Coral Reefs

FISH DENSITY / SIZE ESTIMATES

Location .... Sample ID ....

Reef name .... Reef zone .... Latitude ....

Date .... Time .... Depth .... Replicate .... Longitude ....

Remarks .... Collector ....

Target Species						
I. SERRANIDAE (Groupers)						
Anyperodon leucogrammicus						
Cephalopholis argus						
C. boenack						
C. fasciatus						
C. miniatus						
Cromileptes altivelis						
Epinephelus coioides						
E. cyanopodus						
E. fasciatus						
E. fuscoguttatus						
E. maculatus						
E. malabaricus						
E. merra						
Plectropomus areolatus						
P. laevis						
P. leopardus						
P. maculatus						
Variola albimarginata						
V. louti						
II. LUTJANIDAE (Snappers)						
Lutjanus argentimaculatus						
L. biguttatus						
L. bohar						
L. carponotatus						
L. decussatus						
L. fulviflamma						
L. fulvus						
L. gibbus						
L. kasmira						
L. lutjanus						
L. monostigma						
L. quinquelineatus						
L. rivulatus						
L. russelli						
L. sebae						
L. vitta						
Macolor niger						

Target Species						
III. LETHRINIDAE (Emperor Bream)						
Lethrinus atkinsoni						
L. erythropterus						
L. harak						
L. miniatus						
L. nebulosus						
L. olivaceus						
L. ornatus						
Monotaxis grandoculis						
IV. HAEMULIDAE (Sweetlips)						
Plectorhynchus chaetodontoides						
P. diagramma						
P. goldmanni						
P. picus						
Diagramma pictum						
V. CHAETODONTIDAE (Butterflyfishes)						
Chaetodon baronessa						
C. citrinellus						
C. ephippium						
C. kleini						
C. octofasciatus						
C. melannotus						
C. plebeius						
C. trifascialis						
Chelmon rostratus						
Forcipiger longirostris						
Hemitaurichthys polylepis						

Figure 2.38 Preprinted data sheets for estimates of the size and number of reef fish. The species names listed are from the ASEAN-Australia region. Divers should make a list of the dominant species found in their study area before beginning sampling.

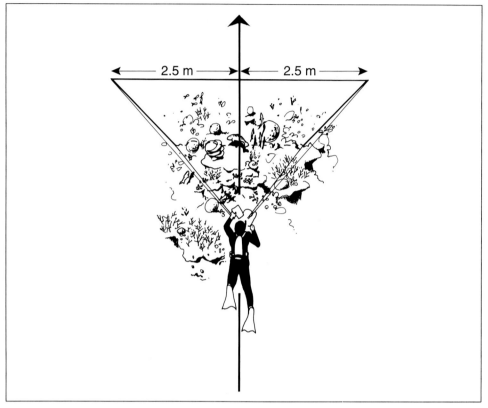

Figure 2.39   The diver swims along the transect counting fish seen within the area specified on either side of the tape (transect strip).

❑ Each transect is censused as a complete 50 x 5 metre belt. Transects should not be broken into smaller units as this will underestimate the abundance of more mobile species.

❑ The observer swims slowly (using SCUBA) along the transect, recording fish encountered within 2.5 metres on either side, and 5 metres above the transect (Fig. 2.39). Always verify the diver's ability to estimate 5 metres before beginning the census.

❑ If the visibility is poor, it may be necessary to reduce the width of the transect belt to 2.5 metres wide, and 2.5 metres above the transect. This should be clearly noted on the data sheet.

❑ Count the actual numbers of 'target' species seen within the transect strip and estimate the size (in centimetres) of each of these fish.

Table 2.7 Logarithmic abundance categories used in estimates of abundance of numerically dominant fish species (Russ 1985).

Log 4 Abundance Category	Number of Fishes
1	1
2	2-4
3	5-16
4	17-64
5	65-256
6	257-1024
7	1025-4096
8	4097-16384

☞ *Experienced observers can count actual numbers of 'visually obvious' species to provide superior data to the abundance categories. For species where fish are particularly numerous, however, abundance categories are the best estimate.*

❑ Count actual numbers of all 'indicator' species.

❑ Estimate the abundances of 'visually obvious' species on a cumulative log 4, abundance scale from 1 to 8 (Russ 1985), Table 2.7.

☞ *Do not compromise getting a good overview of the community by trying to count all individuals of some taxa, while not getting reliable estimates of abundance for others.*

❑ One diver makes the census dive within the transect area while the other serves as a dive buddy swimming behind the observer and making general observations of the reef environment and the fish assemblages.

❑ In areas of high fish diversity and abundance, it is recommended that the tasks be separated. This can be done either by counting in 2 passes (different species each pass); or by having one diver concentrate on the 'target' species, while the second counts other species.

Length estimation

❑ Before undertaking studies of length-estimation through visual census, it is essential that the accuracy of the estimates are known. An exercise known as 'fiddle sticks' is used to test the diver's ability to estimate fish lengths underwater. This test is repeated until estimates are consistent. Details of this exercise are given later in this chapter (Section 2.8).

Coral Reefs

Data recording

❏ Count the fish. If benthic surveys (LIT) are done at the site they should use the same transect as the fish but always complete the fish count first.

❏ Record data onto the prepared data sheets (Figs. 2.37 and 2.38). Also record any relevant notes on the site (e.g. slope, visibility, exposure). If visibility causes a reduction in the width of the transect to 2.5 metres wide, and 2.5 metres above the transect, note this clearly in the data.

❏ Before starting the swim along the transect, the observer should get an overall impression of the species within the census area and tick (✓) all species seen. Estimates using log abundances are recorded by keeping a cumulative total on the data sheet during the swim down the 50 metre transect.

❏ Actual counts of fish are done for (at least) 'target' and 'indicator' species by recording each fish encountered within the transect as it is seen, and totalling the records after the count is completed.

❏ Record length estimates of 'target' species as the selected species are seen. This will give a length frequency histogram for each species.

Standardisation

❏ The observer must be an experienced fish counter. Ideally, censuses should be made by the same observer(s) to ensure consistency. By keeping the number of observers to a minimum, observer bias will be reduced.

❏ The diver's ability to estimate the distance of 2.5 metres (from the tape) should be verified before the fish census. Also verify the distance of 5 metres above the transect.

❏ Repeat training in length-estimation regularly to ensure accuracy. Bell *et al.* (1985) found that the ability to estimate length is reduced if divers do not practise it for 6 months.

❏ The recommended standard identification manuals are "Coral Reef Fishes. Caribbean, Indian Ocean and Pacific Ocean, Including the Red Sea" (Lieske and Myers 1994), "The Fishes of the Japanese Archipelago" (Masuda *et al.* 1984), "Damselfishes of the South Seas" (Allen 1975), "Micronesian Reef Fishes" (Myers 1989) and "Fishes of the Great Barrier Reef and Coral Sea" (Randall *et al.* 1990). Further taxonomic references are given at the end of this section.

❏ The fish surveys and benthic lifeform surveys (LIT method) should use the same sites. Both methods should ensure that replicate sites are as similar as possible. Replicate sites must be within the same reef habitats.

❏ At least 3 replicate censuses of non-overlapping areas of reef slope must be done to determine variability in composition of the communities within a reef site.

❑ The minimum requirements must always be met to ensure that the exchange of data is possible

❑ To avoid the diurnal-nocturnal changeover periods of fish (Carpenter *et al.* 1981), censuses should be done between 0900 and 1600 hours.

❑ As a general rule, no decompression dives should be allowed during censuses.

Data processing

❑ Enter data into the database using the structure described at the end of this chapter (Section 2.9).

❑ Information about the sample is entered into the sample table (XXCRSAMP) and a unique sample identifier (SAMPLE_ID) is allocated. The type of data collected in the sample is described by the DATA_TYPE field, which for the fish data is denoted by the letter "F".

❑ Enter data collected for the fish census into the data table (XXCRFDAT) using the SAMPLE_ID allocated in the sample table.

❑ Calculate the average length (AV_SIZE) of the 'target' species from the length estimates. Individual records from 'target' species can be stored in another table containing the SAMPLE_ID, FIELDCODE, size estimate (SIZE_EST) for each fish.

❑ When ambient environmental parameters are measured at the site another entry is made into the sample table and a unique sample identifier is allocated. The ambient parameters are denoted in the sample table by the letter "A".

❑ **Always check and verify data after entry.**

❑ Always backup data regularly.

Analysis

❑ The mid-point of an abundance category is used as the best estimate of abundance, except in the two highest log abundance categories (categories 7 and 8) in which the minimum of the category range is used: for category 7, an abundance of 1025 is used; and for category 8, an abundance of 4097 is used.

❑ Multivariate techniques or parametric and non-parametric statistics can be used to compare abundance data of many species.

❑ Simple linear regression techniques or multivariate ordination techniques can be used to relate the abundance and species richness and diversity of fishes to benthic community data (e.g. coral cover).

❑ Graphical presentation of patterns of species richness and abundance provide useful exploratory analysis.

Coral Reefs

❑ Other options for data presentation include partitioning the fishes into trophic groupings (eg. algal grazers, planktivores) and presenting estimates of the abundance of such groups.

❑ Rough estimates of species density and average lengths, together with length-weight relationships of many of the species can produce 'first estimates' of standing crop for biomass models, such as the ECOPATH model (Polovina 1984). It is emphasised that such biomass estimates are only 'first estimates'.

❑ Rigorous statistical comparisons of fish community structures will require greater replication. A pilot study should identify the best design, and determine what level of replication is needed within and between sites, to optimise statistical power of the analysis. See Chapter 7 and Russ and Choat (1988) for further discussion of experimental design and analysis.

Comments

❑ The baseline data collected by these protocols are part of a stratified sampling design (Fig. 2.40). Each reef fish visual census should sample all sites, depths and replicates of this stratified design.

❑ Fixed transects help to reduce variability caused by habitat heterogeneity during repeated surveys. If permanently marked transects are surveyed then different (e.g. repeated measures) analysis will be required.

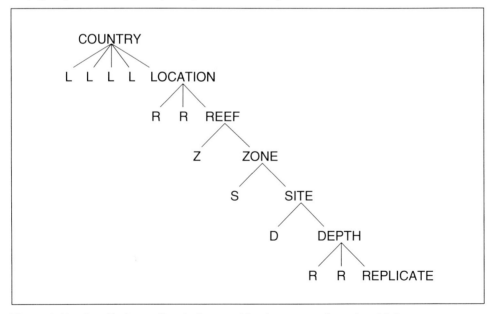

Figure 2.40 Stratified sampling design used for the survey of coral reef fish.

References

Allen, G.R. (1975). "Damselfishes of the South Seas". TFH Publications, Neptune City, New Jersey. 240pp.

Bell, J.D., G.J.S. Craik, D.A. Pollard and B.C Russell (1985). Estimating length frequency distributions of large reef fish underwater. Coral Reefs, 4: 41-44.

Carpenter, K.E., R.I. Miclat, V.D. Albaladejo and V.T. Corpuz (1981). The influence of substrate structure on the local abundance and diversity of Philippine reef fishes. Proceedings Fourth International Coral Reef Symposium, 2: 497-502.

Craik, G.J.S. (1981). Underwater survey of coral trout *Plectropomus leopardus* (Serranidae) populations in the Capricornia Section of the Great Barrier Reef Park. Proceedings Fourth International Coral Reef Symposium, 1: 53-58.

GBRMPA, (1978). Great Barrier Reef Marine Park Authority workshop on reef fish assessment and monitoring. GBRMPA Workshop Series, ISSN 0156-5842, No. 2, Great Barrier Reef Marine Park Authority, Townsville Australia.

GBRMPA, (1979). Workshop on Coral Trout Assessment Techniques. GBRMPA Workshop Series No. 3, Great Barrier Reef Marine Park Authority, Townsville Australia. 85pp.

Gomez, E.D., W.Y. Licuanan and V.V. Hilomen (1988). Reef fish-benthos correlations in the northwestern Philippines. Proceedings Sixth International Coral Reef Symposium, 3: 245-249.

Lieske, E. and R. Myers (1994). "Coral Reef Fishes. Caribbean, Indian Ocean and Pacific Ocean, Including the Red Sea". Harper Collins, London. 400pp.

McManus J.W., R.I. Miclat and V.P. Palaganas (1981). Coral and fish community structure of Sombrero Island, Batangas, Philippines. Proceedings Fourth International Coral Reef Symposium, 2: 271-280.

Masuda, H., K. Amaoka, C. Araga, T. Uyeno and T. Yoshiro (editors) (1984). "The Fishes of the Japanese Archipelago". 2 volumes. Tokai University Press. 807pp.

Myers, R.F. (1989). "Micronesian Reef Fishes". Coral Graphics, Guam. 298pp.

Polovina, J.J. (1984). An overview of the ECOPATH model. Fishbyte 2(2): 5-7.

Randall, J.E., G.R. Allen and R. Steene (1990). "Fishes of the Great Barrier Reef and Coral Sea". Crawford House Press, Australia. 507pp.

Russ, G.R. (1984a). Distribution and abundance of herbivorous grazing fishes in the Central Great Barrier Reef. I: Levels of variability across the entire continental shelf. Marine Ecology Progress Series, 20: 23-34.

Russ, G.R. (1984b). Distribution and abundance of herbivorous grazing fishes in the central Great Barrier Reef. II: Patterns of zonation of mid-shelf and outer shelf reefs. Marine Ecology Progress Series, **20**: 35-44.

Russ, G.R. (1985). Effects of protective management on coral reef fishes in the central Philippines. Proceedings Fifth International Coral Reef Symposium, **4**: 219-224.

Russ, G.R. and A.C. Alcala (1989). Effects of intense fishing pressure on an assemblage of coral reef fishes. Marine Ecology Progress Series, **56**: 13-27.

Russ, G.R. and J.H. Choat (1988). Reef resources: survey techniques and methods of study. South Pacific Commission/Inshore Fish. Res./WP.10.

Williams, D.McB. (1982). Patterns in the distribution of fish communities across the central Great Barrier Reef. Coral Reefs, **1**: 34-43.

Williams, D.McB. (1986). Temporal variation in the structure of reef slope fish communities (central Great Barrier Reef): Short-term effects of *Acanthaster* infestation. Marine Ecology Progress Series, **28**: 157-164.

Williams, D.McB. (1991). Patterns and processes in the distribution of coral reef fishes. In: P.F. Sale (editor). "The Ecology of Coral Reef Fishes". Academic Press, San Diego. pp 437-474.

Suggested reading

Allen, G.R. (1979). "Butterfly and Angel Fishes of the World. Volume 2". Mergus, Germany. 352pp.

Allen, G.R. (1991). "Damsel Fishes of the World". Mergus, Germany. 271pp.

Allen, G.R. (1985). Snappers of the world. FAO Fisheries Synopsis No. 125, Volume 6, 208pp., Plates I-XXVIII.

Carpenter, K.E. and G.R. Allen (1989). Emperor fishes and large-eye breams of the world. FAO Fisheries Synopsis, No. 124, Volume 9, 118pp., Plates I-VIII.

Christensen, V. and D. Pauly (1992). A guide to the ECOPATH II software system (version 2.1). ICLARM Software 6. International Center for Living Aquatic Resources Management, Manila, Philippines. 72 pp.

Phuket Marine Biological Center. "Taxonomy and Biology of Fishes from the Andaman Sea". Phuket Marine Biological Center. Special Publication Number 12 (1993). 143pp.

Randall, J.E. and P.C. Heemstra (1991). Revision of Indo-pacific groupers (Perciformes: Serranidae: Epinephelinae), with descriptions of five new species. Indo-pacific fishes, Number 20, 332pp.

Steene, R.C. (1977). "Butterfly and Angel Fishes of the World. Volume 1". Mergus, Germany. 144 pp.

2.6 Coral Recruitment

Coral Reefs

Abstract

The larval supply of coral species is examined by estimating the number of new corals settling on replicated units of substratum (terracotta tiles). The tiles are deployed at 5 metres depth on a regular basis (e.g. monthly), and are collected after exposure for equal amounts of time. After collection they are examined microscopically to count the new corals. Year-round sampling should be undertaken to determine the period, or periods, of recruitment. When they are known, sampling effort can be concentrated in these periods.

Background

Studies of coral recruitment have fallen into two categories: those that have measured the number of young colonies appearing on reefs between successive sampling periods (Connell 1973, Sakai and Yamazato 1984); and those that have used artificial substrata, which are removed from the reef and examined in the laboratory using a binocular microscope (Wallace and Bull 1981, Sammarco and Andrews 1989, Baggett and Bright 1985). After attaching to the substratum, coral larvae begin to lay down a permanent skeleton which is detectable almost immediately. However, it may take more than a year for newly settled corals to become visible to divers on the reef (Babcock 1988). Therefore, these two types of studies measure quite different things.

Artificial substrata (settlement plates) have frequently been used as tools to understand aspects of the life history of corals. The plates allow observation of the corals soon after settlement, and hence reduce the effect of post-settlement mortality on the measure of recruits arriving in a population. This mortality may be as high as 75% to 95% in the first year (Babcock 1985, Sato 1985). Studies of the seasonality of recruitment onto plates suggested the presence of a highly seasonal reproductive behaviour for some corals on the Great Barrier Reef (Wallace and Bull 1981). Further investigations of the reproductive timing of common corals subsequently revealed the synchronous mass spawning phenomenon (Harrison *et al.* 1984) as one of the causes of this seasonality. Patterns of recruitment onto settlement plates have also been used in attempts to understand the dispersal of coral larvae, both on a local scale around reefs (Sammarco and Andrews 1989), and on wider geographic scales (Baggett and Bright 1985).

These studies of recruitment have been limited, at least in the Indo-Pacific region, by the difficulty of identifying newly settled corals to species level. The use of larvae from known species, which have been reared in the laboratory, can give a more reliable measure of post-settlement mortality (Babcock and Mundy 1996). In addition,

Babcock and others have raised representative specimens of almost all major Indo-Pacific families. Photographs of these are presented in this manual (see Section 2.10 later in this chapter), and show that it is possible to reliably separate certain taxa. However, there are some groups, including whole families (e.g. Pectinidae and Faviidae) which cannot be separated or identified. Therefore, a cautious approach should be made in the identification of newly settled corals.

Advantages

❑ Sampling of newly settled coral larvae using tiles will minimise the effect of post-settlement mortality on observed recruitment.

❑ Racks to hold settlement plates are more easily relocated.

❑ Attachment and removal of plates onto racks is easier and quicker.

Disadvantages

❑ Identification of juvenile corals to species level is difficult.

Logistics

Personnel
❑ Dive teams consist of at least 2 divers and a person in the boat.

Equipment
❑ Small boat with outboard motors and safety equipment.

❑ SCUBA equipment.

❑ Slate and pencils.

❑ Labelled terracotta tiles (unglazed) which are flat, and uniform on each surface. Dimensions to be approximately 12 centimetres x 12 centimetres square and 1 centimetre thick.

❑ Racks of wire mesh to hold tiles.

❑ Stainless steel wire or cable ties to attach tiles to racks.

❑ Binocular dissecting microscope.

Site Selection

❑ Select the sites after a general survey of the reef slope so that sites are representative of that reef, i.e. all sites should be as similar as possible with respect to physical characteristics, slope, coral cover etc. Manta towing is a useful technique for site selection.

❑ The sites for studies of recruitment in corals and/or fish should be the same as those selected for collection of data on the 'adult' communities (see Sections on LIT and reef fish visual census, 2.3 and 2.5 respectively). This will provide a detailed description of the reef area being censused.

❑ At least 2 sites should be selected.

❑ Record the exact positions of all replicate sites. A GPS (Global Positioning System) is useful for relocation of the sites.

General procedure

❑ Attach the racks firmly to the bottom using metal pegs, at approximately 5 metres depth. Avoid sand and rubble areas when selecting sites.

❑ Position the racks so that the tiles are inclined at 45 degrees, and the top of the tile faces into the predominant swell or current (Fig. 2.41).

❑ Attach tiles to the racks using wire ties at a uniform distance above the bottom (approximately 20 centimetres).

❑ Each rack has 2 to 4 tiles which are separated so that they are not directly affected by adjacent tiles.

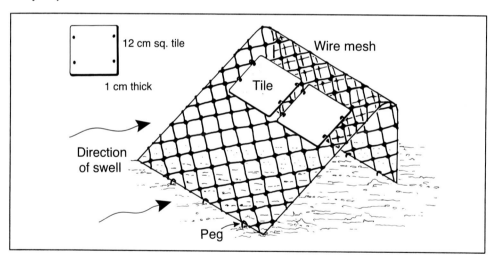

Figure 2.41   Tiles attached to racks for coral recruit settlement.

❑ 20 to 30 tiles are recommended for each site (i.e. 5 to 10 racks).

❑ Each rack should be 0.5 to 1 metre from other racks.

☞ *The sampling interval should not be less than 2 to 3 months to assess seasonal trends in recruitment. Times of successive deployment of tiles must be equal, and should not overlap.*

❏ Label tiles with an identification number before deployment. Put the number on the undersurface of the tile by engraving the tile or by using an indelible marker pen.

☞ *Preconditioning of tiles, by soaking in salt water, is desirable but optional. Ensure equal conditioning of all tiles used during the study, and take care to avoid settlement of corals.*

❏ Record the location of each tile (rack and site) after deployment.

❏ During collection, handle the tiles with great care to ensure that the surfaces are not rubbed, since this will crush newly settled corals.

❏ Transport the tiles back to the laboratory, ensuring that the surfaces are separated from each other by newspaper, or other padding.

❏ Wash the tiles in fresh water and dry in the sun.

❏ Store the tiles with suitable padding between each tile.

Standardisation

❏ Suitable tiles should be supplied from a single source and supplied to groups participating in regional studies. This can be done for minimal cost and will eliminate the need for cross-comparison and standardisation.

Data recording

❏ Record details of each tile i.e. location, rack number, tile number and dates of deployment.

❏ Identify the coral recruits on each tile using a dissecting microscope (see Section 2.10).

❏ Record the position (upper-side or under-surface), taxa and dimensions of each recruit (in millimetres).

Data processing

❏ Enter data into the database using the structure described at the end of this chapter (Section 2.9).

❏ Information about the sample is entered into the sample table (XXCRSAMP) and a unique sample identifier (SAMPLE_ID) is allocated. The type of data collected in the sample is described by the DATA_TYPE field, which for the coral recruitment data is denoted by the letter "C".

❏ Enter data collected for coral recruits into the data table (XXCRCRDT) using the SAMPLE_ID allocated in the sample table.

❏ Recruitment can be standardised as the number of recruits per unit area.

❏ **Always check and verify data after entry.**

❏ Always backup data regularly.

Analysis

❑ Summaries of species composition, and distribution and abundance of coral recruits, can be made.

❑ A variety of multivariate techniques can be used for data analysis.

❑ Where specific questions are to be addressed by surveys, greater replication will be required. Assess the level of replication using pilot studies to measure the level of variability over the scales being examined. See Chapter 7 for a discussion of experimental design.

References

Babcock, R.C. (1985). Growth and mortality of juvenile corals (*Goniastrea, Platygyra, Acropora*): the first year. Proceedings Fifth International Coral Reef Congress, Tahiti, **4**: 355-360.

Babcock, R.C. (1988). Fine-scale spatial and temporal patterns in coral recruitment. Proceedings Sixth International Coral Reef Symposium, Townsville, **2**: 635-641.

Babcock, R.C. and C.N. Mundy (1996). Coral recruitment: consequences of settlement choice for early growth and survivorship in two scleractinians. Journal of Experimental Marine Biology and Ecology, **206**: 179-201.

Baggett, L.S. and T.J. Bright (1985). Coral recruitment at the East Flower Garden reef (Northwestern Gulf of Mexico). Proceedings Fifth International Coral Reef Congress, Tahiti, **4**: 379-384.

Connell, J.H. (1973). Population ecology of reef building corals. In: Biology and geology of coral reefs. Volume II Biology 1. O.A. Jones and R. Endean (editors). Academic Press, New York, 480pp.

Harrison, P.L., R.C. Babcock, G.D. Bull, J.K. Oliver, C.C. Wallace and B.L. Willis (1984). Mass spawning in tropical reef corals. Science, **223**: 1186-1189.

Sakai, K. and K. Yamazato (1984). Coral recruitment to artificially denuded natural reef substrates on an Okinawan reef flat. Galaxea, **3**: 57-69.

Sammarco, P.W. and J.C. Andrews (1989). The Helix experiment: differential localised dispersal and recruitment patterns in Great Barrier Reef corals. Limnology and Oceanography, **34**: 898-914.

Sato, M. (1985). Mortality and growth of juvenile coral *Pocillopora damicornis* (Linnaeus). Coral Reefs, **4**: 27-33.

Wallace, C.C. and G.D. Bull (1981). Patterns of juvenile coral recruitment on a reef front during a spring-summer spawning period. Proceedings Fourth International Coral Reef Symposium, Manila, **2**: 345-350.

Coral Reefs

2.7 Coral Reef Fish Recruitment

Abstract

The replenishment of reef fish stocks with conspicuous sedentary juveniles is monitored by quantitative underwater visual surveys. Absolute counts of all recruits encountered are made along transects (50 metres in length) on the reef slope between 6 to 9 metres depth. Year-round sampling should be undertaken until the period, or periods of recruitment, are firmly established. Once the timing of recruitment is established, sampling effort can be concentrated in a few optimal periods.

Background

The sedentary nature of juveniles of many coral reef fish species, and their conspicuous colours, make it possible to monitor their abundance from very soon after they settle from the plankton to benthic habitats (Sale 1980). This offers the opportunity to investigate the roles of initial abundance and post-settlement mortality on future abundance in the population.

The replenishment of reef fish stocks has traditionally been monitored by quantitative visual counts of recruited juveniles. Such studies have shown that the settlement of reef fishes can be highly variable (Doherty and Williams 1988, Doherty 1991) and that major variations in initial abundance can become permanently fixed in the age structures and abundance of populations. This is consistent with the hypothesis that reef fish populations are 'recruitment-limited' (Doherty 1981). Monitoring of recruitment patterns can therefore be used to project future abundance (Doherty and Fowler 1994 a,b), in addition to hindcasting the spatial and temporal scales of the processes affecting larval supply (Doherty 1983).

Visual census is only applicable to those species which have conspicuous, countable juveniles. While this is satisfactory for many groups (e.g. the majority of pomacentrids and chaetodontids), it is not universal because the juveniles of many food fishes are either cryptic (e.g. serranids) or rare (e.g. lutjanids). Species which have cryptic or rare juveniles cannot be monitored by any adaptation of this technique. Similarly, the juveniles of some species are so mobile after settlement that the patterns of initial colonisation cannot be obtained except by continuous surveillance. Likewise, species subject to very high or variable post-settlement mortality will not be usefully monitored by infrequent surveys (Shulman and Ogden 1987). However, in species with relatively low post-settlement mortality rates and discrete recruitment pulses (e.g. summer), end-of-season recruitment surveys provide relative patterns of early post-settlement distributions (Williams et al. 1994).

Advantages

❑ The method is rapid and non-destructive.

❑ Simplicity and low cost permit repeated assessments.

❑ It utilises a minimum number of personnel and specialised equipment.

❑ It can be used to re-census the same area through time.

Disadvantages

❑ Observers must be well-trained and experienced in fish identification.

❑ Visual census of fish recruits is limited to species with conspicuous sedentary juveniles.

❑ The method is not useful for pelagic species.

Logistics

Personnel

❑ Dive teams should consist of at least 2 divers and a person on watch in the boat.

❑ At least 1 of the divers must be able to identify the fish recruits of the area and be familiar with the size limits that discriminate the recruits (young-of-the-year) from other year-classes.

Equipment

❑ Small boat with outboard motors and safety equipment.

❑ SCUBA equipment.

❑ Slates and pencils.

❑ 50 metre transect tapes, or transect lines, marked at regular intervals.

❑ 1 metre yardstick (reference length). For ease of operation, it is convenient to attach the metre-length to a handle, thus forming a T-piece (Fig. 2.42).

Maintenance

❑ Wash equipment, especially the tapes, with freshwater after use.

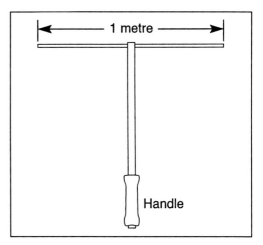

Figure 2.42 T-piece which is carried by the diver as a reference length.

Coral Reefs

Site Selection

❏ Conduct a general survey of the reef to select suitable sites on the windward reef slope which are representative of the reef. All sites should be as similar as possible with respect to physical characteristics, slope, and coral cover. Manta towing is useful for site selection.

❏ Flat or gently sloping sites are best since they contain the highest species diversity. Avoid variable habitats, such as spur formations, where divers are likely to encounter sand and fissures.

❏ At least 3 sites should be selected.

❏ The positions of all replicate sites should be recorded onto an aerial photograph or sketch of the reef. A GPS (Global Positioning System) can be very useful for positioning and relocating sites.

❏ Transects should be laid between 6 to 9 metres since this provides a workable compromise between the shallow surge zone and limits set by decompression.

General procedure

❏ At each site on a reef, at least 3 transect lines (50 metres) are laid haphazardly at 6 to 9 metres depth (below the crest).

❏ Transect lines should not overlap, each transect being separated by 10 to 20 metres.

❏ Lay the transect lines straight, following topographic contours within the recommended depth range (use depth gauge).

☞ *If a sudden change of slope is encountered, it is better to change the depth of the transect slightly if this will allow counts to be made on similar gradients.*

❏ Collect data on the benthic community structure at each site. If Line Intercept Transects are conducted at the site (see method earlier in this chapter), it is recommended that the LIT technique be used along the entire length of the transect laid for the visual census of fish recruits. The fish transects must be 50 metres, and should always be completed first.

❏ Wait 5 to 15 minutes before counting is begun to allow fishes to resume normal behaviour after laying the transects (Carpenter *et al.* 1981).

❏ The observer swims slowly (using SCUBA) along the transect, recording fish encountered within 1 metre either side (left and right) of the transect line. Use a 1-metre yardstick, or T-piece (Fig. 2.43), to verify whether fish recruits (juveniles) observed near the outer edge of the transect belt (1 metre from the transect line) should be included in the count.

❏ Hold the T-piece parallel to the substratum when measuring the transect width.

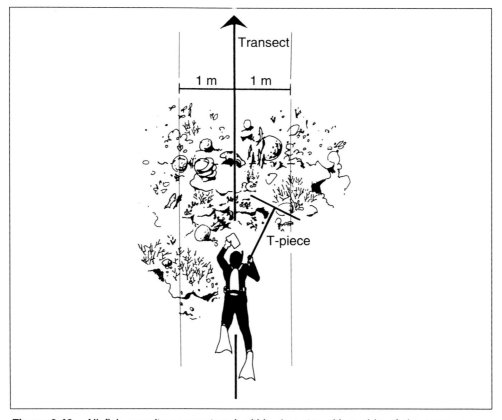

Figure 2.43 All fish recruits encountered within 1 metre either side of the transect are recorded.

❑ Count all recruits (absolute counts) by careful searching of benthic habitats along the transect. Count schooling species well ahead of the observer.

❑ Transects should not be broken into smaller units, as many species are uncommon to rare.

❑ As a general rule, decompression dives should be avoided and are not necessary using this protocol.

Standardisation

❑ The observer must be an experienced fish counter. Ideally, censuses should be made by the same observer(s) to ensure consistency among counts (i.e. reduce observer error by minimising the number of observers).

❑ The recommended standard identification manuals are "Coral Reef Fishes. Caribbean, Indian Ocean and Pacific Ocean, Including the Red Sea" (Lieske and Myers 1994), "The Fishes of the Japanese Archipelago" (Masuda *et al.* 1984), "Damselfishes of the South Seas" (Allen 1975), "Micronesian Reef Fishes" (Myers

1989) and "Fishes of the Great Barrier Reef and Coral Sea" (Randall *et al*. 1990). Further taxonomic references are given at the end of this section.

Data recording

❏ Record onto data sheets actual counts of all recruits encountered up to 1 metre either side of the transect.

Data processing

❏ At the end of each day, data should be entered into the database using the structure described at the end of this chapter (Section 2.9).

❏ Information about the sample is entered into the sample table (XXCRSAMP) and a unique sample identifier (SAMPLE_ID) is allocated. The type of data collected in the sample is described by the DATA_TYPE field, which for the coral recruitment data is denoted by the letter "R".

❏ Enter data collected for coral recruits into the data table (XXCRFRDT) using the SAMPLE_ID allocated in the sample table.

❏ **Always check and verify data after entry.**

❏ Always backup data regularly.

Analysis

❏ Summaries of species composition, and distribution and abundance of recruits, can be made.

❏ A variety of multivariate techniques can be used for data analysis to identify similarities among locations, or to map fish data onto benthic community data.

❏ Where specific questions are to be addressed by surveys, greater replication may be required. Assess the appropriate level of replication using pilot studies to measure the level of variability over the scales of space and time for the planned comparisons. Statistical power to detect differences should always be an important part of planning detailed surveys. See Chapter 7 for a discussion of sampling design.

Comments

❏ Any expansion of the protocol described here to monitor reef fish recruitment should increase the sampling at the habitat level within the study reef. For example, replicate sites could be surveyed on the leeward side of the reef or the reef flat.

This will allow comparison of reef habitat in addition to within reef and inter-reef comparisons.

References

Allen, G.R. (1975). "Damselfishes of the South Seas". TFH Publications, Neptune City, New Jersey. 240pp.

Carpenter, K.E., R.I. Miclat, V.D. Albaladejo and V.T. Corpuz (1981). The influence of substrate structure on the local abundance and diversity of Philippine reef fishes. Proceedings Fourth International Coral Reef Symposium, Manila, **2**: 497-502.

Doherty, P.J. (1981). Coral reef fishes: recruitment-limited assemblages? Proceedings Fourth International Coral Reef Symposium, Manila, **2**: 465-470.

Doherty, P.J. (1983). Recruitment surveys of coral reef fishes as tools for science and management. pp. 191-196 In: Baker, J.T., Carter, R.M., Sammarco, P.W. and Stark, K.P. (editors) "Proceedings: Inaugural Great Barrier Reef Conference", Townsville, Aug 28-Sept 2, 1983, JCU Press.

Doherty, P.J. (1991). Spatial and temporal patterns in recruitment. pp. 261-293. In: Sale, P.F. (editor) "The Ecology of Coral Reef Fishes". Academic Press. 754 pp.

Doherty, P.J. and D. McB. Williams (1988). The replenishment of coral reef fish populations. Oceanography and Marine Biology Annual Review, **26**: 487-551.

Doherty. P.J. and A.J. Fowler (1994a). Demographic consequences of variable recruitment: A congeneric comparison of two damselfishes. Bulletin of Marine Science, **54**: 297-313.

Doherty. P.J. and A.J. Fowler (1994b). An empirical test of recruitment limitation in a coral reef fish. Science, **263**: 935-939.

Lieske, E. and R. Myers (1994). "Coral Reef Fishes. Caribbean, Indian Ocean and Pacific Ocean, Including the Red Sea". Harper Collins, London. 400pp.

Masuda, H., K. Amaoka, C. Araga, T. Uyeno and T. Yoshiro (editors) (1984). "The Fishes of the Japanese Archipelago". 2 volumes. Tokai University Press. 807pp.

Myers, R.F. (1989). "Micronesian Reef Fishes". Coral Graphics, Guam. 298pp.

Randall, J.E., G.R. Allen and R. Steene (1990). "Fishes of the Great Barrier Reef and Coral Sea". Crawford House Press, Australia. 507pp.

Sale, P.F. (1980). The ecology of fishes on coral reefs. Oceanography and Marine Biology Annual Review, **18**: 367-421.

Coral Reefs

Shulman, M.J. and J.C. Ogden (1987). What controls tropical reef fish populations: recruitment or benthic mortality? An example in the Caribbean reef fish *Haemulon flavolineatum*. Marine Ecology Progress Series, **39**: 233-242.

Williams, D. McB., S. English and M.J. Milicich (1994). Annual recruitment surveys of coral reef fishes are good indicators of patterns of settlement. Bulletin of Marine Science, **54**(1): 314-331.

Suggested reading

Allen, G.R. (1979). "Butterfly and Angelfishes of the World. Volume 2". Mergus, Germany. 352pp.

Allen, G.R. (1991). "Damselfishes of the World". Mergus, Germany. 271pp.

Bellwood, D.R. and J.H. Choat (1989). A description of the juvenile phase colour patterns of 24 parrotfish species (family Scaridae) from the Great Barrier Reef, Australia. Records of the Australian Museum, **41**: 1-41.

Steene, R.C. (1977). "Butterfly and Angel Fishes of the World. Volume 1". Mergus, Germany. 144pp.

2.8 Training Techniques for Length Estimation

Abstract

This technique is used as part of the training required by divers conducting the visual census of fish (see Section 2.5). Divers are trained to estimate the lengths of fish underwater using a modification of the methods developed by the Great Barrier Reef Marine Park Authority Workshop (GBRMPA 1979).

Background

Counts of fish, together with estimates of their total length, allow the population size structure of the species counted to be calculated. Using length-weight relationships, the estimates of the length of fish can produce 'first estimates' of standing crop. In order to do this, divers must be able to estimate consistently the length of fish underwater. Therefore, before undertaking studies relying on length estimation, it is essential that the observers are trained to estimate lengths underwater, and that the accuracy of their estimates is known. The divers must be consistent.

To test the ability of the observer, they are asked to estimate underwater, the length of orange 17 millimetre (outer diameter) PVC electrical conduit, which is cut into lengths ('sticks') of between 0 and 100 centimetres. The use of fish models (Fig. 2.44) instead of, or in addition to, the 'sticks', improves the ability of the observer to transfer their size estimate skills to live fish, because the fish silhouette gives depth as well as length (Bell *et al.* 1985).

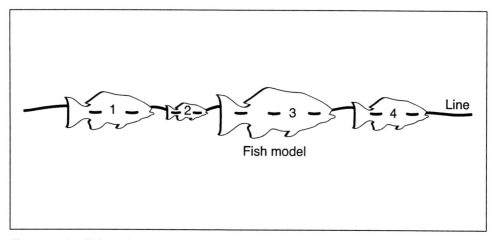

Figure 2.44 Fish models cut out of marine plywood.

Coral Reefs

Equipment

❏ Fish models, made of marine plywood (Fig. 2.44), and 'sticks' of assorted sizes. These can be attached to a 100 metre line to practice estimating total lengths of fishes while diving. Attach weights to the line to keep stop excessive movement

❏ Cut PVC into 50 lengths (sticks) so that when the 'sticks' are grouped into five 20-centimetre length classes (< 20, 21-40, 41-60, 61-80 and 81-100), they form a histogram approximating a normal curve, with a mean length of 50 centimetres and standard deviation of ±20 centimetres (Table 2.8).

❏ Slates, with data sheets (A4 underwater paper is recommended). Printed data sheets will assist the observer (and 'tester') to record the length estimates (Fig. 2.45).

❏ Pencils.

Table 2.8   Lengths used to train divers to consistently estimate fish length underwater.

<20 cm	21-40 cm	41-60 cm	61-80 cm	81-100 cm
6	22	41	61	82
12	24	42	62	88
18	26	43	63	94
	28	44	64	
	30	45	66	
	32	46	68	
	34	47	70	
	36	48	72	
	37	49	74	
	38	50	76	
	39	51	78	
	40	52	80	
		53		
		54		
		55		
		56		
		57		
		58		
		59		
		60		

ESTIMATION OF SIZE CLASSES

Name .... Date ....

Estimate		Trial 1 Size (cm)		Trial 2 Size (cm)		Trial 3 Size (cm)		Trial 4 Size (cm)	
1	26	___	___	___	___	___	___	___	___
2	27	___	___	___	___	___	___	___	___
3	28	___	___	___	___	___	___	___	___
4	29	___	___	___	___	___	___	___	___
5	30	___	___	___	___	___	___	___	___
6	31	___	___	___	___	___	___	___	___
7	32	___	___	___	___	___	___	___	___
8	33	___	___	___	___	___	___	___	___
9	34	___	___	___	___	___	___	___	___
10	35	___	___	___	___	___	___	___	___
11	36	___	___	___	___	___	___	___	___
12	37	___	___	___	___	___	___	___	___
13	38	___	___	___	___	___	___	___	___
14	39	___	___	___	___	___	___	___	___
15	40	___	___	___	___	___	___	___	___
16	41	___	___	___	___	___	___	___	___
17	42	___	___	___	___	___	___	___	___
18	43	___	___	___	___	___	___	___	___
19	44	___	___	___	___	___	___	___	___
20	45	___	___	___	___	___	___	___	___
21	46	___	___	___	___	___	___	___	___
22	47	___	___	___	___	___	___	___	___
23	48	___	___	___	___	___	___	___	___
24	49	___	___	___	___	___	___	___	___
25	50	___	___	___	___	___	___	___	___

Coral Reefs

Figure 2.45 Datasheet used in the 'size-estimation' exercise to test diver's ability to accurately estimate fish lengths underwater.

General procedure

❑ Several methods can be used to test the ability of each diver to estimate lengths underwater.

❑ Method 1:

» Thread the 'sticks' onto a 100 metre rope in random order. Each 'stick' is separated from the next by at least its own length and should be identified by a number.

» An 80 centimetre 'stick', marked in intervals of 10 centimetres, is located at one end of the rope as a reference length.

» Lay the rope across the reef slope at a depth between 8-10 metres.

» The divers swim along the 'stick' transect at a distance of 3 metres, and record the estimated lengths of each 'stick' (recorded in centimetres).

❑ Method 2 - the preferred method:

» Using plywood silhouettes of fish (Fig. 2.44), instead of the PVC 'sticks', repeat the process described above. The length is marked on the back of each model, and models are attached to a rope in random order.

❑ Method 3:

» 2 divers make up the team: a tester; and the diver being tested. The roles should be reversed after testing.

» The divers should remain approximately 3 metres apart.

Figure 2.46 A diver testing underwater length estimation with "sticks" cut from PVC conduit. Other divers record their estimates for later comparison.

» The diver conducting the test (tester) selects the sticks randomly from a pile and records the length onto a datasheet(Fig 2.46). As each stick is held up, the diver being tested estimates the length of the stick, recording the estimate onto a datasheet (Fig. 2.45).

» After the length of the stick is estimated it is placed in a second pile. On completion of the 50 sticks, the process is repeated.

» The actual lengths of the sticks in centimetres are estimated during several trials. In some trials, the sticks are held against a 'standard' - a 80 centimetre stick marked into 10 centimetre intervals.

Analysis

❏ After each trial, analyse the difference between the estimates (observer) and the actual length of the models (tester) using a paired T test (Sokal and Rohlf 1981).

❏ Inform the divers of their results after each trial, (that is, how their estimations compared to the known sizes), so they can adjust their estimation according to any bias shown in their estimates.

❏ Repeat the training exercises until the size frequency histogram from estimates attained by each diver is close to the known size frequency.

Discussion

❏ All divers who estimate lengths underwater must be trained, including 'experienced' fish length estimators. To correctly estimate length underwater, repeated practice, which includes the use of a marked standard and feedback on the kinds of errors being made, must be undertaken regularly.

❏ Rapid improvement can be made to a level where the observed distribution closely approximates the expected distribution.

❏ The use of plywood silhouettes of fish improves training. If these are not available a sample of freshly caught fish can be measured and then used for training.

References

Bell, J.D., G.J.S. Craik, D.A. Pollard and B.C. Russell (1985). Estimating length frequency distributions of large reef fish underwater. Coral Reefs, 4: 41-44.

GBRMPA (1979). Workshop on Coral Trout Assessment Techniques. GBRMPA Workshop Series No. 3. Great Barrier Reef Marine Park Authority, Townsville. 85pp.

Sokal, R.R. and F.J. Rohlf (1981). "Biometry. The Principles and Practise of Statistics in Biological Research". W.H. Freeman and Co., San Francisco.

Coral Reefs

2.9 Coral Reef Database Structure

Sample table

XXCRSAMP

Name	Type	Length/ Decimal	Description
SAMPLE_ID	C	9.0	The standard sample identification. This links the sample table to the data files. Format XXGGGNNNN XX = ISO country code. See codes in Appendix I GGG = study group code NNNN = running number
LOCATION	C	30.0	Location name e.g. Seribu Islands
REEF_NAME	C	30.0	Name of the reef surveyed (e.g. Malinjo, which is part of the Seribu Islands)
DATE	D	8.0	Date when data were gathered (using the format MM/DD/YY)
TIME	C	4.0	Time of sampling using the format HHMM (e.g. 1330 = 1:30 pm).
LATITUDE	C	7.0	Latitude of site in format AABBCCD AA = degrees BB = minutes CC = decimal seconds D = N (north) or S (south)
LONGITUDE	C	8.0	Longitude of site in format AAABBCCD AAA = degrees BB = minutes CC = decimal seconds D = E (east) or W (west)
REEF_ZONE	C	8.0	The zone of the reef sampled: FLAT = reef flat CREST = reef crest SLOPE = reef slope BASE = base of slope LAGOON = lagoon The above zone classifications may be prefixed by F=front, B=back, S=sheltered, E=exposed or P=pass/channel; e.g. EFLAT for exposed reef flat, BSLOPE for back reef slope
DATA_TYPE	C	1.0	Data code denoting the nature of the sample. Where: A = ambient; C = coral recruit; F = fish; M = manta tow; Q = quadrat; R = fish recruit; S = sediment; T = transect, V = video. Details are listed in the datacode table
DEPTH_M	N	5.2	Depth of the sampling site with reference to the crest. Measured in metres
TRANS_LENGTH	N	5.0	Length of transect.
TRANS_WIDTH	N	5.0	Width of transect
ACT_DEPTH	N	5.2	Actual depth during sampling. Measured in metres.
COLLECTORS	C	40.0	Name(s) of data collectors and their tasks
REMARKS	C	50.0	Additional observations regarding the site and the data

Ambient parameters table
XXCRADAT

Name	Type	Length/ Decimal	Description
SAMPLE_ID	C	9.0	The standard sample identification. This links the sample table to the data files. Format XXGGGNNNN (see sample table)
TEMP_TOP	N	5.2	Temperature reading at the top of the water column (30 cm below surface). Measured in degrees Celsius
TEMP_BOT	N	5.2	Temperature reading at the transect depth. Measured in degrees Celsius
SALN_TOP	N	5.2	Salinity reading at the top of the water column (30 cm below surface). Measured in ppt
SALN_BOT	N	5.2	Salinity reading at the transect depth. Measured in ppt
TURBIDITY	N	5.2	Visible depth of the standard secchi disc. Measured in metres
LIGHT	N	6.0	Light penetration of the water at transect depth measured with a portable light-meter in μmoles/m^2/sec
CLOUDCOVER	N	1.0	Cloud cover measured in oktas (0-8), where 0 is cloudless and 8 is complete cloud cover (Table 2.1). Listed in the datacode table.
WIND	N	1.0	Scale for wind force and sea state (Table 2.2). Listed in the datacode table.

Manta tow table
XXCRMDAT

Name	Type	Length/ Decimal	Description
SAMPLE_ID	C	9.0	The standard sample identification. This links the sample table to the data files. Format XXGGGNNNN (see sample table)
TOW_NO	N	3.0	Tow number, allocated sequentially for each 2-minute tow conducted at each reef
LC	N	1.0	Live hard coral cover (0-5) as listed in the datacode table, see Fig. 2.8
DC	N	1.0	Dead hard coral cover (0-5) as listed in the datacode table, see Fig. 2.8
SC	N	1.0	Soft coral cover (0-5) as listed in the datacode table, see Fig. 2.8
VIS	N	1.0	Visibility code (1-4) as listed in the datacode table, see Fig. 2.11
COT_NO*	N	3.0	Number of crown-of-thorns starfish (COT) counted
COT_SCAR*	C	1.0	Category of feeding scars as listed in the datacode table, see Table 2.3
COT_SIZE*	C	1.0	Size category of crown-of-thorns starfish (COT) (Table 2.4). Listed in the datacode table
OTHERS	C	40.0	General remarks on the other reef-associated organisms or other observations (e.g. dominant lifeforms or taxa, dynamite fishing site, fish abundance, etc.)

* Included if monitoring crown-of-thorns starfish.

Coral Reefs

Line intercept transect table
XXCRTDAT

Name	Type	Length/Decimal	Description
SAMPLE_ID	C	9.0	The standard sample identification. This links the sample table to the data files. Format XXGGGNNNN (see sample table).
REPLICATE	N	2.0	Replicate number of a transect at a site (each 20 metres in length).
BENTHOS	C	3.0	Coded benthic lifeform encountered along the transect. See Table 2.5. Listed in datacode table.
TRANSITION	N	5.0	The transition points along the transect. Measured in centimetres.
OCCURRENCE	N	1.0	Number of occurrences for an individual lifeform. If a single lifeform intercepts the transect more than once, an occurrence value of "1" is given for its first intercept, "2" for its second, "3" for the third and so on. Single occurrences are given the default value of "1".
LENGTH	N	5.0	Length of lifeform.
FIELDCODE	C	40.0	Code assigned to the taxonomic entity by the field researchers (see Section 2.11 for suggested codes). The code must uniquely link to one taxonomic identity. Description of the entity (i.e. the binomial name) must be given to the database manager* when a new code is created. This information is maintained in the alltaxon table.
NOTES	C	20.0	Additional notes observed by recorder (e.g. type of other fauna).

Permanent quadrat table
XXCRQDAT

Name	Type	Length/Decimal	Description
SAMPLE_ID	C	9.0	The standard sample identification. This links the sample table to the data files. Format XXGGGNNNN (see sample table).
REPLICATE	N	2.0	Replicate number of each 2x2 metre quadrat at the site.
SECTOR	N	2.0	Identifier of the sector within the quadrat (Fig. 2.33). Listed in the datacode table.
FIELDCODE	C	40.0	Code assigned to the taxonomic entity by the field researchers (see Section 2.11 for suggested codes). See XXCRTDAT for detail.
TAG_NO	C	1.0	Tag number of the coral colony inside the sector being measured.
M_TYPE	C	3.0	Measurement type: BR = branding coral (BR1 = branch 1, BR2 = branch 2 etc.) CM = massive coral CE = encrusting coral.
LENGTH_CM	N	5.1	Maximum length of the measured coral colony. Measured in centimetres.
WIDTH_CM	N	5.1	Maximum width of the measured coral colony. Measured in centimetres.
NOTES	C	20.0	Additional notes.

Sedimentation table
XXCRSDAT

Name	Type	Length/Decimal	Description
SAMPLE_ID	C	9.0	The standard sample identification. This links the sample table to the data files. Format XXGGGNNNN (see sample table).
REPLICATE	N	2.0	Replicate number of 2m x 2m quadrats at the site.
TRAP_NO	C	1.0	Collective identifier for each set of 3 sediment traps mounted together on each rod.
TUBE_NO	N	1.0	Identifies each of the individual tubes in the sediment trap.
DATE_SET	D	8.0	Date when sediment traps were set (using the format MM/DD/YY).
DATE_COLL	D	8.0	Date when sediment traps were collected (using the format MM/DD/YY).
DRYWT_GM	N	8.2	Dry weight of the sediment, measured in grams.
NOTES	C	40.0	Observations on disturbance to traps (e.g. fish in trap, fallen traps, etc.).

Reef fish census table
XXCRFDAT

Name	Type	Length/Decimal	Description
SAMPLE_ID	C	9.0	The standard sample identification. This links the sample table to the data files. Format XXGGGNNNN (see sample table).
REPLICATE	N	2.0	Replicate number of a transect at a site (each 50 metres in length).
ABUND_CAT	N	1.0	Log_4 abundance category (Table 2.7). Listed in the datacode table.
ACTUAL_CNT	N	5.0	Actual number or count of individuals of the particular taxon.
AV_SIZE	N	3.0	Average of size estimates for a 'target' species. Measured in centimetres.
FIELDCODE	C	40.0	Code assigned to the taxonomic entity by the field researchers (see XXCRTDAT for detail).
NOTES	C	20.0	Additional notes observed by the recorder.

Coral Reefs

Coral recruit data table
XXCRCRDT

Name	Type	Length/Decimal	Description
SAMPLE_ID	C	9.0	The standard sample identification. This links the sample table to the data files. Format XXGGGNNNN (see sample table).
REPLICATE	C	2.0	Number of rack (within site) on which tiles were placed.
TILE_NO	N	2.0	Number of the settlement tile (within the rack).
DATE_IN	D	8.0	Date when settlement plate was set (using the format MM/DD/YY).
DATE_OUT	D	8.0	Date when settlement plate was removed (format MM/DD/YY).
FIELDCODE	C	40.0	Code assigned to the taxonomic entity by the field researchers (see Section 2.11 for suggested codes). See XXCRTDAT for detail.
MEASURE	N	5.0	Diameter of specimen in millimetres.
POSITION	C	2.0	The position of each recruit on the plate - UP = upper-surface, UN = under-surface
NOTES	C	20.0	Additional notes observed by recorder (e.g. type of other fauna).

Reef fish recruit data table
XXCRFRDT

Name	Type	Length/Decimal	Description
SAMPLE_ID	C	9.0	The standard sample identification. This links the sample table to the data files. Format XXGGGNNNN (see sample table).
REPLICATE	N	2.0	Replicate number of a transect (each 50 metres in length).
ACTUAL_CNT	N	5.0	Actual number of individuals of the particular species
FIELDCODE	C	40.0	Code assigned to the taxonomic entity by the field researchers (see XXCRTDAT for detail).
NOTES	C	20.0	Additional notes observed by recorder (e.g. type of other fauna).

Taxonomic Table
ALLTAXON

Name	Type	Length/Decimal	Description
FIELDCODE	C	40.0	Code assigned to the taxonomic entity by the field researchers. The code must link uniquely to one taxonomic entity. Description of the entity (binomial name) must be given to the database manager when a new code is created.
TAXCODE	C	10	Unique code used to represent individual taxa. The codes are generated by the system manager. The TAXCODE ensures that the same kind of living things have the same code despite the fact that field researchers may give them different FIELDCODEs.
SPECNAME	C	35	Species name (Latin binomial).
GENUSNAME	C	35	Genus name.
FAMILYNAME	C	35	Family name.
ORDERNAME	C	35	Order name.
CLASSNAME	C	35	Class name.
PHYLANAME	C	35	Phylum name.
AUTHORITY	C	50	Name of authority, an organisation, or a system that was used as a reference to classify samples.
REF_CODE	C	20	Reference code for samples which are stored in a reference collection, museum or herbarium. This allows researchers to look at an actual specimen which has been assigned this classification.

Data code table
DATACODE

Field name	Data Value	Explanation
ABUND_CAT	1	1
	2	2 to 4
	3	5 to 16
	4	17 to 64
	5	65 to 256
	6	257 to 1024
	7	1025 to 4096
	8	4097 to 16384
BENTHOS	AA	Algal assemblage
	ACB	*Acropora* coral with branching growth form
	ACD	*Acropora* with digitate growth form
	ACE	*Acropora* coral with encrusting growth form
	ACS	*Acropora* coral with submassive growth form
	ACT	*Acropora* coral with tabulate growth form
	CA	Coralline algae

	CB	Other coral taxon with branching growth form
	CE	Other coral taxon with encrusting growth form
	CF	Other coral growth form with foliose growth form
	CHL	*Heliopora* sp. (blue coral)
	CM	Other coral taxon with massive growth form
	CME	*Millepora* sp. (fire coral)
	CMR	Mushroom corals (Fungiidae), except for *Lithophyllon* sp., *Podabacia* sp.
	CS	Other coral taxon with submassive/digitate growth form
	DC	Recently dead coral
	DCA	Dead coral covered with algae
	DDD	Missing data
	HA	*Halimeda* sp. (algae)
	MA	Macroalgae
	OT	Others (anemone, gorgonians, hydroid, ascidian, giant clam, etc.)
	R	Rubble
	RCK	Rock
	S	Sand
	SC	Soft coral
	SI	Silt
	SP	Sponge
	TA	Turf algae
	WA	Water (fissures deeper than 50 cm)
	ZO	Zoanthid
CLOUDCOVER	0	no cloud
	1	≤ 1 okta, but > 0
	2	2 oktas
	3	3 oktas
	4	4 oktas
	5	5 oktas
	6	6 oktas
	7	7 oktas
	8	8 oktas
COT_SCAR	A	Absent (no feeding scars)
	P	Present (1 to 10 feeding scars)
	C	Common (> 10 feeding scars)
COT_SIZE	S	Small (average size 1 to 15 centimetres)
	L	Large (average size > 15 centimetres)
DATA TYPE	A	Sample record refers to data in the ambient data file XXCRADAT
	C	Sample record refers to data in the coral recruitment data file XXCRCRDT
	F	Sample record referes to data in the fish visual census data files XXCRFDAT
	M	Sample record refers to data in the manta tow data file XXCRMDAT
	Q	Sample record refers to data in the quadrat data file XXCRQDAT
	R	Sample record refers to data in the fish recuitment data file XXCRFRDT
	S	Sample record refers to data in the sediment data file XXCRSDAT
	T	Sample record refers to data in the transect data file XXCRTDAT
	V	Sample record refers to data in the video transect data file XXCRVDAT
DC	0	0% dead coral cover
	1	1 to 10% dead coral cover

	2	11 to 30% dead coral cover
	3	31 to 50% dead coral cover
	4	51 to 75% dead coral cover
	5	76 to 100% dead coral cover
LC	0	0% live coral cover
	1	1 to 10% live coral cover
	2	11 to 30% live coral cover
	3	31 to 50% live coral cover
	4	51 to 75% live coral cover
	5	76 to 100% live coral cover
POSITION	UP	Upper-surface of the settlement tile
	UN	Under-surface of the settlement tile
SC	0	0% soft coral cover
	1	1 to 10% soft coral cover
	2	11 to 30% soft coral cover
	3	31 to 50% soft coral cover
	4	51 to 75% soft coral cover
	5	76 to 100% soft coral cover
SECTOR	#	The top of the quadrat is nearest the crest. Start numbering from the top left. Number sequentially left to right in top row; go down to the next row and number right to left; go down to the next row etc. (see Fig. 2.33)
VIS	1	< 6 metres visibility (Fig. 2.10)
	2	6 to 12 metres visibility (Fig. 2.10)
	3	12 to 18 metres visibility (Fig. 2.10)
	4	> 18 metres visibility (Fig. 2.10)
WIND	1	0 to 5 knots, sea calm (Table 2.2)
	2	6 to 10 knots, sea smooth (Table 2.2)
	3	11 to 15 knots, sea slight (Table 2.2)
	4	16 to 20 knots, sea moderate (Table 2.2)
	5	21 to 25 knots, sea rough (Table 2.2)

Coral Reefs

2.10 Identification of Juvenile Corals

These photo-micrographs were obtained using scanning electron-microscopy on juvenile corals of known parentage. Several colonies of each species represented in this section were collected from the reef prior to spawning. Individual colonies were each placed in a separate aquarium. After spawning, gametes were collected from at least two colonies of the same species. These gametes were mixed, and then placed into buoyant sealed plankton mesh containers which were deployed over the reef. The larvae were then settled onto artificial settlement plates in the laboratory. Individual plates were removed from the aquaria at several time intervals after settlement. Hence, each specimen photographed was of known age and identity.

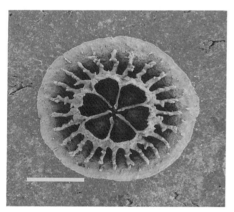

Figure 2.47 *Pocillopora damicornis.*
4 days old. Scale 0.5mm

Figure 2.48 *Pocillopora damicornis.*
2 weeks old. Scale 1mm

Figure 2.49 *Pocillopora damicornis.*
6 weeks old. Scale 0.5mm

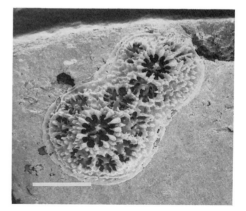

Figure 2.50 *Pocillopora damicornis.*
6 weeks old. Scale 1mm

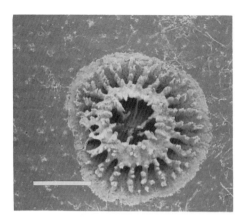

Figure 2.51 *Seriatopora hystrix.*
2 weeks old. Scale 0.7mm

Figure 2.52 *Seriatopora hystrix.*
2 weeks old. Scale 0.5mm

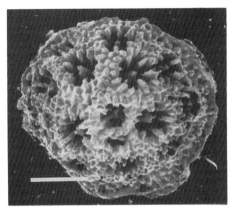

Figure 2.53 *Seriatopora hystrix.*
5 months old. Scale 0.8mm

Figure 2.54 *Stylophora pistillata.*
6 days old. Scale 0.7mm.

Figure 2.55 *Stylophora pistillata.*
6 days old. Scale 0.2mm.

Figure 2.56 *Stylophora pistillata.*
6 weeks old. Scale 1mm.

Coral Reefs

Figure 2.57 *Acropora palifera.*
3 weeks old. Scale 1mm.

Figure 2.58 *Acropora palifera.*
3 weeks old. Scale 0.25mm.

Figure 2.59 *Acropora millepora.*
3 months old. Scale 0.5mm

Figure 2.60 *Acropora millepora.*
3 months old. Scale 0.25mm

Figure 2.61 *Acropora millepora.* 5 months
old, apical polyp has begun
to differentiate. Scale 1mm.

Figure 2.62 *Acropora millepora.* 3 months
old composite colony, note fusion
of right colonies. Scale 1mm.

Figure 2.63 *Acropora tenuis.*
1 month old. Scale 0.25mm.

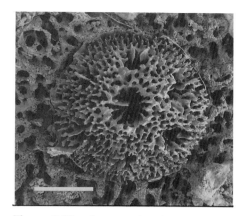

Figure 2.64 *Acropora tenuis.*
5 months old. Scale 1mm.

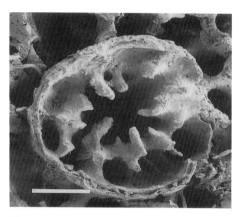

Figure 2.65 *Montipora digitata.*
3 months old. Scale 0.25mm

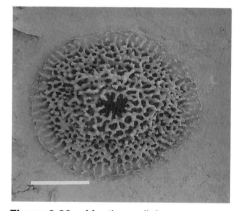

Figure 2.66 *Montipora digitata.*
5 months old. Scale 1mm

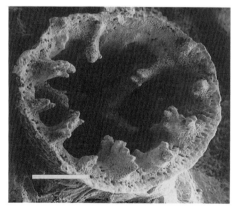

Figure 2.67 *Goniopora lobata.*
4 months old. Scale 0.25mm.

Figure 2.68 *Porites* sp.
<6 weeks old. Scale 0.2mm.

Coral Reefs

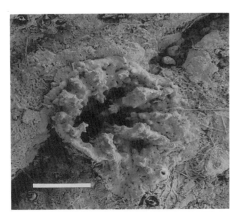

Figure 2.69 *Platygyra sinensis.*
7 months old. Scale 0.5mm.

Figure 2.70 *Platygyra sinensis.*
8 months old. Scale 1mm.

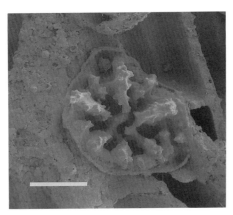

Figure 2.71 *Oxypora lacera.*
5 months old. Scale 0.5mm

Figure 2.72 *Oxypora lacera.*
6 months old. Scale 1mm

Figure 2.73 *Lobophyllia corymbosa.*
3 months old. Scale 0.5mm.

Figure 2.74 *Lobophyllia corymbosa.*
6 months old. Scale 1mm.

Coral Reefs

Figure 2.75 *Galaxea fascicularis.*
3 months old. Scale 0..25mm.

Figure 2.76 *Galaxea fascicularis.*
5 months old. Scale 0.5mm.

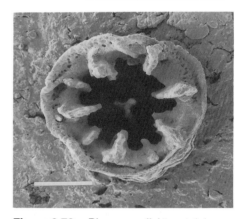

Figure 2.77 *Physogyra lichtensteini.*
6 weeks old. Scale 0.25mm

Figure 2.78 *Physogyra lichtensteini.*
5 months old. Scale 0.25mm

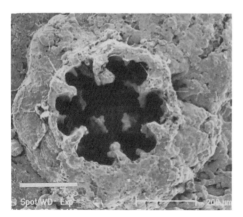

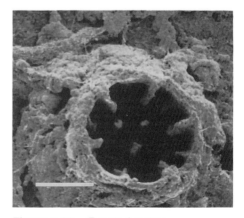

Figure 2.79 *Fungia fungites.*
3 months old. Scale 0.2mm.

Figure 2.80 *Fungia fungites.*
5 months old. Scale 0.2mm.

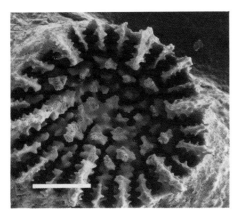

Figure 2.81   *Culicia* sp.
Adult. Scale 1mm.

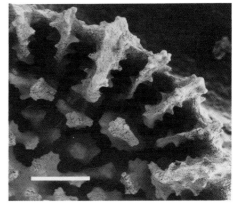

Figure 2.82   *Culicia* sp.
Adult. Scale 0.25mm.

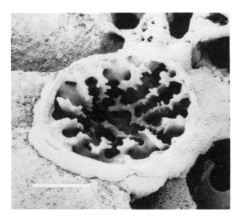

Figure 2.83   *Tubastrea diaphana.*
4 months old. Scale 1mm

Figure 2.84   *Tubastrea diaphana.*
4 months old. Scale 0.25mm

2.11 Coral Species Codes

Acanthastrea echinata . . . . . ACAECHI

Acanthastrea hillae . . . . . . ACAHILL

Acanthastrea lordhowensis . ACALORD

Acanthastrea rotundoflora . ACAROTU

Acrhelia horrescens . . . . . ACHHORR

Acropora aculeus . . . . . . ACRACUL

Acropora acuminata . . . . . ACRACUM

Acropora anthocercis . . . . ACRANTH

Acropora aspera . . . . ACRASPE

Acropora austera . . . . ACRAUST

Acropora brueggemanni . . . . ACRBRUE

Acropora carduus . . . . . . ACRCARD

Acropora caroliniana . . . . ACRCARO

Acropora cerealis . . . . . . ACRCERE

Acropora chesterfieldensis . . ACRCHES

Acropora clathrata . . . . . . ACRCLAT

Acropora copiosa . . . . ACRCOPI

Acropora cuneata . . . . . ACRCUNE

Acropora cytherea . . . . . ACRCYTH

Acropora danai . . . . ACRDANA

Acropora dendrum . . . . . ACRDEND

Acropora digitifera . . . . . . ACRDIGI

Acropora divaricata . . . . ACRDIVA

Acropora donei . . . . ACRDONE

Acropora echinata . . . . . . ACRECHI

Acropora elseyi . . . . ACRELSE

Acropora exquisita . . . . . . ACREXQU

Acropora florida . . . . ACRFLOR

Acropora formosa . . . . . . ACRFORM

Acropora gemmifera . . . . . ACRGEMM

Acropora grandis . . . . . . ACRGRAD

Acropora granulosa . . . . . ACRGRAN

Acropora horrida . . . . ACRHORR

Acropora humilis . . . . . . ACRHUMI

Acropora hyacinthus . . . . . ACRHYAC

Acropora kirstyae . . . . ACRKIRS

Acropora latistella . . . . ACRLATI

Acropora listeri . . . . ACRLIST

Acropora longicyathus . . . . ACRLONG

Acropora loripes . . . . ACRLORI

Acropora lovelli . . . . ACRLOVE

Acropora lutkeni . . . . ACRLUTK

Acropora magnifica . . . . ACRMAGN

Acropora microclados . . . . ACRMICL

Acropora microphthalma . . ACRMICR

Acropora millepora . . . . . ACRMILL

Acropora monticulosa . . . . ACRMONT

Acropora multiacuta . . . . . ACRMULT

Acropora nana . . . . ACRNANA

Acropora nasuta . . . . ACRNASU

Acropora nobilis . . . . ACRNOBI

Acropora palifera . . . . ACRPALI

Acropora paniculata . . . . . ACRPANI

Acropora parilis . . . . ACRPARI

Acropora pruinosa . . . . ACRPRUI

Acropora pulchra . . . . . . ACRPULC

Acropora rambleri . . . . . . ACRRAMB

Acropora robusta . . . . . . ACRROBU

Acropora samoensis . . . . . ACRSAMO

Acropora sarmentosa . . . . ACRSARM

Acropora secale . . . . ACRSECA

Acropora selago . . . . ACRSELA

Coral Reefs

Acropora solitaryensis	ACRSOLI	*Australomussa rowleyensis*	AUMROWL
Acropora spicifera	ACRSPIC	*Barabattoia amicorum*	BARAMIC
Acropora stoddarti	ACRSTOD	*Blastomussa merleti*	BLAMERL
Acropora subglabra	ACRSUBG	*Blastomussa wellsi*	BLAWELL
Acropora subulata	ACRSUBU	*Cataphyllia jardinei*	CATJARD
Acropora tenella	ACRTENE	*Caulastrea curvata*	CAUCURV
Acropora tenuis	ACRTENU	*Caulastrea echinulata*	CAUECHI
Acropora teres	ACRTERE	*Caulastrea furcata*	CAUFURC
Acropora valenciennesi	ACRVALE	*Caulastrea tumida*	CAUTUMI
Acropora valida	ACRVALI	*Coeloseris mayeri*	COEMAYE
Acropora vaughani	ACRVAUG	*Coscinaraea columna*	COSCOLU
Acropora verweyi	ACRVERW	*Coscinaraea crassa*	COSCRAS
Acropora willisae	ACRWILL	*Coscinaraea exesa*	COSEXES
Acropora yongei	ACRYONG	*Coscinaraea wellsi*	COSWELL
Alveopora allingi	ALVALLI	*Cycloseris costulata*	CYCCOST
Alveopora catalai	ALVCATA	*Cycloseris cyclolites*	CYCCYCL
Alveopora excelsa	ALVEXCE	*Cycloseris erosa*	CYCEROS
Alveopora fenestrata	ALVFENE	*Cycloseris hexagonalis*	CYCHEXA
Alveopora marionensis	ALVMARI	*Cycloseris marginata*	CYCMARG
Alveopora spongiosa	ALVSPON	*Cycloseris patelliformis*	CYCPATE
Alveopora tizardi	ALVTIZA	*Cycloseris sinensis*	CYCSINE
Alveopora verrilliana	ALVVERR	*Cycloseris somervillei*	CYCSOME
Anacropora forbesi	ANAFORB	*Cycloseris vaughani*	CYCVAUG
Anacropora matthaii	ANAMATT	*Cynarina lacrymalis*	CYALACR
Anacropora puertogalerae	ANAPUER	*Cyphastrea agassizi*	CYPAGAS
Anacropora reticulata	ANARETC	*Cyphastrea chalcidicum*	CYPCHAL
Anacropora spinosa	ANASPIN	*Cyphastrea glomerata*	CYPGLOM
Astreopora cucullata	ASTCUCU	*Cyphastrea japonica*	CYPJAPO
Astreopora explanata	ASTEXPL	*Cyphastrea microphthalma*	CYPMICR
Astreopora gracilis	ASTGRAC	*Cyphastrea ocellina*	CYPOCEL
Astreopora listeri	ASTLIST	*Cyphastrea serailia*	CYPSERA
Astreopora myriophthalma	ASTMYRI	*Cyphastrea tanabensis*	CYPTANA
Astreopora ocellata	ASTOCEL	*Diaseris distorta*	DIADIST
Astreopora suggesta	ASTSUGG	*Diaseris fragilis*	DIAFRAG
Ausralogyra zelli	AUSZELL	*Diploastrea heliopora*	DIPHELI

Echinophyllia aspera	ECLASPE	*Favites russelli*	FVSRUSS
Echinophyllia echinata	ECLECHI	*Fungia concinna*	FUNCONC
Echinophyllia echinoporoides	ECLECHP	*Fungia corona*	FUNCORO
Echinophyllia orpheensis	ECLORPH	*Fungia danai*	FUNDANA
Echinophyllia patula	ECLPATU	*Fungia echinata*	FUNECHI
Echinopora gemmacea	ECHGEMM	*Fungia fralinea*	FUNFRAL
Echinopora hirsutissima	ECHHIRS	*Fungia fungites*	FUNFUNG
Echinopora horrida	ECHHORR	*Fungia granulosa*	FUNGRAN
Echinopora lamellosa	ECHLAME	*Fungia horrida*	FUNHORR
Echinopora mammiformis	ECHMAMM	*Fungia klunzingeri*	FUNKLUN
Euphyllia ancora	EUPANCO	*Fungia moluccensis*	FUNMOLU
Euphyllia cristata	EUPCRIS	*Fungia paumotensis*	FUNPAUM
Euphyllia divisa	EUPDIVI	*Fungia repanda*	FUNREPA
Euphyllia glabrescens	EUPGLAB	*Fungia scabra*	FUNSCAB
Euphyllia yaeyamaensis	EUPYAEY	*Fungia scruposa*	FUNSCRU
Favia danae	FAVDANA	*Fungia scutaria*	FUNSCUT
Favia favus	FAVFAVU	*Fungia simplex*	FUNSIMP
Favia helianthoides	FAVHELI	*Fungia spinifera*	FUNSPIN
Favia laxa	FAVLAXA	*Galaxea astreata*	GALASTR
Favia lizardensis	FAVLIZA	*Galaxea fascicularis*	GALFASC
Favia maritima	FAVMARI	*Gardineroseris planulata*	GARPLAN
Favia matthaii	FAVMATT	*Goniastrea aspera*	GOSASPE
Favia maxima	FAVMAXI	*Goniastrea australensis*	GOSAUST
Favia pallida	FAVPALL	*Goniastrea edwardsi*	GOSEDWA
Favia rotumana	FAVROTU	*Goniastrea favulus*	GOSFAVU
Favia rotundata	FAVROTD	*Goniastrea palauensis*	GOSPALA
Favia speciosa	FAVSPEC	*Goniastrea pectinata*	GOSPECT
Favia stelligera	FAVSTEL	*Goniastrea retiformis*	GOSRETI
Favia veroni	FAVVERO	*Goniopora burgosi*	GONBURG
Favites abdita	FVSABDI	*Goniopora columna*	GONCOLU
Favites chinensis	FVSCHIN	*Goniopora djiboutiensis*	GONDJIB
Favites complanata	FVSCOMP	*Goniopora fruticosa*	GONFRUT
Favites flexuosa	FVSFLEX	*Goniopora lobata*	GONLOBA
Favites halicora	FVSHALI	*Goniopora minor*	GONMINO
Favites pentagona	FVSPENT	*Goniopora norfolkensis*	GONNORF

Coral Reefs

Goniopora palmensis	. . . GONPALM	*Lithophyllon lobata*	. . . . . LITLOBA
Goniopora pandoraensis	. . GONPAND	*Lithophyllon undulatum*	. . . LITUNDU
Goniopora pendulus	. . . . GONPEND	*Lobophyllia corymbosa*	. . . LOBCORY
Goniopora somaliensis	. . . GONSOMA	*Lobophyllia hataii*	. . . . . . LOBHATA
Goniopora stokesi	. . . . . . GONSTOK	*Lobophyllia hemprichii*	. . . LOBHEMP
Goniopora stutchburyi	. . . GONSTUT	*Lobophyllia pachysepta*	. . . LOBPACH
Goniopora tenuidens	. . . . GONTENU	*Madracis kirbyi*	. . . . MADKIRB
Halomitra pileus	. . . . . . HALPILE	*Merulina ampliata*	. . . . . . MERAMPL
Heliofungia actiniformis	. . . HELACTI	*Merulina scabricula*	. . . . . MERSCAB
Heliopora coerulea	. . . . . . HEPCOER	*Millepora exaesa*	. . . . MILEXAE
Herpolitha limax	. . . . . . HERLIMA	*Montastrea annuligera*	. . MORANNU
Herpolitha weberi	. . . . . . HERWEBE	*Montastrea curta*	. . . . . MORCURT
Heteropsammia cochlea	. . . HETCOCH	*Montastrea magnistellata*	. MORMAGN
Hydnophora exesa	. . . . . . HYDEXES	*Montastrea multipunctata*	. MORMULT
Hydnophora grandis	. . . . HYDGRAN	*Montastrea valenciennesi*	. . MORVALE
Hydnophora microconos	. . . HYDMICR	*Montipora aequituberculata*	MONAEQU
Hydnophora pilosa	. . . . . HYDPILO	*Montipora altasepta*	. . . . MONALTA
Hydnophora rigida	. . . . . HYDRIGI	*Montipora angulata*	. . . . MONANGU
Leptastrea inaequalis	. . . . LERINAE	*Montipora cactus*	. . . . . MONCACT
Leptastrea pruinosa	. . . . . . LERPRUI	*Montipora caliculata*	. . . . MONCALI
Leptastrea purpurea	. . . . . LERPURP	*Montipora capitata*	. . . . MONCAPI
Leptastrea transversa	. . . . . LERTRAN	*Montipora capricornis*	. . . MONCAPR
Leptoria phrygia	. . . . LEPPHRY	*Montipora cebuensis*	. . . . MONCEBU
Leptoseris explanata	. . . . . LESEXPL	*Montipora confusa*	. . . . . MONCONF
Leptoseris foliosa	. . . . LESFOLI	*Montipora corbettensis*	. . . MONCORB
Leptoseris gardineri	. . . . . LESGARD	*Montipora crassitiberculata*	. MONCRAS
Leptoseris hawaiiensis	. . . . LESHAWA	*Montipora danae*	. . . . . MONDANA
Leptoseris incrustans	. . . . LESINCR	*Montipora digitata*	. . . . . MONDIGI
Leptoseris mycetoseroides	. . . LESMYCE	*Montipora efflorescens*	. . . MONEFFL
Leptoseris papyracea	. . . . LESPAPY	*Montipora effusa*	. . . . . MONEFFU
Leptoseris scabra	. . . . . . LESSCAB	*Montipora florida*	. . . . . MONFLOR
Leptoseris solida	. . . . LESSOLI	*Montipora foliosa*	. . . . . MONFOLI
Leptoseris yabei	. . . . LESYABE	*Montipora foveolata*	. . . . MONFOVE
Lithophyllon edwardsi	. . . . LITEDWA	*Montipora friabilis*	. . . . . . MONFRIA
Lithophyllon levistei	. . . . . . LITLEVI	*Montipora gaimardi*	. . . . . MONGAIM

116

Montipora grisea	MONGRIS	*Pavona cactus*	PAVCACT
Montipora hirsuta	MONHIRS	*Pavona clavus*	PAVCLAV
Montipora hispida	MONHISP	*Pavona danai*	PAVDANA
Montipora hoffmeisteri	MONHOFF	*Pavona decussata*	PAVDECU
Montipora informis	MONINFO	*Pavona explanulata*	PAVEXPL
Montipora mactanensis	MONMACT	*Pavona frondifera*	PAVFRON
Montipora malampaya	MONMALA	*Pavona maldivensis*	PAVMALD
Montipora millepora	MONMILL	*Pavona minuta*	PAVMINU
Montipora mollis	MONMOLL	*Pavona varians*	PAVVARI
Montipora monasteriata	MONMONA	*Pavona venosa*	PAVVENO
Montipora orientalis	MONORIE	*Pectinia alcicornis*	PECALCI
Montipora peltiformis	MONPELT	*Pectinia lactuca*	PECLACT
Montipora samarensis	MONSAMA	*Pectinia paeonia*	PECPAEO
Montipora setosa	MONSETO	*Pectinia teres*	PECTERE
Montipora spongodes	MONSPON	*Physogyra lichtensteini*	PHYLICH
Montipora spumosa	MONSPUM	*Physophyllia ayleni*	PHIAYLE
Montipora stellata	MONSTEL	*Platygyra daedalea*	PLADAED
Montipora tuberculosa	MONTUBE	*Platygyra lamellina*	PLALAME
Montipora turgescens	MONTURG	*Platygyra pini*	PLAPINI
Montipora undata	MONUNDA	*Platygyra ryukyuensis*	PLARYUK
Montipora venosa	MONVENO	*Platygyra sinensis*	PLASINE
Montipora verrucosa	MONVERR	*Platygyra verweyi*	PLAVERW
Mycedium elephantotus	MYCELEP	*Plerogyra eurysepta*	PLEEURY
Mycedium robokaki	MYCROBO	*Plerogyra exerta*	PLEEXER
Oulastrea crispata	OURCRIS	*Plerogyra simplex*	PLESIMP
Oulophyllia bennettae	OULBENN	*Plerogyra sinuosa*	PLESINU
Oulophyllia crispa	OULCRIS	*Plerogyra turbida*	PLETURB
Oxypora crassispinosa	OXYCRAS	*Plesiastrea versipora*	PLSVERS
Oxypora glabra	OXYGLAB	*Pocillopora damicornis*	POCDAMI
Oxypora lacera	OXYLACE	*Pocillopora eydouxi*	POCEYDO
Pachyseris gemmae	PACEMM	*Pocillopora meandrina*	POCMEAN
Pachyseris rugosa	PACRUGO	*Pocillopora verrucosa*	POCVERR
Pachyseris speciosa	PACSPEC	*Pocillopora woodjonesi*	POCWOOD
Palauastrea ramosa	PALRAMO	*Podabacia crustacea*	PODCRUS
Pavona bipartita	PAVBIPA	*Polyphyllia talpina*	POLTALP

Coral Reefs

Porites annae	PORANNA
Porites aranetai	PORARAN
Porites attenuata	PORATTE
Porites australiensis	PORAUST
Porites cf. evermanni	POREVER
Porites cumulatus	PORCUMU
Porites cylindrica	PORCYLI
Porites deformis	PORDEFO
Porites eridani	PORERID
Porites horizontalata	PORHORI
Porites latistellata	PORLATI
Porites lichen	PORLICH
Porites lobata	PORLOBA
Porites lutea	PORLUTE
Porites mayeri	PORMAYE
Porites murrayensis	PORMURR
Porites nigrescens	PORNIGR
Porites rus	PORRUS
Porites sillimaniana	PORSILL
Porites solida	PORSOLI
Porites stephensoni	PORSTEP
Porites tenuis	PORTENU
Porites vaughani	PORVAUG
Psammocora contigua	PSACONT
Psammocora digitata	PSADIGI
Psammocora explanulata	PSAEXPL
Psammocora haimeana	PSAHAIM
Psammocora nierstraszi	PSANIER

Psammocora profundacella	PSAPROF
Psammocora superficialis	PSASUPE
Pseudosiderastrea tayami	PSETAYA
Sandalolitha robusta	SANROBU
Scapophyllia cylindrica	SCACYLI
Scolymia vitiensis	SCOVITI
Seriatopora caliendrum	SERCALI
Seriatopora hystrix	SERHYST
Siderastrea savignyana	SIDSAVI
Stylocoeniella armata	STLARMA
Stylocoeniella guentheri	STLGUEN
Stylophora pistillata	STYPIST
Symphyllia agaricia	SYMAGAR
Symphyllia radians	SYMRADI
Symphyllia recta	SYMRECT
Symphyllia valenciennesii	SYMVALE
Trachyphyllia geoffroyi	TRAGEOF
Tubastraea aurea	TUBAURE
Turbinaria frondens	TURFRON
Turbinaria heronensis	TURHERO
Turbinaria irregularis	TURIRRE
Turbinaria mesenterina	TURMESE
Turbinaria peltata	TURPELT
Turbinaria radicalis	TURRADI
Turbinaria reniformis	TURRENI
Turbinaria stellulata	TURSTEL
Zoopilus echinatus	ZOOECHI

CHAPTER 3 MANGROVE ECOSYSTEMS

General Introduction

Mangrove ecosystems presently cover an area of about 20 million hectares worldwide. They are the main vegetation type in protected intertidal areas along tropical and subtropical coastlines. Within this broad geographic range, mangroves grow in environmental settings ranging from highly humid to extremely arid conditions, and on soils which range from pure clays to peat, sand, or coral rubble. It is therefore not surprising that mangrove ecosystems display extreme variations in plant composition, forest structure and growth rate.

Mangrove ecosystems have significant ecological, environmental and socioeconomic value. These include:

❑ Maintenance of coastal water quality.

❑ Reduction in the severity of coastal storm, wave and flood damage.

❑ Nursery areas and feeding grounds for commercial and artisanal fisheries.

❑ Important habitat and feeding grounds for a range of benthic and pelagic marine animals and bird species.

❑ Production of timber and other forest products.

During this century, large areas of mangrove forests have been destroyed by overexploitation and conversion to other uses. Anthropogenic activities still continue to be the major cause of degradation and loss of mangrove ecosystems in all parts of the world. Monitoring programs, and more specific environmental studies, are required to ensure that mangrove ecosystems are conserved and managed sustainably to maintain their environmental, ecological and socioeconomic benefits.

Many environmental factors influence the diversity and productivity of mangrove ecosystems. These include climate, geomorphology, tidal range, freshwater input and soil characteristics. All mangrove surveys should include measurements of environmental parameters that characterise the conditions existing at the site at the time of data collection.

A variety of methods are available to study the environmental characteristics and community structure of mangrove ecosystems at varying levels of detail. Selection of the most appropriate method depends, among other things, on the desired end product, time constraints, personnel available and budget. This chapter focuses on methods for describing major environmental characteristics and community structure of mangrove vegetation. These survey methods have been chosen to generate baseline data that can be used to monitor changes and make comparisons between mangrove ecosystems in different parts of the world.

Two sampling methods are described for studying the community structure of mangrove forests. The first is based on angle count cruising techniques using a relascope, and the second is the 'transect line plot' (TLP) method. The relascope method is easy and fast to execute, but the results are relative rather than absolute. This method is particularly suited to quick initial surveys, but is not suitable for more detailed or long-term quantitative monitoring. The 'transect line plot' method is required for a more detailed study of the community structure, but it is more laborious and time consuming.

The primary productivity of plant communities is often correlated with the area of leaves per unit ground area (leaf area index, L). Generally, gross primary production (i.e. gross canopy photosynthesis) increases with increasing leaf area index. Furthermore, leaf area index is a useful indicator of environmental stress, because leaf shedding and leaf growth are usually sensitive to a wide range of environmental factors. Hence, a method for estimating leaf area index in mangrove canopies is included in this chapter. Estimates of leaf area index may be converted to estimates of nett canopy photosynthesis by multiplying leaf area index by the average rate of photosynthesis per unit leaf area, if the latter is known.

Methods are also described for the collection of soil samples and the measurement of soil salinity, pH and redox potential (Eh). These are important physicochemical characteristics which influence local species distributions and growth, either directly or indirectly, through their effect on nutrient availability and other soil properties. Two methods for fractionating the soil into different particle sizes are included. The 'hydrometer method' of Bouyoucos (1962) provides faster processing of samples (with acceptable accuracy) than the more robust 'pipette method' described by Buchanan (1984).

Tidal regime is a major factor influencing species distribution, abundance and growth, and soil physicochemical properties. Hence, a simple method is decribed to quantify the frequency and duration of tidal inundation.

3.1 Mangrove Soils

Abstract

Soil characteristics are one of the most important environmental factors directly affecting mangrove productivity and structure. This section contains simple and practical field methods for the analysis of mangrove soils. These methods concentrate on major physical and chemical properties of the soils, such as pH (hydrogen ion concentration), Eh (Redox potential), salinity and particle size. Two methods are presented for the analysis of soil particle size: a 'hydrometer method' (after Bouyoucos 1962) and 'pipette method' (after Buchanan 1984).

Samples are collected at low tide, when the substratum is uncovered, and should be taken in conjunction with methods describing the plant community structure for the area (Angle-Count Cruising, Transect Line Plots). It should be emphasised that for a complete picture of the effects of soil factors on mangrove productivity and structure, longer time-scale effects must be considered and long-term studies of factors, including nutrient status, must be made.

Background

Since mangrove soils are typically waterlogged, and hence anaerobic, microbial decomposition takes place through a series of oxygen-reduction (redox) processes. The redox potential (Eh) is a quantitative measure of reducing power which provides a diagnostic index of the degree of anaerobiosis or anoxia (Patrick and Delaune 1977). Totally anoxic sediments have redox potentials below -200 mV, while typical oxygenated soils have potentials of above +300 mV. The measurement of Eh has been used as a rapid means of assessing the potential impact of additional organic input to a marine sediment (Pearson and Stanley 1979). Reliable measurements of redox potential require great care to minimise exposure of the soil sample to air.

All soils and sediments (unconsolidated or 'loose' deposits) are composed of particles with a wide range of sizes. These are generally divided into 3 major groups: gravel (greater than 2 millimetres), sand (0.062 - 2 millimetres) and mud (silt and clay). The mud fraction is further divided into coarse silt (62 - 15.6 µm), fine silt (15.6 - 3.9 µm) and clay (less than 3.9 µm). A graded scheme for soils is given by the Wentworth Grade Scale (Table 3.1, see Folk 1974). The species composition and growth of mangroves is directly affected by the physical composition of mangrove soils. The proportions of clay, silt and sand, together with the grain size, dictate the permeability (or hydraulic conductivity) of the soil to water, which influences soil salinity and water content. Nutrient status is also affected by the physical composition of the soil, with clay soils generally higher in nutrients than sandy soils.

The acidity of the soil influences the chemical transformation of most nutrients and their availability to plants. Most mangrove soils are well buffered, having a pH in the range of 6 to 7, but some have a pH as low as 5. Measurement of the acidity or alkalinity of soils using pH must be done with fresh samples to avoid oxidation of iron pyrites (a common constituent of mangrove soils) to sulphuric acid, thus giving a much lower value of pH than normally occurs *in situ*.

The salinity of mangrove soils has a significant affect on the growth and zonation of mangrove forests. The majority of mangrove species grow best in low to moderate salinities (25 ppt), although there appear to be marked differences in the ability of species to tolerate very high salinities. In the past, soil salinity was measured in pore water that drained into a hole made by removing a sediment core. This is not a reliable measure of soil salinity because of uncertainty about the source of water filling the core hole. The method presented in this manual, where pore water is physically squeezed from the soil sample, is preferred.

Table 3.1 Wentworth Grade Scale.

	Name	Grade limits	
		mm	µm
Gravel	Boulder	>256	
	Cobble	256 - 64	
	Pebble	64 - 4	
	Granule	4 - 2	
Sand	Very coarse sand	2 - 1	2000 - 1000
	Coarse sand	1 - 0.5	1000 - 500
	Medium sand	0.5 - 0.25	500 - 250
	Fine sand	0.25 - 0.125	250 - 125
	Very fine sand	0.125 - 0.062	125 - 62
Mud	Silt	0.062 - 0.0039	62 - 3.9
	Clay	<0.0039	<3.9

Advantages

❑ The methods use simple, inexpensive and easy to maintain equipment.

❑ The instruments used are easily carried and do not restrict the movement of the field investigator.

❑ The methods are quick and are easily repeatable, and therefore enable the collection of statistically significant sample sizes.

Disadvantages

❑ The particle-size fractionation assumes that all the particles are spheres and that they all have specific densities similar to that of quartz. However, if the prescribed methodological conditions are closely followed the method has been shown to be accurate.

❑ The laboratory fractionation of the soil particles is a relatively long and tedious task.

❑ Preparation of the sample and the process of sedimentation analysis can be very time consuming.

Logistics

Personnel
❑ Teams of 3 field personnel are optimal for the collection of samples and onsite determination of the soil parameters. The same team will usually do the onsite structural study of the mangrove community.

❑ Other personnel may be needed for the laboratory analysis of soil samples.

Field equipment
❑ A stainless steel D-section corer to collect soil samples (Fig. 3.1).

❑ A pH/millivoltmeter with a platinum electrode to measure Eh and pH.

❑ Mercury thermometer enclosed in a protective casing - used to measure temperature with an accuracy of ±0.5 degrees Celsius. If available, use a thermoprobe which is compatible with the millivoltmeter used for Eh and pH measurements.

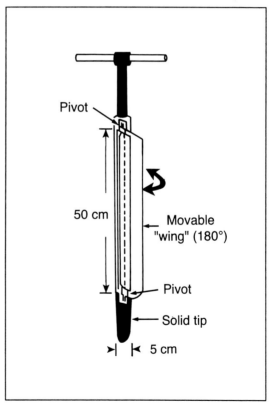

Figure 3.1   A D-section corer is used to collect soil samples.

Mangroves

❏ A refractometer (Fig. 2.1) to measure salinity. A portable conductivity-salinity analyser can be used, if available.

❏ Airtight containers to hold soil samples, e.g. plastic jars or sealed plastic bags.

❏ A pore water squeezer. An improvised squeezer for use in the field may be made from a 10 or 20 millilitre syringe (Fig. 3.2). For this technique a small piece of filter paper or tissue is placed in the bottom of the syringe, after which the soil is added. Squeeze the water through the filter using the plunger. Other more sophisticated squeezers may be used, if available.

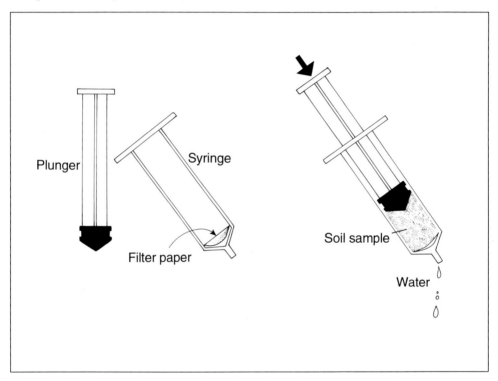

Figure 3.2 Water can be squeezed from the soil sample using a pore water squeezer.

❏ Soil colour charts.

❏ Preprinted data sheets (Fig.3.3) and pencils. Small notebooks can also be used, but care should be taken to reduce their exposure to water. A new notebook should be used for each field trip.

Laboratory equipment
❏ Laboratory equipment is listed with the laboratory techniques described later in this section.

MANGROVE SOIL, FIELD MEASUREMENTS

Location .... Sample ID ....
Site... Transect N° .... Plot N° ....
Date .... Time .... Latitude .... Longitude ....
Impact code .... Impact assement ....
Forest type .... Drainage conditions ....
Soil colour .... Remarks ....

Parameter	Replicate	Depth 10cm	40cm
Eh	1	_____	_____
	2	_____	_____
	3	_____	_____
	$\bar{x}$ = _____		$\bar{x}$ = _____
pH	1	_____	_____
	2	_____	_____
	3	_____	_____
	$\bar{x}$ = _____		$\bar{x}$ = _____
Temp. (°C)	1	_____	_____
	2	_____	_____
	3	_____	_____
	$\bar{x}$ = _____		$\bar{x}$ = _____
Salinity (‰)	1	_____	_____
	2	_____	_____
	3	_____	_____
	$\bar{x}$ = _____		$\bar{x}$ = _____

Figure 3.3 A data sheet with suggested format for the recording and processing of the measurements in the field.

Mangroves

Figure 3.4   Taking a soil sample using a D-section corer.

Maintenance

❏ After field use, clean off all soil particles adhering to the surfaces of the D-section corer. Rinse with freshwater and wipe dry with a clean cloth.

❏ Keep the Platinum electrode surface of the millivoltmeter well cleaned by overnight immersion in 10% sulphuric or chromic acids. Remove batteries from the meter and store in a cool, dry place.

Site selection

❏ Soil samples should be taken from all plots in conjunction with methods describing forest structure (plotless and permanent plot methods) and measurement of forest primary productivity. See relevant sections in this chapter.

❏ The number of sites sampled at each location will depend on the observed structural heterogeneity of the ecosystem in terms of topography and/or plant species distribution. See relevant sections in this chapter.

❏ At each site, 5 to 10 replicates should be regarded as a minimum for soil samples. For specific studies the minimum number of replicate samples required can be calculated statistically, while the available analytical facilities may set the upper limit.

General procedure

❏ Record the depth from which each sample is collected, the soil colour, site drainage conditions, the forest type (dominant species) and note the soil consistency and texture. See relevant sections in this chapter.

❏ Take at least 3 replicates in each plot. See relevant sections in this chapter.

❏ Take a core of soil using a D-section corer (Fig. 3.4). This type of corer minimises disturbance and compaction of the soil sample and allows direct measurement of soil parameters. In very hard soils, where it is difficult to use the corer, a hole should be dug to a depth of about 50 centimetres.

❏ It is recommended that Eh, pH and salinity be measured at the site (*in situ*). Always measure the Eh as soon as the core is removed. If it is not possible to measure *in situ*, store the soil samples in airtight containers in a cold box to keep the temperature of the samples below ambient, and take them to the laboratory as quickly as possible. Storing on ice keeps the soils anaerobic and inhibits further microbial activity. Some procedures for the initial treatment of mangrove soils are given in Table 3.2.

☞ *Freezing is not advisable.*

Table 3.2 Procedures for the initial treatment of mangrove soils (after Allen 1989).

Analysis Required	Recommended Treatment
pH; Eh	rapid examination of fresh material
organic nitrogen and phosphorous fraction; extractable ions, humic fractions and all peat extractions	analysis of fresh material or short, cold storage periods
proximate organic analysis; nitrogen availability	air drying (40 °C)
particle fractionation; loss on ignition; total concentration of mineral constituents, phosphorous and sulphur	oven drying at 100 °C to 105 °C, without boiling

Soil pH and Eh

❏ Calibrate electrodes with appropriate standards just before measurements are taken.

❏ Measure the redox potential (Eh) as soon as the core is removed.

❏ Carefully insert the electrode into the core of sediment 10 centimetres below the top of the core (Fig. 3.5).

❏ Ensure that the contacts of the electrode are properly connected to the digital pH/millivoltmeter, which measures the electrical potential. Leave the probe in the soil until the readings have stabilised (it may take some time for the electrodes to equilibrate).

❏ Correct the measured potentials to Eh (vs. a reference electrode) by addition of + 244 mV to the reading.

❏ If a corer has not been used, then dig a hole and insert the probes into the wall of the hole 5 to 10 centimetres below the surface.

Figure 3.5 Taking readings from a core sample collected using a D-corer.

❑ In soft soils, the electrodes can be probed directly into the soil; in hard soils, however, remove the sample and mix 1 part soil to 2 parts water (by volume) before using the meter.

☞ *Do not measure pH of air dried and re-wetted soils because oxidation of iron pyrites to sulphuric acid will give artificially low pH values.*

❑ Always measure both pH and Eh.

❑ Always carry out replicate determinations to obtain reproducible results.

Temperature
❑ Carefully insert the thermometer or thermoprobe into the core of sediment 10 centimetres below the top of the core.

Salinity
❑ Salinity is measured with a refractometer (Fig 2.1), or a conductivity-salinity analyser, if available.

❑ Remove a sample of soil from the core at 10 centimetres and 40 centimetres along the core (measured from the soil surface).

❑ Place the soil in the bottom of a 10 or 20 millilitre syringe (with filter paper in place) and push the plunger until a few drops of water are extracted (Fig. 3.2).

❑ Place a few drops of the water squeezed from the soil under the cover of the refractometer. Hold the cover down, and looking through the eyepiece, face the instrument to the light so that the salinity can be read (Fig. 2.1).

❑ If using a conductivity-salinity analyser a larger water sample will be required. Calibrate electrodes with appropriate standards before samples are measured.

Soil particle-size analysis
❑ Take subsamples of soil from the core for particle-size analysis.

❑ Take approximately 100 grams of soil at 10 centimetres and 40 centimetres along the core (see Fig. 3.4). Measure the distance from the soil surface.

❑ Place samples in labelled airtight containers (plastic bags or jars) for transport back to the laboratory.

Laboratory procedure

Two methods are described for analysis of soil particle-size. The choice of method will depend on the equipment available. The method described by Buchanan (1984) is robust and widely used; however, the samples take some time to process. Hence, an alternative method developed by Bouyoucos (1962) has been included, which uses simple equipment and speeds up the processing time.

Hydrometer method for particle size analysis (after Bouyoucos, 1962).

The hydrometer method determines the percentage of sand, silt and clay in the soil using the differential settling rates of soil particles from suspension in water (Bouyoucos 1962). Large particles (i.e. sand) settle out of suspension more rapidly than do small particles (i.e. clay). The hydrometer is designed to measure the density of the suspension.

The percentage of material in suspension at the end of 40 seconds represents the silt/clay in the sample. To determine the amount of clay in the sample the percentage of material still in suspension after 2 hours is calculated. From these readings it is then possible to calculate the percentage of silt and sand in the sample. The hydrometer method determines the total amount of sand; it cannot subdivide the sands into their various fractions. Fractionation of the sand can be achieved by sieving.

The settling rate is affected by temperature because the density and viscosity of water change with temperature - settling time is faster at higher temperature. Hence, it is necessary to correct the hydrometer readings for temperature:

>> **Add** 0.36 graduations for every 1 °C **above** 20 °C.

>> **Subtract** 0.36 graduations for every 1 °C **below** 20 °C.

Equipment

❑ Amyl alcohol to dissipate froth on the top of the soil solution.

❑ Balance accurate to 1 milligram - to weigh the soil samples.

❑ Beaker - 600 millilitre .

❑ Deionised water - used to leach highly charged cations (e.g. Ca^{2+}, Al^{3+}) that may cause soil to aggregate.

❑ Drying oven - able to heat to 105° C.

❑ 6% hydrogen peroxide - to dissolve organic matter.

❑ Hydrometer.

❑ Measuring cylinder - 1 litre .

❑ Mortar and pestle.

❑ Parafilm.

❑ Pencils.

❑ Petri dish.

❑ Plastic wash bottle for deionised water.

❑ Preprinted data sheets (Fig. 3.6) or notebooks.

MANGROVE SOIL, HYDROMETER ANALYSIS

Location .... Sample ID ....

Site.. Transect N° .... Plot N° ....

Date .... Time .... Latitude .... Longitude ....

Forest type .... Remarks ....

Depth	10 cm			40 cm		
Replicate	1	2	3	1	2	3
Wt. of total sample (g)						
Blank: temperature						
hydrometer						
reading + correction						
40 secs: temperature						
hydrometer						
reading + correction						
2 hours: temperature						
hydrometer						
reading + correction						
Hydrometer correction						
Weight of clay (g)						
Weight of silt (g)						
Weight of sand (g)						
MEAN % SAND						
MEAN % SILT						
MEAN % CLAY						

Figure 3.6 Preprinted data sheet to record laboratory analysis of soils using the hydrometer method (Bouyoucos).

Mangroves

❑ 1N sodium hexametaphosphate or 1N sodium hydroxide - dispersing agent.

❑ Stirrer.

❑ Stopwatch.

❑ Water bath - useful to maintain sediment solutions at 20 ℃.

Maintenance

❑ Wash all equipment after use with freshwater.

Procedure for hydometer method

❑ Place soil sample on a petri dish and oven dry (105 ℃).

❑ Break up soil aggregates using a mortar and pestle.

❑ Weigh 50 grams of dried sediment (to produce approximately 15 grams of silt and clay fraction - 100 grams of sediment is needed in the case of very sandy soils).

❑ Place soil into the beaker (600 millilitre volume).

❑ Half fill the beaker with deionised water, and add 100 millilitres of 6% hydrogen peroxide. Use the hydrogen peroxide until oxidation is complete (i.e. no further frothing is seen).

❑ Mix well, cover and stand overnight (15 to 20 hours).

❑ Add 5 millilitres of dispersing agent (1N sodium hexametaphosphate or 1N sodium hydroxide).

❑ Calibrate the hydrometer - take blank readings of the dispersing solution (no soil):

» Pour 5 millilitres of dispersing agent into a 1 litre measuring cylinder.

» Make up the volume to 1 litre with deionised water.

» Place the hydrometer in the cylinder, determine the scale reading and note the temperature.

» If temperature is above 20 ℃ then use a water bath to maintain temperature at 20 ℃. If a water bath is not available then readings will need to be corrected.

» Empty and wash the measuring cylinder.

❑ Place the beaker on a stirrer and stir until any soil aggregates are broken down.

❑ Transfer the contents of the beaker to a 1 litre measuring cylinder. Use the wash bottle of deionised water to wash out the beaker, and make up the volume to exactly 1 litre with deionised water.

❏ Seal the mouth of the cylinder with a piece of parafilm, then place the palm of one hand over the top of the cylinder and shake the cylinder thoroughly (invert several times) until the sediment is evenly suspended throughout the water column.

❏ Add a few drops of amyl alcohol if there is froth on the top of the soil suspension.

❏ Place the cylinder on a solid, level table and note the exact time.

❏ At 40 seconds place the hydrometer gently into the cylinder and immediately take a hydrometer reading. Note the temperature of the soil suspension.

❏ Remove the hydrometer carefully and wash it.

☞ *The hydrometer must be clean each time it is used.*

❏ Take another hydrometer reading exactly 2 hours after sedimentation was begun and note the temperature of the soil suspension.

☞ *Temperature affects the hydrometer readings which have been calibrated to 20 °C. While corrections can be made to the readings, it is recommended that a water bath (preferably thermostatically-controlled) be used to maintain sediment solutions at about 20 °C .*

Particle-size Fractionation (after Buchanan, 1984).

The sample is sieved to separate the gravel and sand from the silt-clay fraction. The silt-clay fraction is then graded using pipette analysis of a column of sediment based on the principle of sedimentation, which says that large particles will fall faster and farther than small particles through a column of distilled water in a given time (Table 3.3).

Table 3.3 Times of settling for the Wentworth Grade Scale (at 20 °C).

Diameter (μm)	Settling distance (cm)	Time		
		Hours	Minutes	Seconds
62.5	20			58
31.2	10		1	56
15.6	10		7	44
7.8	10		31	0
3.9	10	2	3	0

From this table it can be seen that particles of 15.6 μm will fall 10 centimetres in 7 minutes 44 seconds. Hence, if a 20 millilitre pipette sample is taken from 10 centimetres below the surface after 7 minutes 44 seconds has lapsed, and if the

133

material in the pipette is subsequently dried and weighed, it should represent the weight of the material less than 15.6 µm that is contained in a volume of 20 millilitres of the original solution. To obtain an estimate for the litre of suspension this figure is multiplied by 50. The weights of material lying between the grade limits 62 µm to 15.6 µm can be calculated using the known weights of materials 62 µm and 15.6µm.

☞ *All calculations in Table 3.3 assume that fractionation is done at 20 °C. If a thermostatically-controlled water bath is not available, immerse the cylinder in a simple water bath at the ambient temperature in order to buffer the effects of room temperature fluctuations.*

❏ If temperature is not 20 °C, recalculate settling velocities before analysing soil samples. A new table can be calculated from the *Stoke's Law Formula*:

$$V = C r^2$$

where: V = settling velocity in centimetres sec^{-1}

C is a constant, and

r = radius of particle in centimetres

$$C = \frac{2 (d_1 - d_2) g}{9z}$$

where: d_1 = density of the particle = 2.65 (quartz);

d_2 = density of water

g = acceleration of gravity = 980 cm sec^{-2}

z = viscosity of water in dyne sec cm^{-2} (this value can be extracted from physical tables for water viscosity; 1 dyne sec/cm^2 = 1 poise; 1 centipoise = 0.01 poise).

» At 15 °C to 30 °C, d2 = 1, therefore:

$$C = \frac{2 (2.65 - 1) 980}{9z} = \frac{3234}{9z}$$

Equipment
❏ Balance accurate to 1 milligram - to weigh the soil samples.

❏ Beaker - 1 litre .

❏ Buchner funnel.

❏ Camel hair brush.

❏ Crystallising dish.

❏ Desiccator.

❏ Drying oven.

MANGROVE SOIL, PIPETTE ANALYSIS

Location ………………….......................…................................ Sample ID …………......

Site……………....….................…. Transect Nº …………….…… Plot Nº ……………..

Date ….................…. Time ……………..… Latitude ……............. Longitude …………….

Forest type ……………………..…................. Remarks ………………………………….

	Depth	10 cm			40 cm		
	Replicate (g)	1	2	3	1	2	3
SIEVE ANALYSIS							
Wt. of total sample							
Wt. of sand fraction (> 62 μm)							
Wt. of silt-clay fraction							
PIPETTE ANALYSIS							
1.							
Wt. of first pipette sample & dish							
Wt. of dish							
Wt. of material < 62 μm in 20 ml suspension							
Wt. of material < 62 μm in 1 litre							
2.							
Wt. of second pipette sample & dish							
Wt. of dish							
Wt. of material < 15.6 μm in 20ml suspension							
Wt. of material < 15.6 μm in 1 litre							
Wt. of material finer than 62 μm							
Wt. of material finer than 15.6 μm							
By diff: amount in 62 - 15.6 μm grade							
3.							
Wt. of third pipette sample & dish							
Wt. of dish							
Wt. of material < 3.9 μm in 20 ml suspension							
Wt. of material < 3.9 μm in 1 litre							
Wt. of material < 15.6 μm							
Wt. of material < 3.9 μm							
By diff: amount in 15.6 - 3.9 μm grade							
MEAN % SAND							
MEAN % SILT							
MEAN % CLAY							

Mangroves

Figure 3.7 Preprinted data sheet to record laboratory analysis of soils using the pipette method.

❑ Electric beverage mixer. The cup for the mixer should be 500 to 600 millilitres with baffles and lid to prevent loss of material. Mixing speeds should be 16,000 revolutions per minute (rpm). An ordinary laboratory stirrer with a glass beaker fitted with baffles will suffice.

❑ Flat-bottomed white basin.

❑ Filter funnel.

❑ Filter paper (Whatman No. 50).

❑ 6% hydrogen peroxide to dissolve organic matter.

❑ Measuring cylinder - 1 litre .

❑ Pencils.

❑ 20 millilitre pipette with a minimum stem length of 20 centimetres. The stem should be marked at 10 centimetres and 20 centimetres from the tip (Fig. 3.8).

❑ Preprinted data sheets (Fig. 3.7) or small notebooks.

❑ Plastic wash bottle with distilled water.

❑ Rubber stopper to fit the mouth of the cylinder, or parafilm.

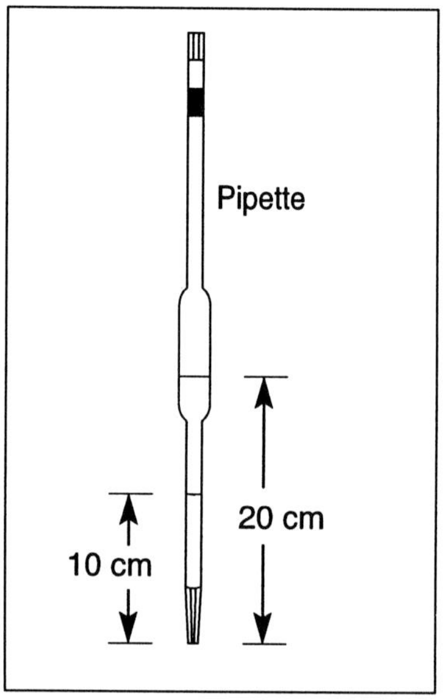

❑ Sheets of white glazed paper.

❑ Sodium hexametaphosphate $(NaPO_3)_6$ solution (6.2 grams per litre aqueous) - dispersing agent

❑ Standard set of sieves which suit the Wentworth Grade Scale, given in Table 3.1. A sieve shaker is useful, if available.

❑ Stopwatch.

❑ Water bath (preferably thermostatically-controlled) to maintain sediment solutions at 20 °C.

Figure 3.8   A marked pipette to sample soil solution.

Maintenance

❑ Wash all equipment with freshwater after use. Soil particles caught in the mesh of finer sieves can be removed by brushing both surfaces with a camel hairbrush or air blowing.

Fractionation procedure

☞ *It may take a few trials to determine the best starting weight for soil analysis. Sandy soils will require a larger sample size to obtain sufficient silt-clay fraction for sedimentation analysis. For example, if the sample contains 50% sand and 50% silt and clay, then the initial sample should be 30 grams, while a sample containing 30% sand and 70% silt and clay would only require an initial sample of 22 grams.*

Pretreatment

❑ Weigh an appropriate amount of air-dried (40 °C) sediment to produce approximately 15 grams of silt and clay fraction (see note above).

❑ Transfer the sediment to a 1 litre beaker containing 100 millilitres of 6% hydrogen peroxide to completely dissolve the organic matter. Stand overnight and heat gently on a water bath until no further frothing is seen. If roots/leaves are present add 100 millilitres of 50% hydrogen peroxide.

❑ Wash the contents of the beaker thoroughly with distilled water onto a filter paper (Whatman No. 50) fitted to a Buckner funnel.

❑ Wash the sediment from the filter into the cup of the mixer/stirrer using a jet of distilled water from the wash bottle (200 to 300 millilitres) and a camel hair brush.

❑ Add 10 millilitres of dispersing agent - sodium hexametaphosphate $(NaPO_3)_6$.

❑ Stir for 15 minutes and leave the sediment to soak overnight.

Initial splitting of silt-clay fraction

❑ Restir the sediment for 15 minutes and transfer to a 62 μm sieve placed in the flat-bottomed white basin.

❑ Add about 300 to 400 millilitres distilled water, enough to flood the sieve surface. Do not exceed 1 litre.

❑ Wet sieve the sediment (by agitating and puddling) until the fine fraction has passed through the sieve into the basin.

❑ Lift and drain the sieve over the basin and transfer sieve with its contents, to a drying oven at 100 °C.

❑ Wet-sieving will remove most of the material less than 62 μm.

Dry-sieving of the sand fraction

❑ Agitate the dried sample on the 62 μm sieve over a large sheet of white glazed paper to remove any remaining material that is less than 62 μm.

❑ Transfer any fine material on the paper to the suspension in the basin.

❑ When no further material passes through the sieve, transfer the sieve contents to the uppermost (most coarse) of the stacked series of graded sand sieves. Put a clean 62 μm sieve at the bottom of the stack with a pan below it, to catch the last of any fine material which may still pass through.

❑ Shake the stack of sieves for 15 minutes (use a sieve shaker, if available).

❑ When the sieving has been completed, empty the contents of one of the sieves on to the sheet of glazed paper. Gently brush any grains that remain in the sieve.

❑ Weigh the contents (fractions) of each sieve and record weights onto the data sheet (Fig. 3.7).

❑ This analysis continues sieve by sieve through the series until any material passing the 62 μm sieve into the pan is transferred into the silt-clay suspension in the basin.

Grading of the silt-clay fraction:
i. First pipette sample
❑ Wash the material remaining in the basin into a 1-litre cylinder using a large filter funnel and a wash bottle of distilled water. Make up the volume to exactly 1 litre of distilled water.

❑ Place the cylinder in the thermostatic bath until the temperature has equilibrated at 20 °C.

❑ Remove the cylinder and seal the mouth with a rubber stopper or piece of parafilm. Place the palm of one hand over the top of the cylinder and shake the sealed cylinder thoroughly (invert several times) until the sediment is evenly suspended throughout the water column.

❑ Place the cylinder upright in the water bath and start a stopwatch.

❑ Immediately lower the pipette gently, to 20 centimetres below the surface of the solution. Withdraw a 20 millilitre sample after 58 seconds has elapsed on the stopwatch (see Table 3.3).

❑ Transfer the pipette sample to a pre-weighed crystallising dish and oven dry at 100 °C. Do not boil the sample.

❑ Cool the dried sample in a desiccator and weigh accurately (in grams to the third decimal place).

❑ Record the weight of the first pipette sample onto the data sheet (Fig. 3.7). The weight of this material represents the total amount of sediment, less than 62 μm in the 20 millilitre sample of the soil suspension.

ii. Second pipette sample
❑ A few seconds before 7 minutes 44 seconds has elapsed, lower the pipette tip to a depth of exactly 10 centimetres below the surface of the suspension. At exactly 7 minutes 44 seconds, withdraw the 20 millilitre pipette sample (see Table 3.3).

❑ Transfer to a pre-weighed crystallising dish.

❑ Dry at 100 °C without boiling.

❑ Cool the dried sample in a desiccator and weigh accurately (in grams to the third decimal place).

❑ Record the weight of the second pipette sample onto the data sheet (Fig. 3.7). The weight of this material represents the total amount of sediment, less than 15.6 µm in the 20 millilitre sample of the soil suspension.

iii. Third pipette sample
❑ Take the third pipette sample 10 centimetres below the surface of the suspension, after 2 hours 3 minutes has elapsed (see Table 3.3) - 15.6 to 3.9 µm grade.

❑ Transfer to a pre-weighed crystallising dish.

❑ Dry and weigh the sample as before.

❑ Record the weight of the third pipette sample onto the data sheet (Fig. 3.7). The weight of this material represents the total amount of sediment, less than 3.9 µm in the 20 millilitre sample of the soil suspension.

Data recording

❑ Record the field data onto data sheets at the study site (Fig. 3.3).

❑ Sampling depth, soil colour, texture, site drainage conditions and forest type should be noted for each sample.

❑ Climate data should be collected for all locations. This should include mean monthly rainfall and monthly temperature (maximum and minimum).

❑ Calculate the means of pH, Eh, salinity and temperature at each depth measured in the field.

❑ Calculate the weight of material in each size grade of the sediment using the corrected hydrometer readings or the results collected from the pipette method (see worked examples).

Data processing

❑ Combine the results of the sieve analysis with those from the hydrometer or pipette analysis to give the weights in each grade of soil. These weights are expressed as a percentage of the dry weight of the total sample.

❑ After the data have been processed and summarised, enter them into the database using the data structure described at the end of this chapter (Section 3.6).

Mangroves

❏ Information about the sample is entered into the sample table (XXMVSAMP) and a unique sample identifier (SAMPLE_ID) is allocated. The type of data collected in the sample is described by the DATA_TYPE field. Soil data are entered into the ambient data table, which is denoted by the letter "A".

❏ Enter the soil data (mean values for the sample) into the ambient data table (XXMVADAT) using the sample identification allocated in the sample table.

❏ The soil type is described by the format abc, where a is the dominant soil fraction, b is the next most common fraction, and c is the least common fraction. See the datacode table in Section 3.6 for details.

❏ Additional environmental parameters recorded for each site:

  » Climate data such as rainfall (mean annual and mean monthly), and monthly temperature (maximum and minimum) is entered into the climate table (XXMVCDAT). This would be the same for all sites in a location.

  » Index of 'human pressure'. The impact may be direct (D), indirect (I), or both direct and indirect (B). Codes for the **types** of impacts are given in Table 3.4 (see also DATACODE in Section 3.6).
  Impact is **assessed** on a scale from 0 to 5, where 0 is no impact and 5 is severely impacted (Table 3.5). These data are entered into the sample table (XXMVSAMP).

Table 3.4 Codes used to describe the type of impact at a site (IMPCT_CODE).

Code	Type of impact
BU	bunding or dyking
CO	infrastructure, including jetties, fish landing sites, construction sites or other coastal developments
ER	erosion
IC	illegal cutting
MI	mining activities
MU	multiple impact
OT	others
PP	prawn or fish ponds
SC	shell collecting
SS	severe storm

Table 3.5 Codes used to record the impact of human pressure on mangrove ecosystems.

Code	Impact
0	No impact
1	Slight impact
2	Moderate impact
3	Rather high impact
4	High impact
5	Severe impact

❏ **Always check and verify data after entry.**

❏ Always backup data regularly.

Analysis

❏ Size frequency distribution of grain size diameter can be calculated and represented graphically using cumulative frequency curves. For further discussion see Buchanan (1984).

Worked example

1. Hydrometer method

❏ Blank readings are taken of the dispersing solution with no soil added.

❏ Data for worked example is presented in Figure 3.9.

Temperature blank	= 24 °C
Temperature at 40 seconds	= 24 °C
Temperature at 2 hours	= 24 °C
Hydrometer reading of blank	= 0.996
Hydrometer reading after 40 seconds	= 1.011
Hydrometer reading after 2 hours	= 1.007

MANGROVE SOIL, HYDROMETER ANALYSIS

Location ...*Hinchinbrook Island*................................ Sample ID ....

Site......*Coral Creek*.............. Transect N° ......*2*............ Plot N° ....*1*............

Date .*12/9/85*.... Time .*1115*..... Latitude .*18°15.0'S*.. Longitude .*146°12.0E*.

Forest type ...*Bruguiera*.................. Remarks ....

	Depth	10 cm			40 cm		
	Replicate	1	2	3	1	2	3
Wt. of total sample (g)		50.9	50.6	50.8	51.0	51.1	50.9
Blank: temperature		24°	24°	24°	24°	24°	24°
hydrometer		0.996	0.995	0.980	0.989	0.986	0.998
reading + correction		997.44	987.44	994.44	997.44	997.54	997.40
40 secs: temperature		24°	24°	24°	24°	24°	24°
hydrometer		1.011	1.021	1.011	1.011	1.011	1.011
reading + correction		1012.44	1012.44	1012.44	1012.44	1012.44	1012.44
2 hours: temperature		24°	24°	24°	24°	24°	24°
hydrometer		1.007	1.010	1.058	1.024	1.015	1.025
reading + correction		1008.41	1007.25	1006.28	1005.91	1007.31	1010.415
Hydrometer correction		+1.44	+1.43	+1.50	+1.39	+1.50	+1.40
Weight of clay (g)		11	11	12	12	11	10
Weight of silt (g)		4	3	3	4	5	4
Weight of sand (g)		35	39	32	36	35	36
MEAN % SAND		70	70	70	68	71	72
MEAN % SILT		8	9	8	9	7	8
MEAN % CLAY		22	21	22	23	22	20

Figure 3.9   Completed data sheet for soil analysis using the Bouyoucos hydometer method.

❑ If temperature differs from 20 °C, then hydrometer reading must be corrected.

$$\Delta\ temperature = temperature\ of\ sample - 20\ °C$$

$$\Delta\ t = (24\ °C - 20\ °C) = 4 \tag{3-1}$$

❑ Correct the hydrometer readings for temperature. Temperature is above 20 °C, therefore add 0.36 graduation for every 1 °C. From equation (3-1) the correction factor is:

$$\Delta\ t\ x\ 0.36 = 4\ x\ 0.36 = 1.44 \tag{3-2}$$

» Blank plus correction factor from (3-2):

$$(0.996\ x\ 1000\ gm/litre) + 1.44 = 997.44 \tag{3-3}$$

» 40 second reading plus correction factor from (3-2):

$$(1.011\ x\ 1000\ gm/litre) + 1.44 = 1012.44 \tag{3-4}$$

» 2 hour reading plus correction factor from (3-2):

$$(1.007\ x\ 1000\ gm/litre) + 1.44 = 1008.44 \tag{3-5}$$

❑ Calculate the weight using the corrected readings:

» Weight of silt and clay is the difference between the corrected readings for 40 seconds (3-4) and the corrected blank (3-3):

$$Silt\ and\ clay = 1012.44 - 997.44$$

$$= 15\ grams \tag{3-6}$$

» Weight of clay is the difference between the corrected readings for 2 hours (3-5) and the corrected blank (3-3):

$$Clay = 1008.44 - 997.44$$

$$= 11\ grams \tag{3-7}$$

» Therefore, the weight of silt is the difference between the weight of silt and clay (3-6) and the weight of clay (3-7):

$$Weight\ of\ silt\ and\ clay - weight\ of\ clay = 15 - 11 = 4\ grams$$

» The weight of sand is the difference between the total weight of the sample (in this case 50 grams) and the weight of silt and clay:

$$Sand = Total\ weight\ of\ sample - weight\ of\ silt\ and\ clay$$

Mangroves

$$= 50 - 15 = 35 \; grams$$

» Calculate the percentages:

$$Percentage \; of \; sand = \frac{Weight \; of \; sand}{Total \; weight \; of \; sample} \; x \; 100$$

$$= \frac{35}{50} \; x \; 100 = 70\%$$

» Similarly, the percentages of silt (8%) and clay (22%) can be calculated.

2. Particle-size fractionation (hypothetical figures)

❏ Data for worked example is presented in Figure 3.10.

❏ Material <62 μm - first pipette sample.

    » Weight of material <62 μm in 20 millilitres suspension:

weight of first pipette sample and dish	= 31.799 g	(3-8)
weight of dish	= 31.317 g	(3-9)

    ∴ weight of material <62 μm ((3-8) - (3-9))= 0.482 g

    » Convert to weight of material in a 1 litre suspension:

    ∴ weight of material <62 μm in sample   = 0.482 x 50 g
        = 24.100 g   (3-10)

❏ Material <15.6 μm - second pipette sample.

    » Weight of material <15.6 μm in 20 millilitres suspension:

weight of second pipette sample and dish	= 30.247 g	(3-11)
weight of dish	= 30.126 g	(3-12)

    ∴ weight of material <15.6 μm ((3-11) - (3-12))= 0.121 g

    » Convert to weight of material in a 1 litre suspension:

    ∴ weight of material <15.6 μm in sample   = 0.121 x 50 g
        = 6.050 g   (3-13)

❏ The amount of silt in the 62 to 15.6 μm grade is the difference between the material finer than 62 μm (3-10) and the material finer than 15.6 μm (3-13)

$$24.100 - 6.050 = 18.050 \; g$$

❏ Do similar calculations for the third pipette sample to give the weight of material in the 15.6 to 3.9 μm grade together with the amount less than 3.9 μm (clay).

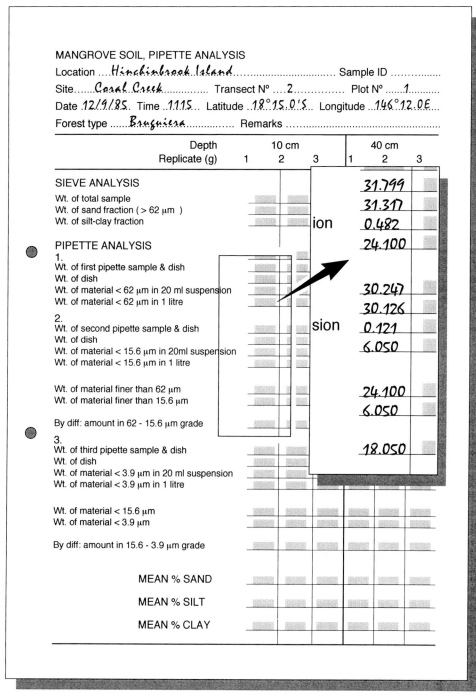

Figure 3.10 Completed data sheet for soil analysis using the particle-size fractionation method.

❏ The results of the pipette analysis are combined with those of the sieve analysis and the weights in each grade expressed as a percentage of the dry weight of the total sample.

References

Allen, S.E., H.M. Grimshaw, J.A. Parkinson and C. Quarmby (1989). "Chemical analysis of ecological materials". 2nd ed. John Wiley and Sons, New York. 368pp.

Bouyoucos, G.J. (1962). Hydrometer method improved for making particle size analysis of soils. Agronomy Journal, **54**: 464-465.

Buchanan, J.B. (1984). Sediment analysis. pp. 41-65. In: N.A. Holme and A.D. McIntyre (editors). "Methods for the Study of Marine Benthos". Blackwell Scientific Publications. London.

Folk, R.L. (1974). "Petrology of sedimentary rocks". Hemphill Publishing Co., Austin, Texas. 182pp.

Patrick, W.H. Jr. and R.D. Delaune (1977). Chemical and biological redox systems affecting nutrient availability in the coastal wetlands. Geoscience and Man, **18**: 131-137.

Pearson, T.H. and S.O. Stanley (1979). Comparative measurement of the redox potential of marine sediments as a rapid means of assessing the effect of organic pollution. Marine Biology, **53**: 371-379.

Suggested reading

Boto, K.G. (1984). Waterlogged saline soils. pp. 114-129. In: S.C. Snedaker and J.G. Snedaker (editors). "The Mangrove Ecosystem: Research Methods". UNESCO.

Boto, K.G. and J.T. Wellington (1984). Soil characteristics and nutrient status in a northern Australian Mangrove Forest. Estuaries **7**: 61-69.

Day, J.W., C.A.S. Hall, W.M. Kemp and A. Yanez-Araancibia (1989). "Estuarine ecology". John Wiley and Sons, New York. 558pp.

Fenchel, T. (1969). The Ecology of Marine Microbenthos. IV. Structure and function of the benthic ecosystem, its chemical and physical factors and the microfauna communities, with special reference to the ciliated protozoa. Ophelia, **6**: 1-182.

3.2 Mangrove Forest Leaf Area Index and Nett Canopy Photosynthesis

Abstract

Measurements of light absorption by the forest canopy are used to estimate leaf area index (m^2 leaf area m^{-2} ground area). The leaf area index (L) may then be converted to nett canopy photosynthesis using the average rate of photosynthesis per unit leaf area (A). The method is useful for comparisons between forests over a wide range of forest types and distributions, and for monitoring changes in a particular forest. However, it does not provide a reliable estimate of the nett primary productivity.

Background

The method described by Bunt *et al.* (1979) has been used widely in recent years to estimate 'potential' primary productivity in mangrove forests. The method was based on that originally described by Kirita and Hozumi (1973) in studies of oak forests, where the amount of light absorbed by the mangrove canopy is related to the total canopy chlorophyll content. Canopy chlorophyll concentration was then multiplied by a rate of carbon fixation per unit of chorophyll to give an estimate of 'potential' primary productivity. However, recent work (Clough *et al.* submitted) suggests that figures calculated using the method of Bunt *et al.* significantly underestimate 'potential' primary productivity.

The method described here uses the same techniques to collect data, and the same primary dataset as the method of Bunt *et al.* (1979), but uses a different, and theoretically more robust, method of calculation to provide an estimate of canopy leaf area index. This index can be multiplied by the average rate of canopy photosynthesis (if it is known) to provide an estimate of nett canopy photosynthesis during the daytime. The estimation of the leaf area index assumes that radiation decreases exponentially as it passes through the canopy, according to the relationship:

$$I = I_0 \, e^{-kL} \tag{3-14}$$

where: I = photon flux density beneath the canopy

       I_0 = photon flux density incident on the top of the canopy (in this case at ground level in a fully exposed position outside the canopy)

       L = leaf area index (m^2 leaf area m^{-2} ground area)

       k = canopy light extinction coefficient that is determined by the angle and spatial arrangement of the leaves

Mangroves

This relationship is used widely in agriculture and forestry. Equation 3-14 can be rewritten as

$$L = \frac{\log_e (I/I_0)}{-k} \quad (m^2 \text{ leaf area } m^{-2} \text{ground area})$$

(3-15)

which allows the direct estimation of leaf area index from the ratio of light flux density below and above the canopy (I/I_0), and the canopy light extinction coefficient, k.

The ratio, I/I_0, is measured using the same technique as that described by Bunt *et al.* (1979). However, this manual recommends that the value of k used to obtain an estimate of leaf area index should be 0.5. This is based on a number of studies that have shown that k commonly lies between 0.4 and 0.65 in mangrove canopies, with an average about 0.5 (Clough *et al.* submitted; and unpublished data). Using a value for k of 0.5, and values for I/I_0 obtained from field measurements, it is possible to obtain an estimate of leaf area index (L). Nett canopy photosynthesis can then be estimated by multiplying L by the average rate of photosynthesis per unit leaf area (A) and daylength. Values for A vary with species, soil salinity, and climatic conditions: in harsh conditions (hot, dry, and cloudless climate and a high soil salinity of 25 ppt) A is usually about 0.216 g C m^{-2} leaf hour^{-1}; under favourable conditions (cloudy and humid climate and a low soil salinity of 20 ppt) A may reach 1.0 g C m^{-2} leaf hour^{-1} (Andrews and Muller 1985; Clough and Sim 1989; Cheeseman *et al.* 1991). While it is desirable to measure the actual rates of photosynthesis at each site, approximate rates of 0.216 g C m^{-2} leaf hour^{-1} can be used for harsh conditions and 0.648 g C m^{-2} leaf hour^{-1} for favourable conditions.

While the present method is imprecise, due to uncertainty in the actual average rate of photosynthesis per unit leaf area (unless it is measured at each site), it is based on widely used and reasonably robust concepts, which will permit progressive refinement in estimates of primary productivity using the same measurements of I and I_0.

Therefore, previous estimates of nett canopy photosynthesis, made using the values presented in Bunt *et al.* (1979), can be recalculated using the values for the extinction coefficient (k) and average rate of photosynthesis (A), detailed in this manual.

Advantages

❏ The method is quick and economical.

❏ The leaf area index of forests in different climatic conditions can be compared, and estimates of nett canopy photosynthesis can be obtained provided that reasonable estimates of average canopy photosynthesis are available.

MANGROVE PRIMARY PRODUCTION DATA

Location .... Site...................................

Transect N° .... Plot N° .... Latitude .... Longitude ....

Date .... Time start .... Light - I_o initial .... I_o final ....

Air temp.(°C) .... Soil temp.(°C) .... Forest type ....

1

2

3

4

5

6

7

8

9

10

11

12

13

14

15

16

17

18

19

20

Mangroves

Figure 3.11   Preprinted data sheets assist in data collection.

Disadvantages

❏ The relationship between the potential nett canopy photosynthesis estimated by this method and the actual productivity has yet to be elucidated.

❏ The constants used in the calculations are calculated from different mangrove systems: $k = 0.5$ (value obtained using *Rhizophora* species); $A = 0.216$ to 0.864 (values obtained from mangrove species in Australia, Malaysia, Papua New Guinea and Thailand).

❏ The method does not estimate nett primary productivity since it does not account for respiration by the branches, stems or roots, or night-time respiration by the leaves.

Logistics

Equipment

❏ A portable light meter with an underwater quantum sensor is used to measure photosynthetically active radiation (PAR). An underwater sensor is used because of its greater resilience under mangrove conditions. A model widely used for surveys conducted as part of the ASEAN-Australia project is the LI-COR® 1000 readout/logger, coupled with a LI-COR® quantum sensor.

❏ A clinometer, or other measuring device, to measure solar zenith angle.

❏ Pencils and preprinted data sheets; A4 underwater paper is recommended (Fig. 3.11). Small notebooks can also be used but care should be taken to keep them dry. A new notebook should be used for each field trip.

Maintenance

❏ If the meter is not digital, make sure that the meter is set on the 3000 scale when it is first switched on and then lower the setting to the scale required so as not to 'shock' the instrument.

❏ Wipe the meter and sensor cable with a moist cloth after every field trip. Clean the sensor very gently.

❏ Check the batteries regularly.

General procedure

❏ Take light meter readings on a sunny day, between true noon ±2 hours, so that the sun is more or less overhead (Fig. 3.12).

❏ Take a reading of *Io* (the incident photosynthetically active radiation, PAR) outside the forest (in an open area) at the start and the end of a set of readings. It may be necessary to take a boat out into the creek to find open space for these readings.

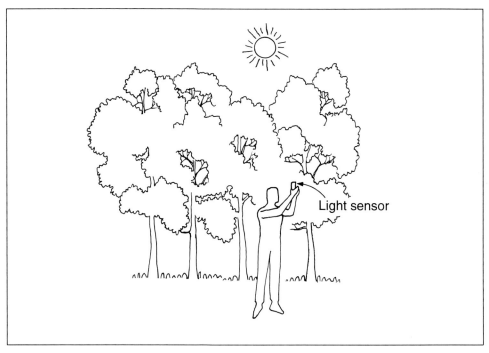

Figure 3.12 Light meter readings should be taken at noon ± 2 hours.

❏ Measure the PAR penetrating the forest canopy (*I*). Avoid bias in taking the readings by mentally dividing the area to be studied (say a 50 metre x 50 metre plot) into a grid.

❏ At least 100 readings of *I* should be taken under well-developed canopies, but as many as 1000 in areas with numerous gaps. The number of points depends on the variability of the readings obtained (the more open the canopy, the more gaps, the more readings required).

❏ Each set of readings should be taken within a 30-minute timeframe.

❏ Record whether the forest has more than one stratum, but only one of the strata is studied.

❏ If an analog quantum meter is available, select a suitable scale (300 µEinsteins m^{-2} sec^{-1} for dense canopies, and 1000 µEinsteins m^{-2} sec^{-1} for more open canopies) and record values exceeding the scale as 300 or 1000. These values will eventually be excluded in the estimation of canopy cover.

❏ Measure ambient environmental factors for each plot (quadrat). These include soil salinity, redox potential (Eh), soil temperature and the soil pH (see section on mangrove soils in this chapter).

❑ Take note of any impact in the area, that is, record any activities such as bunding, storm damage etc., and assess the degree of impact (Tables 3.4 and 3.5).

☞ *If individual readings fluctuate, estimate the mean reading. If the highest and lowest values are very different (say 50 and 200 on the 300 scale; or 100 and 500 on the 1000 scale), take the lowest and highest values and record as two separate readings.*

Data recording

❑ Record the physical variables before beginning light meter readings (e.g. soil type, soil salinity, and soil temperature). The observer should include any other relevant site information (e.g. details of vegetation) at the top of the data sheet (Fig. 3.11).

❑ Climate data should be collected for all sites. These should include mean monthly rainfall and monthly temperature (maximum and minimum).

❑ Record Io (incident PAR), the date and time, before beginning forest light meter readings.

❑ Record I, the PAR penetrating the forest canopy.

❑ Return to an open area and remeasure Io after completing forest PAR readings, and record the time of the reading.

❑ Record the zenith angle (θ) of the sun (angle of sun from the vertical) using a clinometer. If this is not available, the zenith angle (θ) for a given latitude, longitude, date and time of day can be obtained from a nautical almanac or from a suitable computer program.

Data processing

❑ An estimate of canopy cover (η) is not required to calculate leaf area index using this method (used by method described by Bunt *et. al.* 1979). However, an estimate of canopy cover should be calculated independently of leaf area index and this estimate of canopy cover entered into the database.

Estimation of canopy cover (η) :
❑ Use the mean value of Io (incident PAR) in the calculations.

❑ Calculate the mean value of the light readings taken under the canopy (I), I_{mean}.

❑ Any value of I that is greater than $3 \times I_{mean}$ is left out of further calculations. The value chosen represents a gap in the canopy and is based on comparisons with photographs of the forest canopy in Australian mangroves (K.G. Boto, pers. comm.).

❑ Calculate a new I_{mean} with the remaining values.

❑ Repeat the process until there are no more light readings greater than 3 times the last I_{mean}.

□ The cover of the forest canopy (η) is taken as

$$\eta = \frac{\text{remaining number of readings}}{\text{total number of readings}} \qquad \text{(3-16)}$$

Estimation of leaf area index (L):

□ This part of the method assumes that light transmission through a well-developed forest canopy follows an exponential relationship of the form given in equation 3-15.

$$L = \frac{\log_e (I/I_o)}{-k} \quad (m^2 \text{ leaf area } m^{-2} \text{ground area})$$

□ When the angle of the sun is not vertical the solar beam passes through more leaves, overestimating leaf area index. These readings therefore represent the apparent leaf area index (L').

□ Take the natural logarithms of each measurement beneath the canopy.

□ Take the natural logarithms of each measurement above the canopy.

□ Average the logged values of $\log_e(I)$ and $\log_e(Io)$ to get $\log_e(I)_{mean}$ and $\log_e(Io)_{mean}$ respectively.

□ Therefore the equation for apparent leaf area index (L') is:

$$L' = \frac{[\log_e (I)_{mean}] - [\log_e (I_o)_{mean}]}{-k} \quad (m^2 \text{ leaf area } m^{-2} \text{ground area}) \qquad \text{(3-17)}$$

□ The apparent leaf area index (L') must be corrected for the solar zenith angle (θ) at the time that measurements of I and I_o were made, that is, corrected for the angle of the sun from the vertical.

□ The corrected leaf area index (L) is given by:

$$L = L' \cdot \cos (\theta_r) \qquad \text{(3-18)}$$

where: θ_r = is the zenith angle in radians

$$\theta_r = \theta \cdot \frac{\pi}{180}$$

$$\cos \theta_r = \cos (\theta \cdot \frac{\pi}{180}) \qquad \text{(3-19)}$$

Mangroves

Estimation of nett canopy photosynthesis (P$_N$):

❏ The approximate nett photosynthesis of the whole plant canopy above a unit area (1 metre x 1 metre) of ground can be described by:

$$P_N = A . d . L \tag{3-20}$$

where: A = average rate of photosynthesis (gC m^{-2} leaf area hr^{-1}) for all leaves in the canopy

d = daylength (hr)

L = total leaf area index of the canopy above the ground

❏ The canopy light extinction coefficient (k) and the average rate of photosynthesis (A) require sophisticated, expensive equipment for exact calculation. Estimates, using data collected from a range of mangrove forests, are therefore used in calculations.

❏ The value of k for *Rhizophora* canopies is close to 0.5 (UNESCO, 1991). While values of k for the canopies of other mangrove species are not available, a value of 0.5 can probably be used without introducing significant error.

❏ The rate of nett photosynthesis (A), varies with the species, the position of the leaf in the canopy, the time of day, the soil salinity and the prevailing climatic conditions. The rates of nett photosynthesis in *Rhizophora* species of northern Australia and Southeast Asia, vary between the dry (A $\approx$ 0.216 gC m^2 hour^{-1}; salinities greater than 35 ppt) and wet seasons (A $\approx$ 0.648 gC m^2 hour^{-1}; low salinities) (Clough and Sim, 1989; UNESCO, 1991). Similar rates of nett photosynthesis have been found in other species (Clough and Sim, 1989).

❏ Ideally, calculation of the rate of nett photosynthesis should be made when light attenuation is measured. Since this is usually not practical, average values for A should be used:

In the dry season or at high soil salinities:

$$A \approx 0.216 \ gC \ m^{-2} \ hour^{-1}$$

In the wet season and for low salinities:

$$A \approx 0.648 \ gC \ m^{-2} \ hour^{-1}$$

❏ After the data have been processed and summarised, enter the data into the database using the structure described at the end of this chapter (Section 3.6).

❏ Information about the sample is entered into the sample table (XXMVSAMP) and a unique sample identifier (SAMPLE_ID) is allocated. The type of data collected in the sample is described by the DATA_TYPE field. The light absorption data are denoted by the letter "L".

MANGROVE PRIMARY PRODUCTION DATA

Location ......*Hinchinbrook Island*..................... Site...*Coral Creek*...........

Transect N° ..*2*... Plot N° ....*1*.. Latitude ..*18°15.0'S.* Longitude .*146°12.0E*...

Date ..*12/9/85*... Time start ...*1115*.... Light - I_o initial ..*2100*.... I_o final ...*2100*...

Air temp.(°C) .*25.1*........... Forest type ....*Bruguiera*...............................

1	150	130	300	50	40
2	50	100	300	110	40
3	40	35	300	50	220
4	55	40	45	300	110
5	300	85	300	60	300
6	15	40	50	45	70
7	300	45	300	70	80
8	90	60	45	100	300
9	65	35	45	300	190
10	115	60	45	200	130
11	65	40	50	50	300
12	60	80	60	80	300
13	62	45	300	300	60
14	63	95	60	110	50
15	280	60	45	50	300
16	220	70	37	300	150
17	42	50	60	45	60
18	95	55	30	45	50
19	65	60	55	80	300
20	67	70	300	45	150

Figure 3.13   Completed light attenuation data sheet. Data are used in calculations presented in the worked example.

Mangroves

❑ Enter the calculated light data into the data table (XXMVLDAT) using the SAMPLE_ID allocated in the sample table.

❑ An entry is made into the sample table (XXMVSAMP) to describe the ambient data collected in conjunction with the light attenuation measurements, i.e. DATA_TYPE is "A". The ambient data record the soil characteristics of the sample (e.g. soil type, temperature, salinity, Eh and pH), which are entered into the ambient data table (XXMVADAT) using the sample identification allocated in the sample table.

❑ Additional environmental parameters recorded for each site:

» climate data such as rainfall (mean annual and mean monthly), and monthly temperature (maximum and minimum) - entered into the climate table (XXMVCDAT) ;

» index of 'human pressure'. Codes for the types of impacts are given in Table 3.4. Impact is assessed on a scale from 0 to 5, where 0 is no impact and 5 is severely impacted (Table 3.5) - entered into the sample table (XXMVSAMP).

❑ **Always check and verify data after entry.**

❑ Always backup data regularly.

Comments

❑ Measurements of light attenuation made when the sun is not directly overhead will overestimate the leaf area index and the nett canopy photosynthesis. For most mangrove canopies, the greater the angle of the sun from the vertical, the greater the corresponding error.

❑ Both the leaf area index and the rate of photosynthesis per unit leaf area vary seasonally, so surveys should be carried out during the different seasons.

❑ Estimates of the nett canopy photosynthesis (P_N) are only approximate unless direct measurements of k and A have been made.

❑ The method presented in this manual calculates the nett canopy photosynthesis to be almost 7 times greater than that estimated from the method used by Bunt *et al.* (1979). In the worked example given at the end of this method the estimate for P_N (kgC ha^{-1} day^{-1}) is calculated to be 137.9, compared to an estimate of 19.96 using the Bunt equations.

Worked Example

❏ A dataset for this example is presented in Figure 3.13.

❏ The estimation of canopy cover of the forest (η):

» 19 of the values recorded are greater than, or equal to, 300 (the threshold value for dense canopies - see General Procedure). Therefore, exclude these readings and calculate the mean for the remaining 81 values:

$$I_{mean} = 75.7 \quad (n = 81)$$

$$3 \times I_{mean} = 227 \quad (n = 81)$$

» Look through the data and exclude values >227. Thus, we exclude 280.

» Calculate a new mean for the remaining values:

$$I_{mean} = 73.1 \quad (n = 80)$$

$$3 \times I_{mean} = 219 \quad (n = 80)$$

» Look through the data and exclude values >219. Therefore, we exclude both readings of 220.

» Calculate the new mean for the remaining (78) values:

$$I_{mean} = 69.4 \quad (n = 78) \tag{3-21}$$

$$3 \times I_{mean} = 208 \quad (n = 78)$$

» Since there are no values greater than 208, we can conclude (using equation 3-14) that the cover in this site is:

$$\eta = (\frac{78}{100}) = 0.78 \tag{3-22}$$

❏ Estimation of leaf area index (L):

» According to equation 3-17

$$L' = \frac{[log_e\ (I)_{mean}] - [log_e\ (I_o)_{mean}]}{-k} \quad (m^2\ leaf\ area\ m^{-2} ground\ area)$$

where:

$$log_e\ (I)_{mean} = mean\ log_e\ (I) = 4.475$$

$$log_e\ (I_o)_{mean} = mean\ log_e\ (I_o) = 7.650$$

Mangroves

$$k = 0.5$$

$$L' = \frac{(4.475 - 7.650)}{-0.5} = 6.35 \quad (m^2 \, leaf \, area/m^2 ground \, area)$$

» For this example, we use a solar zenith angle (θ) of 20°.

» Convert θ to radians (θ_r). From equation 3-19

$$cos \, \theta_r = cos \, (\theta \, . \, \frac{\pi}{180})$$

$$= cos \, (20 \, . \, \frac{3.141593}{180}) = 0.94$$

» Therefore the corrected leaf area index (L) is given by equation 3-18:

$$L = L' \, . \, cos(\theta_r)$$

$$= 6.35 \, x \, 0.94 = 5.97$$

❑ Estimation of nett canopy photosynthesis (P_N):

» According to equation 3-20:

$$P_N = A \, . \, d \, . \, L$$

» In a stressed environment: A = 0.216 gC m^{-2} leaf area hour^{-1}; d = 12 hours; and L = 5.97. Therefore:

$$P_N = 0.216 \, x \, 12 \, x \, 5.97 = 15.5 \quad gC \, m^{-2} \, ground \, day^{-1}$$

$$= 155 \quad kgC \, ha^{-1} \, day^{-1}$$

$$= 56 \quad tC \, ha^{-1} \, year^{-1}$$

References

Andrews, T.J. and G.J. Muller (1985). Photosynthetic gas exchange of the mangrove, *Rhizophora stylosa* Griff., in its natural environment. Oecologia, **65**: 449-455.

Bunt, J.S., K.G. Boto and G. Boto (1979). A survey method for estimating potential levels of mangrove forest primary production. Marine Biology, **52**: 123-128.

Cheesman, J.M., B.F. Clough, D.R. Carter, C.E. Lovelock, Ong J.E. and R.G. Sim (1991). The analysis of phtotsynthetic performance in leaves under field conditions: A case study using *Bruguiera* mangroves. Photosynthetic Research, **29**: 11-22.

Clough, B.F. and R.G. Sim (1989). Changes in gas exchange characteristics and water use efficiency of mangroves in response to salinity and vapour pressure deficit. Oecologia, **79**: 38-44.

Clough, B.F., Ong, J.E. and Gong, W.K. (Submitted). Estimating leaf area index and photosynthetic production in mangrove forest canopies. Marine Ecology Progress Series.

Kirita, H. and Hozumi, K. (1973). Estimation of the total chlorophyll amount and its seasonal change in a warm-temperature evergreen oak forest at Minimata, Japan. Japanese Journal of Ecology, **23**: 195-200.

UNESCO (1991). Soils and forestry studies. pp. 35-81. In: "Final Report of the Integrated Multidisciplinary Survey and Research Programme of the Ranong Mangrove Ecosystem". Unesco in cooperation with the National Research Council of Thailand, Paris.

Suggested reading

Ong, J.E., W.K. Gong, C.H. Wong and Zubir Din (1985). "Productivity of the Mangrove Ecosystem: A Manual of Methods". Universiti Sains Malaysia, Penang.

Mangroves

3.3 Angle Count Cruising Method

Abstract

This method estimates the stem density and basal area of mangrove trees per hectare in a relatively fast and simple way. Supplemented with measurement of diameter at breast height (DBH) of the counted trees, the method can also be used to describe the size distribution of trees in mangrove forests, and provides a useful method for comparison of mangrove forests at different locations.

Background

The Angle Count Cruising (ACC) method was first developed by Bitterlich in 1948 to estimate stand basal area, and has been widely used since then. The advantage of this method is that it can be implemented by making use of a simple wooden device or a more sophisticated instrument called a relascope, described in this chapter.

The underlying principles of the angle count cruising method were reviewed by Cintrón and Novelli (1984). It is a plotless method, in that it does not sample a specific, known area of the forest. Instead, it uses angular sighting, covering an area of forest in accordance with the size class of the trees which fall within the scale used. The observer stands at the sampling point, and while sighting through the relascope, turns through 360°, tallying trees greater in size than a specified horizontal angle. The number of trees counted is then multiplied by a constant, which is determined by the angle used. This calculation gives the basal area per unit ground area. If the DBH's of each tree is measured, stem densities per hectare can also be calculated.

Advantages

❏ It is easy to apply and is relatively fast.

❏ Equipment is simple to use and relatively cheap.

❏ It can be used to describe major forest types and their distribution.

Disadvantages

❏ The size of the plot sampled in this method is undefined.

❏ It cannot be used for temporal measurement of change since it does not leave a permanent plot that can be measured through time.

Logistics

Personnel
❑ All observers must be familiar with the species of mangrove trees in the region to be surveyed.

❑ At least 2 observers are recommended; one observer does a sweep with the relascope, counting the trees encountered, while the other observer measures trees counted during the sweep.

Equipment
❑ The relascope is an optical device used to estimate the stand basal area of trees. The relascope has a measuring scale of alternating stripes of black and white bands. Trees appearing within the field of view are to be compared with any of these bands; but for most purposes white band 1 (Fig. 3.14) is most convenient.

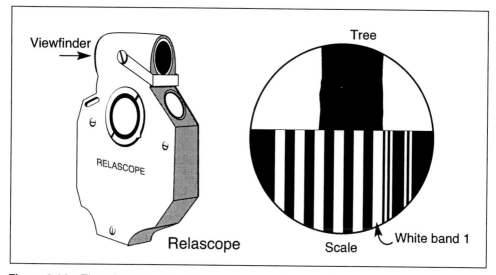

Figure 3.14 The relascope - the observer compares trees to the scale seen in the lower half of the field of view.

❑ Fibreglass tape measures - a short tape (2 to 3 metres long) to measure the girth of the tree (GBH). The girth can be converted to DBH by dividing by π.

☞ *Specialist tapes for measuring the diameter of the trees at breast height (DBH tape) are available. However, since many mangrove trees do not have a round cross-section, girth measurements are preferred.*

❑ Pencils and preprinted data sheets. A4 underwater paper is recommended (Fig. 3.15). Small notebooks can also be used but care should be taken to reduce their exposure to water. A new notebook should be used for each field trip.

MANGROVE BASAL AREA DATA

Location ………………....................…….................. Site………………....…..........

Transect Nº ……. Plot Nº .... Latitude ……...…...... Longitude …..............…..

Date …................ Time ….......….. Air temp.(°C) ….............. Soil temp.(°C) …...........…

Relascope scale …….................. Forest type …..

Nº	Species	GBH(cm)	Nº	Species	GBH(cm)	Nº	Species	GBH(cm)
1	___	___	21	___	___	41	___	___
2	___	___	22	___	___	42	___	___
3	___	___	23	___	___	43	___	___
4	___	___	24	___	___	44	___	___
5	___	___	25	___	___	45	___	___
6	___	___	26	___	___	46	___	___
7	___	___	27	___	___	47	___	___
8	___	___	28	___	___	48	___	___
9	___	___	29	___	___	49	___	___
10	___	___	30	___	___	50	___	___
11	___	___	31	___	___	51	___	___
12	___	___	32	___	___	52	___	___
13	___	___	33	___	___	53	___	___
14	___	___	34	___	___	54	___	___
15	___	___	35	___	___	55	___	___
16	___	___	36	___	___	56	___	___
17	___	___	37	___	___	57	___	___
18	___	___	38	___	___	58	___	___
19	___	___	39	___	___	59	___	___
20	___	___	40	___	___	60	___	___

Figure 3.15   Preprinted data sheet for recording measurements taken in the field.

Maintenance

❏ The relascope is made of metal and hence is susceptible to corrosion. Care should be taken to prevent its immersion in seawater. Wipe with a moist, clean tissue or cloth after use to remove salt spray. Store the relascope in a dry and cool compartment to reduce fungal growth on glass parts.

Site selection

❏ Sites should be as representative as possible of the general area.

❏ Determine the extent of the mangrove forest using aerial photographs. The photographs (Fig. 3.16) will indicate changes in forest types and geomorphic features (see below). When at the site confirm any changes in forest type indicated in the photograph (ground truthing).

❏ At least 3 transect lines should be walked into the forest, perpendicular to the shoreline, and samples taken wherever the forest types change.

❏ Geomorphic features, such as sand ridges, filled river bends, barrier islands, hinterland margin etc., should be considered when sampling. If a general survey of the entire mangrove forest is required, then all the geomorphic features should be sampled.

Figure 3.16 Aerial photograph showing changes in vegetation types and geomorphic features.

Mangroves

General procedure

❏ Survey at least 3 randomly selected, replicate sample 'plots' in each forest type along the transect using the relascope. The centre of each 'plot' should be well apart from the other samples in order to avoid double counting of trees.

❏ Sight the forest through the viewfinder of the relascope keeping the instrument perpendicular to the line of sight (Fig. 3.17). The target tree will be seen within the circular field of view, superimposed by alternating stripes of black and white bands (Fig. 3.14).

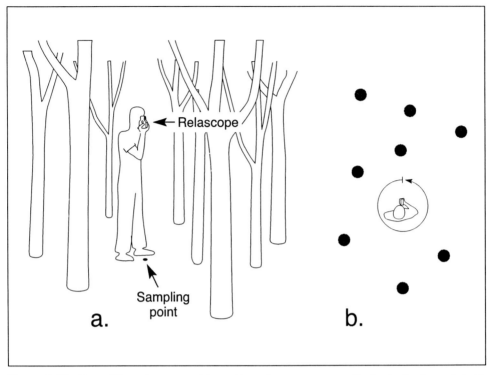

Figure 3.17 Use of the relascope: **a)** keep the relascope perpendicular to the line of sight; **b)** stay on the sampling point and turn through 360°.

❏ From the centre of the chosen 'plot' count the trees in a 360° sweep (Fig. 3.17) around the sampling point that are equal to, or larger than, the whiteband 1 of the relascope.

❏ The relascope can be held at any distance from the observer's eye provided that the image is in focus and the relascope is kept above the sample point.

❏ Count only those stems where the image of the tree is greater than, or equal to, the image of the width of the white band (Fig. 3.14). Trees exactly on the scale are included.

❏ If a tree is blocked from view by another tree, the observer may step to the side of the pivot point to get an unobstructed view of the hidden tree. In so doing, however, care should be taken that the distance between the observer and the tree be kept unchanged.

❏ If the tree is leaning, the relascope must be held so that the black and white bands of the scales are approximately parallel to the trunk of the leaning tree.

❏ Each sweep should contain a sample of at least 30 to 40 trees.

❑ It may be necessary to select a different scale on the relascope to achieve this sample size. For example, in a forest of mostly young trees, the use of the normal unit scale (relascope band 1) will result in undersampling because trees are small (e.g. saplings which have a girth of less than 4 centimetres). In this case, the 360° sweep should be repeated using a smaller scale which will sample 30 to 40 trees. The resulting count must then be corrected to give true basal area (see worked example).

☞ *While in theory it may be necessary to continuereducing the size of the scale so that a sample of 30 to 40 saplings is sampled, it is rarely necessary to use a band size of less than the half unit scale.*

❑ The observer indicates to another member of the team, who has the tape, which trees are larger than the selected band width. These trees are then indentifed and measured.

❑ Measure the girth of each tree included in the 360° sweep, at breast height (GBH), i.e. approximately 1.3 metres above the ground (Fig. 3.18).

❑ Measurement of trees can be difficult for some shape and growth forms of mangrove trees. The following procedures are therefore recommended (Fig. 3.19):

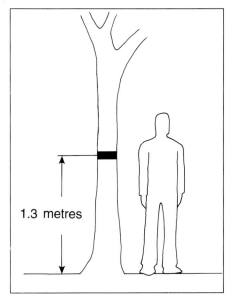

1.3 metres

Figure 3.18 Tree measurements are taken at breast height.

» When a tree forks below breast height, or sprouts from a single base close to the ground or above it, measure each branch as a separate stem.

» When the stem forks at breast height or slightly above, measure the girth at breast height or just below the swelling caused by the fork.

» When the stem has prop roots or fluted lower trunk, measure the girth 20 centimetres above the root collar.

» When the stem has swellings, branches or abnormalities at the point of measurement, take the diameter slightly above or below the irregularity, where it stops affecting normal form.

❑ If seedlings are of interest in the study, or if they predominate in an area, then quadrats should be used to count the number of seedlings per square metre. The number of quadrats will be determined by the aims of the study, but there should be at least 2 in each forest type.

Mangroves

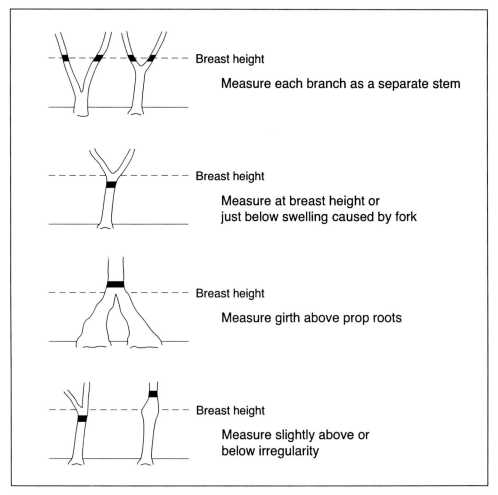

Figure 3.19   Procedure for measuring trees with unusual or different growth forms.

❏ Measure ambient environmental factors for each 'plot' . These include soil salinity, redox potential (Eh), soil temperature and pH (Section 3.1). Collect soil samples for grain size analysis (Section 3.1). Light measurements may also be taken (Section 3.2).

❏ Take note of any impact at the site, that is, record any activities such as bunding, storm damage, etc. and assess the degree of impact (Tables 3.4 and 3.5).

❏ A greater number of samples (replicates) may be needed to answer specific questions relating to forest types. After a pilot study, the number of sampling points for a desired sampling error can be estimated using the following formula (see Chapter 7 for further discussion of experimental design):

$$n = \frac{t^2 \cdot CV^2}{SE^2}$$

where: n = number of sampling points required

t = Student's t for the probability level defined
for the standard error (SE)

CV = coefficient of variation in percent for the forest to be sampled

SE = size of allowable standard error in percent (see Table 3.6).

Data recording

❏ Record the ambient environmental factors for each sampling 'plot' (Section 3.1) on the top of the data sheet (Fig. 3.15). Light measurements may also be recorded (see Section 3.2).

❏ Record the relascope scale used.

❏ Record the scientific name or fieldcode (Section 3.7) for each of the trees counted in the 360° sweep, and measure their girth at breast height (GBH). See example data in Figure 3.20.

❏ Collect climate data for all sites. These should include monthly temperature (maximum and minimum) and average monthly rainfall.

Data processing

❏ Girth measurements of trees may be converted to diameter (DBH) by dividing GBH by π.

❏ Enter data into the database at the end of each day using the structure described at the end of this chapter (Section 3.6).

❏ Information about the sample is entered into the sample table (XXMVSAMP) and a unique sample identifier (SAMPLE_ID) is allocated. The type of data collected in the sample is described by the DATA_TYPE field. The relascope data are denoted by the letter "R".

❏ Enter the relascope data into the data table (XXMVRDAT) using the sample identification allocated in the sample table. Each tree within the sample will have the same SAMPLE_ID.

❏ An entry is made into the sample table (XXMVSAMP) to describe the ambient data collected in conjunction with the relascope, i.e. DATA_TYPE is "A". The ambient data record the soil characteristics of the sample (e.g. soil type, temperature, salinity, Eh and pH), which are entered into the ambient table (XXMVADAT) using the sample identification allocated in the sample table.

Mangroves

Table 3.6 The number of samples needed (from an infinite population with a given coefficient of variation) so that the standard error of the sample will tend to be near the given limit of error (after Grosenbaugh 1952, in Cintrón and Novelli 1984).

Coefficient Variation (%)	Specific Limit for Standard Error			
	± 1-0.5%	± 5%	± 10%	± 20%
	N			
5	12	1	1	1
10	45	4	1	1
15	100	9	3	1
20	178	16	4	1
25	278	25	7	2
30	400	36	9	3
35	545	49	13	4
40	712	64	16	4
45	900	81	21	6
50	1112	100	25	7
55	1345	121	31	8
60	1600	144	36	9
65	1878	169	43	11
70	2178	196	49	13
75	2500	225	57	15
80	2845	256	64	16
85	3212	289	73	19
90	3600	324	81	21
95	4012	361	91	23
100	4445	400	100	25
125	6945	625	157	40
150	10000	900	225	57
175	13612	1225	307	77
200	17778	1600	400	100

❏ If light data is collected in conjunction with the relascope an entry is made into the sample table (XXMVSAMP), i.e. DATA_TYPE "L". The light data are entered into the light table (XXMVLDAT) using the sample identification allocated in the sample table.

❏ Additional environmental parameters recorded for each site:

» climate data such as mean annual and mean monthly rainfall, and monthly temperature (maximum and minimum - entered into the climate table (XXMVCDAT);

» index of 'human pressure'. Codes for the types of impacts are given in Table 3.4. Impact is assessed on a scale from 0 to 5, where 0 is no impact and 5 is severely impacted (Table 3.5) - entered into the sample table (XXMVSAMP).

❏ **Always check and verify data after entry**.

❏ Always backup data regularly.

Analysis

❏ The raw data contain information on the species composition, community structure and density.

❏ Data can be tabulated according to taxonomic categories as well as DBH class. This shows the species composition and distribution of trees according to DBH class, and allows the calculation of the total basal area of the trees per hectare, basal area of each species per hectare, as well as basal area of trees according to the DBH class.

❏ If a scale other than relascope band 1 (normal unit scale) is used, then the resulting count must be corrected to give true basal area (BA)

$$BA = count \; x \; (scale \; factor)^2$$

❏ The number of stems per hectare for DBH measurements up to 50 centimetres, are given in Table 3.7. If the DBH is greater than 50 centimetres calculate the stem density as follows:

$$Stem \; density = \frac{Basal \; Area}{(0.00007854x \; DBH^2)} \; stem \; hectacre^{-1}$$

❏ If data are collected in DBH classes, then the mean value of the DBH class is used to estimate the stem density.

Table 3.7 Stems per hectare represented by a stem of a given diameter. For angle gauges of basal

Diameter (cm)	Tenth of a centimetre				
	0.0	0.1	0.2	0.3	0.4
0	0	1 273 239.5	318 309.9	141 471.1	79 577.5
1	12 732.4	10 522.6	8 841.9	7 534.0	6 496.1
2	3 183.1	2 887.2	2 630.7	2 406.9	2 210.5
3	1 414.7	1 324.9	1 243.4	1 169.2	1 101.4
4	795.8	757.4	721.8	688.6	657.7
5	509.3	489.5	470.9	453.3	436.6
6	353.7	342.2	331.2	320.8	310.8
7	259.8	252.6	245.6	238.9	232.5
8	198.9	194.1	189.4	184.8	180.4
9	157.2	153.8	150.4	147.2	144.1
10	127.3	124.8	122.4	120.6	117.7
11	105.2	103.3	101.5	99.7	98.0
12	88.4	87.0	85.5	84.2	82.8
13	75.3	74.2	73.1	72.0	70.9
14	65.0	64.0	63.1	62.3	61.4
15	56.6	55.8	55.1	54.4	53.7
16	49.7	49.1	48.5	47.9	47.3
17	44.1	43.5	43.0	42.5	42.1
18	39.3	38.9	38.4	38.0	37.6
19	35.3	34.9	34.5	34.2	33.8
20	31.8	31.5	31.2	30.9	30.6
21	28.8	28.6	28.3	28.1	27.8
22	26.3	26.1	25.8	25.6	25.4
23	24.1	23.9	23.7	23.5	23.3
24	22.1	21.9	21.7	21.6	21.4
25	20.4	20.2	20.0	19.9	19.7
26	18.8	18.7	18.5	18.4	18.3
27	17.5	17.3	17.2	17.1	17.0
28	16.2	16.1	16.0	15.9	15.8
29	15.1	15.0	14.9	14.8	14.7
30	14.1	14.1	14.0	13.9	13.8
31	13.2	13.2	13.1	13.0	12.9
32	12.4	12.4	12.3	12.2	12.1
33	11.7	11.6	11.6	11.5	11.4
34	11.0	10.9	10.9	10.8	10.8
35	10.4	10.3	10.3	10.2	10.2
36	9.8	9.8	9.7	9.7	9.6
37	9.3	9.3	9.2	9.2	9.1
38	8.8	8.8	8.7	8.7	8.6
39	8.4	8.3	8.3	8.2	8.2
40	8.0	7.9	7.9	7.8	7.8
41	7.6	7.5	7.5	7.5	7.4
42	7.2	7.2	7.1	7.1	7.1
43	6.9	6.9	6.8	6.8	6.8
44	6.6	6.5	6.5	6.5	6.5
45	6.3	6.3	6.2	6.2	6.2
46	6.0	6.0	6.0	5.9	5.9
47	5.8	5.7	5.7	5.7	5.7
48	5.5	5.5	5.5	5.5	5.4
49	5.3	5.3	5.3	5.2	5.2
50	5.1	5.1	5.1	5.0	5.0

area factor (BAF) equal to 1 metre^2 per hectare (after Citrón and Novelli 1984).

Tenth of a centimetre					Diameter (cm)
0.5	0.6	0.7	0.8	0.9	
50 929.6	35 367.8	25 984.5	19 894.4	15 718.0	0
5 658.8	4 973.6	4 405.7	3 929.8	3 527.0	1
2 037.2	1 883.5	1 746.6	1 624.0	1 514.0	2
1 039.4	982.4	930.1	881.7	837.1	3
628.8	601.7	576.4	552.6	530.3	4
420.9	406.0	391.9	378.5	365.8	5
301.4	292.3	283.6	275.4	267.4	6
226.4	220.4	214.7	209.3	204.0	7
176.2	172.2	168.2	164.4	160.7	8
141.1	138.2	135.3	132.6	129.9	9
115.5	113.3	111.2	109.2	107.2	10
96.3	94.6	93.0	91.4	89.9	11
81.5	80.2	78.9	77.7	76.5	12
69.9	68.8	67.8	66.9	65.9	13
60.6	59.7	58.9	58.1	57.4	14
53.0	52.3	51.7	51.0	50.4	15
46.8	46.2	45.7	45.1	44.6	16
41.6	41.1	40.6	40.2	39.7	17
37.2	36.8	36.4	36.0	35.6	18
33.5	33.1	32.8	32.5	32.2	19
30.3	30.0	29.7	29.4	29.1	20
27.5	27.3	27.0	26.8	26.5	21
25.2	24.9	24.7	24.5	24.3	22
23.1	22.9	22.7	22.5	22.3	23
21.2	21.0	20.9	20.7	20.5	24
19.6	19.4	19.3	19.1	19.0	25
18.1	18.0	17.9	17.7	17.6	26
16.8	16.7	16.6	16.5	16.4	27
15.7	15.6	15.5	15.4	15.2	28
14.6	14.5	14.4	14.3	14.2	29
13.7	13.6	13.5	13.4	13.3	30
12.8	12.8	12.7	12.6	12.5	31
12.1	12.0	11.9	11.8	11.8	31
11.3	11.3	11.2	11.1	11.1	33
10.7	10.6	10.6	10.5	10.5	34
10.1	10.0	10.0	9.9	9.9	35
9.6	9.5	9.5	9.4	9.4	35
9.1	9.0	9.0	8.9	8.9	37
8.6	8.5	8.5	8.5	8.4	38
8.2	8.1	8.1	8.0	8.0	39
7.8	7.7	7.7	7.6	7.6	40
7.4	7.4	7.3	7.3	7.3	41
7.0	7.0	7.0	7.0	6.9	42
6.7	6.7	6.7	6.6	6.6	43
6.4	6.4	6.4	6.3	6.3	44
6.2	6.1	6.1	6.1	6.0	45
5.9	5.9	5.8	5.8	5.8	46
5.6	5.6	5.6	5.6	5.5	47
5.4	5.4	5.4	5.3	5.3	48
5.2	5.2	5.2	5.1	5.1	49
5.0	5.0	5.0	4.9	4.9	50

Mangroves

MANGROVE BASAL AREA DATA

Location ..*Hinchinbrook Island*................... Site...*Coral Creek*.........

Transect N° ..*2*... Plot N° ..*3*.... Latitude .*18°15.0'S*.. Longitude *146°12.0'E*

Date ..*9/9/85*.. Time ..*1035*... Air temp.(°C) ..*25.4*.... Soil temp.(°C) ....

Relascope scale ......*1*.............. Forest type ...*Bruguiera*..............................

N°	Species	GBH(cm)	N°	Species	GBH(cm)	N°	Species	GBH(cm)
1	XG	32.1	21	BG	21.1	41	CT	21.0
2	BG	22.2	22	XG	23.9	42	XG	14.2
3	BG	14.5	23	XG	39.7	43	BG	11.0
4	XG	32.0	24	BG	20.4	44	RS	10.3
5	XG	24.4	25	BG	23.7	45	RS	8.5
6	BG	22.4	26	XG	11.8	46	XG	15.6
7	BG	21.8	27	BG	25.5	47		
8	XG	24.0	28	CT	11.2	48		
9	BG	19.5	29	CT	19.0	49		
10	BG	26.7	30	CT	13.1	50		
11	XG	14.0	31	CT	23.7	51		
12	XG	22.7	32	CT	16.0	52		
13	BG	19.9	33	CT	13.2	53		
14	BG	26.8	34	CT	15.2	54		
15	BG	12.9	35	CT	13.2	55		
16	XG	34.5	36	CT	23.0	56		
17	BG	28.0	37	CT	17.0	57		
18	XG	14.7	38	CT	12.7	58		
19	BG	29.5	39	CT	15.9	59		
20	BG	26.7	40	CT	19.7	60		

Figure 3.20 Completed data sheet. Data from this sample are used in the worked example.

Comments

❏ To accurately measure changes in forest structure or tree growth it is necessary to use permanent plots (see the Transect Line Plots Method).

❏ Great care should be taken when counting smaller trees using the relascope since errors in these size classes can greatly affect the estimation of stem densities.

Worked example

❏ Data used in the worked example are shown in Figure 3.20.

❏ These data are tallied according to taxonomic categories as well as DBH class (Table 3.7). From the data collected we can calculate the species composition, distribution of trees according to DBH class, the total basal area of the trees per hectare, basal area of each species per hectare, as well as basal area of trees according to the DBH class.

❏ To derive the stem density of *Xylocarpus granatum* (XG) in a given DBH class:

» Nominate the DBH class and calculate the mean

DBH class: 10.1 to 15.0 centimetres

Mean DBH = 12.5 cm

» The number of trees counted within each size class is tallied (Table 3.8)

Number of XG = 3

» The density of a tree of a known diameter is taken from Table 3.7 (after Cintrón and Novelli 1984)

Density of tree at DBH 12.5 = 81.5 stem hectacre^{-1}

Stem density XG = 3 x 81.5 = 244.5

❏ Correction of data where scale of the relascope is altered:

» If a sweep using the half-unit scale (Fig. 3.21) gave a count of 40 trees, then the true basal area density is obtained by dividing the result by 4

$$BA = count \; x \; (scale \; factor)^2$$

$$= 40 \; x \; \left\{\frac{1}{2}\right\}^2 = 40 \; x \; \frac{1}{4}$$

$$= 10 \; m^2 \; hectare^{-1}$$

Table 3.8 DBH classes of trees from the worked example (Fig. 3.20). BA is basal area, SD is stem density (stems per hectare)

DBH Class (cm)	Species									
	XG		RS		BG		CT		Sub Total	
	BA	SD	BA	SD	BA	SD	BA	SD	BA	SD
≤ 5.0	0		0		0		0			
5.1-10.0	0		1	226	0		0		1	226
10.1-15.0	3	243	1	81	3	243	5	405	12	972
15.1-20.0	2	84	0		2	84	6	252	10	420
20.1-25.0	4	100	0		8	200	3	75	15	375
25.1-30.0	0		0		5	85	0		5	85
30.1-35.0	3	36	0		0		0		3	36
35.1-40.0										
41.0-45.0										
45.1-50.0										
50.1-55.0										
55.1-60.0										
> 60.1										
Subtotal	12	436	2	307	18	612	14	732		
Total									46	2114

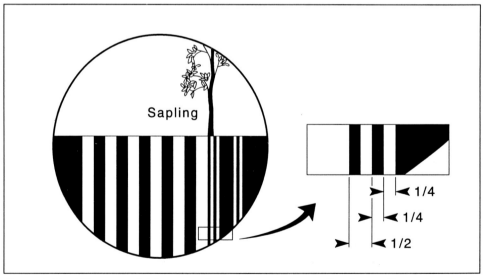

Figure 3.21 When tree girth is narrow (e.g. when counting saplings) a smaller scale must be used to calculate the basal area.

References

Bitterlich, W. (1948). Die winkelzahprobe. Allgemeine Forst- und Holzwirtschaftliche Zeitung, **59**: 4-5.

Cintrón, G. and Y.S. Novelli (1984). Methods for studying mangrove structure. pp. 91-113. In: Snedaker, S.C. and J.G. Snedaker (editors). "The Mangrove Ecosystem: Research Methods". Unesco, Paris. 251pp.

Suggested Reading

Finlayson, W. (1969). "The Relascope: Bitterlich's Spiegel Relaskop; using metric units throughout". Edinburgh. 32pp.

Mangroves

3.4 Transect Line Plots Method

Abstract

The method provides quantitative descriptions of the species composition, community structure and plant biomass of mangrove forests. It provides a convenient framework for relating changes in forest structure and growth to soil, climatic and hydrologic factors. Permanent plots are established along a transect through the mangrove forest in each of the main forest types or zones. Permanent plots are particularly suited to studies that require long-term monitoring of changes in forest structure, biomass and growth.

Background

Temporary or permanent plots have been used extensively by ecologists to study community structure in a wide variety of plant ecosystems. When the plots are marked to enable resurvey of exactly the same site, they can be used to detect changes in the community over time.

Measurements of Girth at Breast Height (GBH) or Diameter at Breast Height (DBH) can be used to calculate above ground biomass using allometric relationships between GBH (or DBH) and the biomass of individual plant parts (Ong *et al.* 1984, Putz and Chan 1986, Clough and Scott 1989). Coefficients for these allometric relationships for a number of species are summarised in Clough (1992) and reproduced in a slightly modified form at the end of this section.

The 3 relative measurements used for this assessment are density, basal area (dominance) and the probability of occurrence throughout the plot (frequency). These relative measures are often combined to give an importance value (Curtis 1959) and should only be used as a supplement to absolute values.

Advantages

❑ This method uses simple equipment and gives accurate results for many aspects of structural characteristics of mangrove forests.

❑ Permanently marked plots allow the measurement of change in forest structure over space and time.

Disadvantages

❑ It is very time consuming.

MANGROVE TRANSECT DATA

Location .... Site..................................

Transect Nº .... Plot Nº .... Latitude .... Longitude ....

Date .... Time .... Forest type ....

Tag Number	X Coord.	Y Coord.	Species	GBH

Species count

Saplings	Seedlings

Tree ≡ D > 4cm; Sapling ≡ D > 4cm, H > 1m; Seedling ≡ H < 1m

Mangroves

Figure 3.22   Preprinted data sheet to record measurements taken in each plot.

❑ The probability of a plant occurring in a plot (frequency measurements) is a function of plot size, since larger plots are most likely to yield larger frequencies. Therefore, comparison of frequencies can only be made between plots of similar size.

Logistics

Equipment
❑ 2 handheld compasses to establish a transect line.

❑ Tapes: 50 metre fibreglass tapes will be required to lay out the plots, and a 2 metre fibreglass tape to measure tree girth (GBH). Special diameter tapes, which are used in forestry to measure tree diameter at breast height (DBH), are not recommended for mangrove studies since many mangrove trees do not have a round cross-section.

❑ Rope or string, approximately 100 metres in length.

❑ Durable tags and stainless steel wire. Cut the tags from a sheet of light gauge aluminium and punch a unique number onto each tag. Do not duplicate numbers.

❑ Stakes - 1.5 metre lengths of 50 millimetre PVC pipe or other material.

❑ Hammer and nails (5 centimetres in length).

❑ Preprinted data sheets. A4 underwater paper is recommended (Fig. 3.22). Small notebooks can also be used but care should be taken to reduce their exposure to water. A new notebook should be used for each field trip.

❑ Pencils.

Site selection

❑ At least 2 sites should be selected at each location.

❑ Sites should be as representative as possible of the general area.

❑ Determine the extent of the mangrove forest using aerial photographs. The photographs will also indicate whether zonation occurs in the forest. Ground truthing is used to confirm any changes in forest type indicated on the photographs.

❑ Record the precise location of the sites. A GPS is useful, if available.

❑ Plots should be established wherever the vegetation type changes.

General procedure

❑ For each site, establish at least 3 transect lines from the seaward margin of the forest at right angles to the edges of mangrove forest (Fig. 3.23).

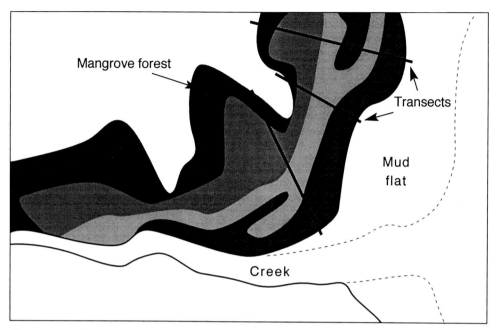

Figure 3.23 Transects are established through the mangrove forest from the seaward edge to the landward margin.

❑ Ensure that edge of forest margins do not confound the measurements. If the mangrove forest is just a narrow 'fringe' along the coast, a number of permanent plots should be set up within the 'fringe'.

❑ Divide the transect into zones corresponding to the main inundation/flooding classes as defined in this manual. The minimum acceptable division is low, mid and high intertidal zones (see Section 3.5).

❑ Subdivide the intertidal zone into the main forest types according to the tree species present.

❑ Establish 3 randomly located replicate plots of equal size in each forest type encountered along the transect.

☞ *For some studies, it may be desirable for plots to be aligned end-to-end along the transect. However, data obtained from end-to-end sequential plots are more difficult to analyse statistically than those obtained from replicate plots placed at random to the side of the transect line.*

❑ The size of the plot is determined by the density of the trees, but should be no less than 10 metres x 10 metres. It may be necessary in some sites to compromise between the minimum number of trees required for statistically significant analyses, and the amount of time required to measure them. Generally, there should be **at least** 40-100 trees in each plot.

Permanent plots

❏ Mark the corners of the plots with stakes (1.5 metre lengths of 50 millimetre PVC pipe or other material). Drive the stakes well into the ground (at least 50 centimetres).

❏ Mark one corner of the plot with tape and a durable numbered tag. This corner is referred to as the origin (0,0) coordinate and the other corners are then referenced according to their XY axis (Fig. 3.24).

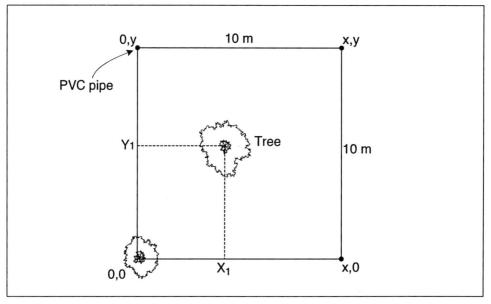

Figure 3.24 Reference system used to locate trees within a permanently marked quadrat. The coordinates of the tree shown in the figure are X_1, Y_1.

❏ Attach numbered tags to each tree with stainless steel wire. Leave enough slack in the wire to allow for tree growth.

❏ Identify and record the species of each tree (larger than 4 centimetres in girth), and its position in the plot to the nearest 10 centimetres. Use the X and Y coordinates set up by the corners of the plot (Fig. 3.24). This method allows relocation of the plot provided a few trees remained tagged.

❏ Measure the girth of the tree stem (GBH) using a 2 metre fibreglass tape. The GBH measurement is taken at breast height, approximately 1.3 metres above the ground (Fig. 3.18).

❏ Hammer a nail (5 centimetres in length) into the stem 10 centimetres beneath the height at which the GBH was measured to provide a reference point for future measurements. Leave about half the nail protruding from the stem to allow for growth.

☞ *The nail should be positioned below the height at which GBH was measured so that any swelling around the nail will not affect future measurements. Other methods of marking the stem, such as painting or notching, are not satisfactory. Sloughing of bark sheds paint marks, and notches grow out, usually with noticeable swelling.*

❑ Measurement of the girth of trees can be difficult for some shape and growth forms of mangrove trees (Fig. 3.19). The following procedures are therefore recommended:

» When a system forks below breast height, or sprouts from a single base close to the ground or above it, measure each branch as a separate stem (the link between these records is denoted by "1" for the main stem, and "2" for the other branches/stems).

» When the stem forks at breast height or slightly above, measure the girth at breast height or just below the swelling caused by the fork.

» When the stem has prop roots or fluted lower trunk (*Rhizophora* species), measure the girth 20 centimetres above the root collar.

» When the stem has swellings, branches or abnormalities at the point of measurement, measure the girth slightly above or below the irregularity (where it stops affecting normal form).

❑ Saplings (girth less than 4 centimetres and height greater than 1 metre) are identified and the number of individuals by species is determined by actual count. If the density of saplings is very high and uniform, smaller subplots can be used (5 metre x 5 metre would be the minimum size). Use the reference corner (origin) of the main plot as the reference corner of the subplot.

❑ Seedlings (height less than 1 metre) are identified and the number of individuals by species is determined by actual count. Subplots can be counted when densities are high, as above.

❑ Measure ambient environmental factors for each plot (quadrat). These include soil salinity, redox potential (Eh), soil temperature and pH (Section 3.1). Collect soil samples for grain size analysis (Section 3.1). Light measurements may also be taken (Section 3.2).

❑ Take note of any impact in the area, that is, record any activities such as bunding, storm damage, etc. and assess the degree of impact.

❑ Index of 'human pressure'. This is assessed on a scale from 0 to 5, where 0 is no impact and 5 is severely impacted (Table 3.5).

Mangroves

Data recording

❏ Record data onto data sheets similar to that shown in Figure 3.22. Species codes are shown in Section 3.7.

❏ Record the ambient environmental factors for each plot (see Sections 3.1) onto the top of the data sheet (Fig. 3.22). Light measurements may also be recorded, see Section 3.2.

❏ Collect climate data for all sites. This should include average monthly rainfall and monthly temperature (maximum and minimum).

Data processing

❏ Enter data into the database at the end of each day using the structure described at the end of this chapter.

❏ Information about the sample is entered into the sample table (XXMVSAMP) and a unique sample identifier (SAMPLE_ID) is allocated. The type of data collected in the sample is described by the DATA_TYPE field, which for the vegetation data collected in the plots along the transect, are denoted by the letter "T".

❏ The tree data from the plots (along the transect) are entered into the data table (XXMVDATA) using the sample identification allocated in the sample table. Each tree within the plot will have the same SAMPLE_ID. If sapling or seedling data are collected from the plot data are entered into the data table XXMVSDAT using the same SAMPLE_ID.

❏ An entry is made into the sample table (XXMVSAMP) to describe the ambient data collected in conjunction with the plot, i.e. DATA_TYPE is "A". The ambient data which record the soil characteristics of the plot (e.g. soil type, temperature, salinity, Eh and PH), are entered into the ambient table (XXMVADAT) using the sample identification allocated in the sample table.

❏ Light data (DATA_TYPE "L") are entered into the data XXMLDAT as above.

❏ Additional environmental parameters recorded for each site:

   » climate data such as mean annual and mean monthly rainfall and monthly temperature (maximum and minimum) - entered into the climate table (XXMVCDAT);

   » Index of 'human pressure'. Codes for the types of impacts are given in Table 3.4. Impact is assessed on a scale from 0 to 5, where 0 is no impact and 5 is severely impacted (Table 3.5) - entered into the sample table (XXMVSAMP).

❏ **Always check and verify data after entry.**

❏ Always backup data regularly.

Analysis

❑ Community structure:

» Calculate the basal area (BA) for the stand in m^2 per hectare (ha)

BA for each tree is the cross-sectional area at breast height

$$BA = \frac{\pi\,DBH^{\,2}}{4}\ (cm^2)$$

The total BA for all species is the sum of BAs for each tree in the plot

$$\Sigma\,BA\ (cm^2)$$

Convert cm^2 to m^2, and ground area from m^2 to hectares

$$Stand\ BA = \frac{\Sigma\,BA}{Area\ of\ the\ plot}\ m^2\,ha^{-2}$$

» The basal area of each species (Basal Area of Species) is calculated by the same method as above, but calculating the total only for trees of the same species.

» Calculate the number of stems per hectare

$$Stems\ per\ ha = \frac{No.\ of\ stems\ in\ plot\ x\ 10,000}{Area\ of\ the\ plot}$$

» The importance of the contribution of each component species to the stand in terms of density, contribution to basal area (dominance) and probability of occurrence throughout the plot (frequency) are described by the following parameters:

$$Relative\ density\ = \frac{no.\ of\ individuals\ of\ a\ species}{total\ of\ no.\ individuals\ (all\ species)}\ x\ 100$$

$$Relative\ frequency\ = \frac{frequency\ of\ a\ species}{\Sigma\,frequency\ of\ all\ species}\ x\ 100$$

$$Relative\ dominance\ = \frac{total\ basal\ area\ of\ species}{basal\ area\ of\ all\ species}\ x\ 100$$

☞ *Frequency is defined as the probability of finding the species in any one plot and can only be compared between plots of equal size.*

» The 'importance value' (Curtis 1959) is the sum of the relative density, relative frequency and relative dominance.

» Above ground biomass can be calculated from the GBH/DBH using relative growth (allometric) relationships between GBH/DBH and biomass.

Mangroves

Equations and coefficients for these relationships have been published for a number of species and localities.

» Species diversity is described according to the Shannon Index (H) as per the following equation:

$$H = -\sum_{i=1}^{s} \left(\frac{N_i}{N}\right) \log \left(\frac{N_i}{N}\right)$$

Where: N_i = importance value of a species i

   N = sum of importance values for all species

$$N = \sum_{i=1}^{s} N_i$$

Where: S = total number of species in the sample

Comments

❏ In fringing mangroves, which only occur in a narrow strip along the coastline, transects are not possible and replicate plots should be done at each site. The size of the plots may be influenced by the width of the fringing strip, since the plot should fit comfortably within the mangrove forest, avoiding the margins of the forest.

References

Clough, B.F. (1992). Primary productivity and growth of mangrove forests. pp. 225-249. In: A.I. Robertson and D.M. Alongi (editors). "Tropical Mangrove Ecosystems". American Geophysical Union, Washington, DC. 329pp.

Clough, B.F. and K. Scott (1989). Allometric relationships for estimating above-ground biomass in six mangrove species. Forest Ecology and Management, 27: 117-127.

Curtis, J.T. (1959). "The Vegetation of Wisconsin. An Ordination of Plant Communities". University of Wisconsin Press, Madison. 657pp.

Ong, J.E., W.K. Gong, C.H. Wong and G. Dhanarajan (1984). Contribution of aquatic productivity in managed mangrove ecosystem in Malaysia. pp. 209-215. In: E. Soepadmo, A.N. Rao and D.J. Macintosh (editors). "Proceedings of the Asian Symposium on Mangrove Environment: Research and Management". University of Malaya, Kuala Lumpur.

Putz, F.E. and H.T. Chan (1986). Tree growth, dynamics and productivity in a mature mangrove forest in Malaysia. Forest Ecology and Management, 17: 211-230.

3.5 Tidal Flooding/Inundation

Abstract

This technique provides a description of the local topography of mangrove areas with respect to tidal inundation (flooding) and drainage patterns. It uses the water level at the tidal peak as a benchmark, below which the height of the soil surface is measured. The technique does not establish absolute topographic levels, but it can be used to determine the frequency and duration of tidal inundation.

The method involves attaching cloth tape or string, previously soaked in a water soluble dye, to trees or stakes in the mangrove community. The tape is left out over a high tide period, which washes the dye from the tape. The height of the washout line above the soil surface is used to estimate the topographic level.

Mangroves

Background

The frequency and duration of tidal flooding is important in determining the zonation, distribution and species composition of mangrove forests. Some workers have been content to subdivide mangrove areas into low-, mid- and high-intertidal areas. This somewhat arbitrary division is hard to quantify and makes comparisons difficult between areas with differing tidal regimes.

A more quantitative approach was used by Watson (1928), who divided mangrove areas into 5 inundation classes:

Class 1 . . inundated by all high tides;
Class 2 . . inundated by medium high tides;
Class 3 . . inundated by normal high tides;
Class 4 . . inundated by spring tides; and
Class 5 . . occasionally inundated by exceptional or equinoctial tides.

In many cases, these inundation classes may be quantified in terms of the number of times per month that an area is inundated tidally. However, Watson's classification scheme is still somewhat arbitrary and its use is restricted largely to the mangrove areas of Malaysia, for which it was originally devised.

There is need for a more quantitative description of tidal inundation classes that is both ecologically and hydrologically meaningful across a wide range of tidal regimes. At this stage, however, there are insufficient data to develop such a description. The technique described here quantifies topographic elevation in mangrove areas with respect to tidal range. The data could be used to develop a more widely acceptable, quantitative description of tidal inundation classes or zones, if the method is applied in a sufficiently wide range of areas.

The method does not require expensive equipment and is easy to use. Conventional surveying techniques using theodolites or laser-based levels provide good absolute topographic levels, but are time consuming and require line of site to established surveying benchmarks.

Advantages

❑ The method does not require expensive equipment and is easy to use.

❑ This method provides a simple means of surveying relatively large areas of mangrove quickly without the need for specialised equipment.

Disadvantages

❑ Estimates of topographic elevation derived from this method are not absolute, nor are they as accurate as those obtained by conventional surveying techniques.

Logistics

Equipment

❑ 2 or 3 fibreglass measuring tapes (3 metres in length) - to measure the height of the watermark. If measurements of topographic level are to be done along line transects, tapes of 50 or 100 metres in length will be needed.

❑ Slates and preprinted data sheets (Fig. 3.25). A4 underwater paper is recommended. Small notebooks can also be used but care should be taken to reduce their exposure to water. A new notebook should be used for each field trip.

❑ Pencils.

❑ Small flat-head nails (about 2 centimetres long) and hammer.

❑ White cotton tape, 0.5 to 2 centimetres in width, cut into lengths of 1 to 3 metres, depending on the expected tide height. Strong cotton, string or other absorbent material may also be suitable, but must be tested before use.

❑ Red, green or blue water-soluble food dye (available from supermarkets or baking suppliers).

❑ Brightly coloured surveying or flagging tape (pink or orange or red is more visible than green, yellow and white).

❑ Timber stakes.

Maintenance

❑ Wash equipment in freshwater after use.

MANGROVE INUNDATION DATA

Location .... Site.....................................

Date .... Time .... Creep .... (cm)

Reference point: Hight above MSL .... Height of tape ....

	Transect 1			Transect 2			Transect 3	
N°	Distance	Height	N°	Distance	Height	N°	Distance	Height
1	_____	_____	1	_____	_____	1	_____	_____
2	_____	_____	2	_____	_____	2	_____	_____
3	_____	_____	3	_____	_____	3	_____	_____
4	_____	_____	4	_____	_____	4	_____	_____
5	_____	_____	5	_____	_____	5	_____	_____
6	_____	_____	6	_____	_____	6	_____	_____
7	_____	_____	7	_____	_____	7	_____	_____
8	_____	_____	8	_____	_____	8	_____	_____
9	_____	_____	9	_____	_____	9	_____	_____
10	_____	_____	10	_____	_____	10	_____	_____
11	_____	_____	11	_____	_____	11	_____	_____
12	_____	_____	12	_____	_____	12	_____	_____
13	_____	_____	13	_____	_____	13	_____	_____
14	_____	_____	14	_____	_____	14	_____	_____
15	_____	_____	15	_____	_____	15	_____	_____
16	_____	_____	16	_____	_____	16	_____	_____
17	_____	_____	17	_____	_____	17	_____	_____
18	_____	_____	18	_____	_____	18	_____	_____
19	_____	_____	19	_____	_____	19	_____	_____
20	_____	_____	20	_____	_____	20	_____	_____
21	_____	_____	21	_____	_____	21	_____	_____
22	_____	_____	22	_____	_____	22	_____	_____
23	_____	_____	23	_____	_____	23	_____	_____
24	_____	_____	24	_____	_____	24	_____	_____
25	_____	_____	25	_____	_____	25	_____	_____

Mangroves

Figure 3.25 Preprinted data sheet to record the height of the watermark measured from each tape after high tide. The distance along the transect of each sampling point (stake or tree) is recorded with the heights. The height of the tide at the reference point is also be recorded.

Location of sites

❏ The selection of a suitable site depends on the nature of the study. It is best to make measurements along a transect from the low-intertidal to the high-intertidal.

❏ For many studies, it is appropriate to combine this method with the Transect Line Plots Method for examining forest structure and growth (Section 3.4).

General procedure

❏ Pre-dye 1.5 to 2.0 metre lengths of cotton tape with a water-soluble food dye and allow to dry for at least 8 hours.

☞ *It is important to test the solubility of the dye before field studies to ensure that the dye will be washed from the tape during the high tide cycle.*

❏ Measurements must be done on a high tide that covers the whole area to be studied.

❏ Lay the transect lines along a topographic gradient from the seaward to the landward margins of the mangrove community (see Fig. 3.23). Mark trees with surveyors tape or other colourful material to identify the transect.

❏ During the low tide preceding height measurements, nail a length of dyed tape to a tree (or stake) at 10 metre or 20 metre intervals along the transect.

❏ Position the tape on the tree so that it extends above and below the expected high tide level (Fig. 3.26), i.e. the dyed tape must span the expected peak water level.

☞ *In open areas, or where trees are sparse, it may be difficult to find suitably spaced trees on which to attach the dyed tape. In such cases, timber stakes may be needed.*

❏ The time of the tidal peak at the transect site should be recorded.

❏ Generally, the watermark on the cloth tape 'creeps' 2 to 3 centimetres above the actual peak water level because of capillary movement of water up the tape (Fig. 3.26). This varies with the type of tape used. To compensate for this, monitor the peak tide level and the watermark on a reference stake at a convenient position in the area.

❏ Immediately after the high tide period, measure the height of the watermark above the soil surface. Be sure to correct for any difference in level between the base of the tree or stake and the surrounding general ground level.

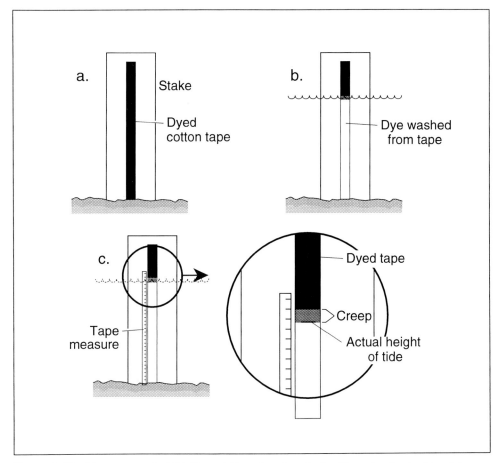

Figure 3.26 Measurement of tidal inundation at a site: **a)** dyed tape is attached to stakes or trees; **b)** water washes dye out of the tape at high tide; **c)** height reached by the tide is measured.

Data recording

❏ Record details of the sampling site, date and all height measurements onto the data sheets (Fig. 3.25).

❏ Record the 'creep' (centimetres) of the watermark on the cloth tape of the observed (reference) stake.

❏ Record the time of the tidal peak at the site.

❏ Record the name of the standard port which is used in the tide tables for the tidal predictions.

Processing data

❏ The height measured at the watermark must be corrected for watermark 'creep' and for any difference in height between the base of the stake (or tree) and general ground level (Hm).

❏ Look up the predicted height of high tide (in metres) in the tide tables for the area. Record the predicted height for the day on which measurements are taken (Hp).

❏ The topographic level (Ht) is then given by:

$$H_t = H_p - H_m$$

❏ Use the tide tables to tally the number of days each year when the predicted level is greater than, or equal to, the topographic level (Ht).

❏ After data have been processed enter them into the database using the structure described at the end of this chapter (Section 3.6).

❏ Enter the inundation data into the ambient data table (XXMVADAT) using the sample identification allocated in the sample table (Section 3.6).

Comments

❏ The accuracy of this method is about 5 centimetres. Simple sources of error, such as the difference between the true peak tide height and the watermark, and the slightly elevated soil surface around the bases of trees, can be minimised by careful measurement.

❏ The main source of error in this method is non-uniformity in the level of the water surface at the tidal peak. In the absence of freshwater flooding, the tidal amplitude in estuaries and coastal rivers decreases with increasing distance from the mouth. Similarly, the tidal amplitude in a mangrove community decreases with increasing distance from the seaward margin. Thus, the peak water level near the landward margins will be lower than that near the seaward margin.

References

Watson, J.G. (1928). "Mangrove Forests of the Malay Peninsular". Fraser and Neave, Ltd., Singapore. 275pp.

3.6 Mangrove Database Structure

Mangrove sample data
XXMVSAMP

Name	Type	Length/ Decimal	Description
SAMPLE_ID	C	9.0	The standard sample identification. This links the sample table to the data files. Format XXGGGNNNN: XX = country code. See codes in Appendix I. GGG = study group code NNNN = running number
LOCATION	C	30.0	Location name e.g. Matang
SITE	C	30.0	Specific study area (e.g. 'Compartment' 17, in Matang, Malaysia)
DATE	D	8.0	Date when data were gathered (using the format MM/DD/YY)
LATITUDE	C	7.0	Latitude of site in format AABBCCD AA = degrees BB = minutes CC = decimal seconds D = N (north) or S (south)
LONGITUDE	C	8.0	Longitude of site in format AAABBCCD AAA = degrees BB = minutes CC = decimal seconds D = E (east) or W (west)
DATA_TYPE	C	1.0	Data code denoting the type of the study: A = ambient data; C = climate data; L = light data; R = relascope data; T = transect/vegetation data. Data file names are listed in the datacode table
IMPCT_CODE	C	3.0	Impact code using the format abb, where: a is direct (D), indirect (I) or both direct and indirect (B); and bb is the type of impact (Table 3.4). Codes are listed in the datacode table
IMPCT_ASSE	N	1.0	Codes for the scale of impact, where 0 is no impact and 5 is severely impacted (Table 3.5). Codes are listed in the datacode table
REMARKS	C	50.0	Relevant observations regarding the site and the data

Mangroves

Mangrove ambient data
XXMVADAT

Name	Type	Length/ Decimal	Description
SAMPLE_ID	C	9.0	The standard sample identification. This links the sample table to the data files. Format XXGGGNNNN (see sample table).
REPLICATE	N	2.0	Replicate transect within a site
FOREST	C	2.0	Forest type within the transect determined by the dominant species (see Section 3.7 for codes)
PLOT_NO	N	2.0	Replicate plot number surveyed within each site (both permanent and relascope plots)
DEPTH	N	2.0	Depth at which sample is collected. Measured in cm
SOIL_COLOUR	C	10.0	Colour of soil
SOIL_TYPE	C	10.0	Texture of soil (e.g. sandy clay loam)
SAND	N	3.0	Mean sand in the plot samples. Recorded as a percentage
SILT	N	3.0	Mean silt in the plot samples. Recorded as a percentage
CLAY	N	3.0	Mean clay in the plot samples. Recorded as a percentage
TEMP	N	6.2	Mean temperature of soil at the plot, measured in degrees Celsius
SALN	N	5.2	Mean salinity of soil at the plot, measured in ppt
Eh	N	8.2	Mean redox potential at the plot
PH	N	5.2	Mean pH of soil at the plot
INUNDATION	N	3.0	Number of days each year when the plot is flooded by the tide

Mangrove climate data
XXMVCDAT

Name	Type	Length/ Decimal	Description
LOCATION	C	30.0	Location name e.g. Matang
TIDAL_RNGE	N	4.1	Tidal range at study site. Measured in metres
RAINFALL	N	5.1	Mean annual rainfall at the location (if monthly values are not available). Measured in millimetres
MONTH	N	2.0	Month (1 to 12)
RAINFALL_M	N	5.1	Mean monthly rainfall at the location. Measured in millimetres
TEMP_MAX	N	3.1	Mean monthly maximum temperature. Measured in degrees Celsius
TEMP_MIN	N	3.1	Mean monthly minimum temperature. Measured in degrees Celsius

Mangrove light data
XXMVLDAT

Name	Type	Length/ Decimal	Description
SAMPLE_ID	C	9.0	The standard sample identification. This links the sample table to the data files. Format XXGGGNNNN (see sample table).
REPLICATE	N	2.0	Replicate transect within a site
FOREST	C	2.0	Forest type within the transect determined by the dominant species (see Section 3.7 for codes)
PLOT_NO	N	2.0	Designated plot number surveyed within forest type along transect
TIME	C	4.0	Time that data were collected. Format HHMM (e.g. 1330 = 1:30 pm)
ZENITH ANGLE	N	2.2	Angle of the sun from the vertical, measured in radians
IMEAN	N	10.0	Mean penetrated light per plot, measured in $\mu E/m^2/s$
IoMEAN	N	10.0	Mean incident light per plot, measured in $\mu E/m^2/s$
CANOPY	N	2.3	Mean canopy cover per plot
L_INDEX	N	2.2	Leaf area index (L), measured in m^2 leaf area m^{-2} ground area
C_PHOTO	N	3.0	Net canopy photosynthesis (P_N), measured in $gC\ m^{-2}$ ground day^{-1}

Mangrove vegetation relascope data
XXMVRDAT

Name	Type	Length/ Decimal	Description
SAMPLE_ID	C	9.0	The standard sample identification. This links the sample table to the data files. Format XXGGGNNNN (see sample table).
REPLICATE	N	2.0	Replicate transect within a site
FOREST	C	2.0	Forest type within the transect determined by the dominant species (see Section 3.7 for codes)
PLOT_NO	N	2.0	The replicate number 'plot' (sampling point) at each forest type along transect
FIELDCODE	C	40.0	Code assigned to the taxonomic entity by the field researchers (see Section 3.7). The code must uniquely link to one taxonomic entity. Description of the entity (i.e. binomial name) must be given to the database manager when a new code is created. This information is maintained in ALLTAXON (see page 102)
GBH	N	6.2	Girth of individual tree at breast height (1.3m above ground level). Measured in centimetres
DBH	N	6.2	Diameter of individual tree at breast height (1.3m above ground level), measured in centimetres
RELA_SCALE	C	5.0	Relascope scale used (e.g. band 1)

Mangroves

Mangrove vegetation data (mature trees)
XXMVDATA

Name	Type	Length/ Decimal	Description
SAMPLE_ID	C	9.0	The standard sample identification. This links the sample table to the data files. Format XXGGGNNNN (see sample table).
REPLICATE	N	2.0	Replicate transect within a site
FOREST	C	2.0	Forest type within the transect determined by the dominant species (see Section 3.7 for codes)
PLOT_NO	N	2.0	Designated plot number surveyed within forest type along transect
TAG_NO	N	2.0	Tag number of tree (girth > 4 centimetres)
X_COORD	N	1.2	Position of tree within plot along X coordinate of quadrat
Y_COORD	N	1.2	Position of tree within plot along Y coordinate of quadrat
FIELDCODE	C	40.0	Code assigned to the taxonomic entity by the field researchers (Section 3.7). See XXMVRDAT for detail
GBH	N	6.2	Girth of tree measured at breast height (1.3 metres above ground level). Measured in centimetres
DBH	N	6.2	Diameter of tree measured at breast height (1.3 metres above ground level). Measured in centimetres
LINK	N	1.0	Code used to separate the main stem from branches when trees sprout close to the ground, where: 1 = main stem; 2 = other branches/stems which sprout from the same base
STATUS	C	1.0	Coded condition of the trees, where: A = living trees; C = cut trees; D = dead trees

Mangrove vegetation data (saplings and seedlings)
XXMVSDAT

Name	Type	Length/ Decimal	Description
SAMPLE_ID	C	9.0	The standard sample identification. This links the sample table to the data files. If trees, saplings and seedlings are sampled at the same time this table would have the same sample_id as XXMVDATA. Format XXGGGNNNN (see sample table).
REPLICATE	N	2.0	Replicate transect within a site
FOREST	C	2.0	Forest type within the transect determined by the dominant species (see Section 3.7 for codes)
PLOT_NO	N	2.0	Designated plot number surveyed within forest type along transect
FIELDCODE	C	40.0	Code assigned to the taxonomic entity by the field researchers (Section 3.7). See XXMVRDAT for detail
AGE_STAGE	C	1.0	Age code of trees, where: 2 = saplings (girth < 4 centimetres, height > 1 metre); 3 = seedlings (height < l metre)
COUNT	N	3.0	Number of saplings or seedlings in the plot

Mangrove Datacodes
DATACODE

Name	Data Type	Explanation
DATA_TYPE	A	Sample record refers to data in the ambient data file XXMVADAT
	C	Sample record refers to data in the climate data table XXMVCDAT
	L	Sample record refers to data in the light data table XXMVLDAT
	R	Sample record refers to data in the relascope data file XXMVRDAT
	T	Sample record refers to data in the transect/vegetation data file XXMVDATA
IMPCT ASSE	0	No impact
	1	Slight impact
	2	Moderate impact
	3	Rather high impact
	4	High impact
	5	Severe impact
IMPCT_CODE	###	Uses the format abb where
		where a = B (both direct and indirect impact)
		= D (direct impact)
		= I (indirect impact)
		where bb = BU (bunding for dyking)
		= CO (infrastructure including jetties, fish landing sites, construction sites, settlements or other coastal developments)
		= ER (erosion)
		= IC (illegal cutting)
		= MI (mining activities)
		= MU (multiple impact)
		= OT (others)
		= PP (prawn/fish ponds)
		= SC (shell collecting)
		= SS (severe storm)
SOIL_TYPE	C	Represents clay soil fraction. In the format abc where a represents the texture of the dominant soil fraction, b the next most common fraction and c the least common fraction, e.g. SLC means clay forms the least common fraction
	L	Represents loam fraction of soil. In the format abc where a represents the texture of the dominant soil fraction, b the next most common fraction and c the least common fraction e.g. SLC means sand forms the dominant fraction
	S	Represents sand fraction of the soil. In the format abc where a represents the texture of the dominant soil fraction, b the next most common fraction and c the least common fraction e.g. SLC means sand forms the dominant fraction
LINK	1	Used to separate the main stem and branches/stems that sprout from a single base close to the ground or above it. Code 1 is for the main stem
	2	Used to separate the main stem and branches/stems that sprout from a single base close to the ground or above it. Code 2 is for other branches or stems that sprout from the same base
STATUS	A	Condition of the trees. Code A is for living trees
	C	Condition of the trees. Code C is for cut trees
	D	Condition of the trees. Code D is for dead trees
AGE_STAGE	1	The code assigned for mature trees (girth > 4 centimetres)
	2	The code assigned for saplings (girth < 4 centimetres, height > 1 metre)
	3	The code assigned for seedlings (height < I metre)

3.7 Mangrove Tree Species Codes

Aegiceras corniculatum	AC	*Kandelia candel*	KC
Aegiceras floridum	AF	*Laguncularia racemosa*	LA
Avicennia alba	AA	*Lumnitzera littorea**	LL
Avicennia bicolor	AB	*Lumnitzera racemosa**	LR
Avicennia germinans	AG	*Lumnitzera X rosea*	LS
Avicennia integra	AI	*Mora oleifera*	MO
Avicennia marina	AM	*Myristica hollrungii**	MH
Avicennia officinalis	AO	*Nypa fruticans*	NP
Avicennia rumphiana	AR	*Osbornia octodonta*	OO
Avicennia schaueriana	AS	*Pemphis acidula*	PA
Bruguiera cylindrica	BC	*Rhizophora apiculata*	RA
Bruguiera exaristata	BE	*Rhizophora mucronata*	RM
Bruguiera gymnorrhiza	BG	*Rhizophora mangle*	RN
Bruguiera hainesii	BH	*Rhizophora racemosa*	RR
Bruguiera parviflora	BP	*Rhizophora samoensis*	RO
Bruguiera sexangula	BS	*Rhizophora stylosa*	RS
*Brownlowia argentata d B. tersa**	BA	*Rhizophora X harrisonii*	RH
Camptostemon philippensis	CP	*Rhizophora X lamarckii*	RL
Camptostemon schultzii	CS	*Rhizophora X selala*	RX
Ceriops australis	CA	*Scyphiphora hydrophyllacea*	SH
Ceriops tagal	CT	*Sonneratia alba*	SA
Ceriops decandra	CD	*Sonneratia apetala*	SP
Conocarpus erectus	CE	*Sonneratia caseolaris*	SC
Cynometra iripa	CI	*Sonneratia griffithii*	SG
Dolichandrone spathacea	DS	*Sonneratia lanceolata*	SL
*Diospyros ferrea**	DF	*Sonneratia ovata*	SO
*Excoecaria agallocha**	EC	*Sonneratia X gulngai*	SU
Excoecaria indica	EI	*Xylocarpus granatum*	XG
Heritiera littoralis	HL	*Xylocarpus moluccensis*	XM
*Heritiera fomes**	HF	*Xylocarpus mekongensis*	XK
Heritiera globosa	HG	* back mangroves, no shrubs included.	
*Intsia bijuga**	IB		

CHAPTER	**SOFT-BOTTOM**
4	**COMMUNITIES**

General Introduction

Extensive soft-bottom coastal environments exist throughout tropical regions of the world. Soft-bottom communities are diverse and play an important role as support systems for many coastal resources. These include large mobile invertebrates, such as penaeid shrimps, which are the basis of important commercial fisheries (Longhurst and Pauly 1987), and higher trophic groups which feed on soft-bottom communities, such as fin fish.

The soft-bottom communities near the coast are subject to increasing effects of domestic and industrial pollution and, since many of the organisms of these communities are sessile, they provide useful indicators of habitat quality. Because of this, soft-bottom communities have often been used in studies of pollution (Chang *et al*. 1992, Gray *et al*. 1992). However, the effects of pollution in tropical soft-bottom communities are poorly documented compared with comparable temperate environments (see reviews by Pearson and Rosenberg 1978, Alongi 1990).

Specific sampling programs are needed to monitor perturbations, such as pollution, and these should involve appropriate sampling design which takes into consideration the objectives of the study (see Chapter 7). All such studies require a knowledge of the natural spatial and temporal variability of benthos. However, there is a lack of this information for tropical soft-bottom benthos. Therefore, the initial sampling program should establish the broader scale variability of the benthos and describe any gradients in community structure as you move offshore (shallow to deep). This is most effectively done using samplers such as dredges and epibenthic sledges, which collect over a wide area. Such sampling can act as a pilot survey for intensive localised studies using more quantitative samplers, such as grabs. Repetitive sampling with sledges can also provide important information on the temporal variability of larger benthos. Sledges and dredges sample quite distinct components of the benthos from those sampled by grabs, hence both are necessary for a comprehensive evaluation of benthic communities.

Tropical soft-bottom communities may show high species diversities and temporal variability. Due to problems with identification of most groups, data collected should be limited to macrobenthos, unless specific expertise in meiofauna and microfauna taxonomy is available. All fauna collected should be identified at least to family level.

The area of study should cover the nearshore areas, and sites should be selected to sample both pristine (or less disturbed) and impacted/disturbed communities. The number of sites chosen in each study region will be affected by manpower availability and logistics. While recognising these limitations, it is important that monitoring programs consider the natural variability in benthic populations.

References

Alongi, D.M. (1990). The ecology of tropical soft-bottom benthic ecosystems. Oceanography and Marine Biology Annual Review, **28**: 381-496.

Chang, S., F.W. Steimle, R.N. Reid, S.A. Fromm, V.S. Zdanowicz and R.A. Pikanowski (1992). Association of benthic macrofauna with habitat types and quality in the New York Bight. Marine Ecology Progress Series, **89**: 237-251.

Gray, J.S., A.D. McIntyre and J. Stirn (1992). Manual of methods in aquatic environment research. Part 11. Biological assessment of marine pollution with particular reference to benthos. FAO Fisheries Technical Paper No. 324. 49pp.

Longhurst, A.R. and D. Pauly (1987). "Ecology of Tropical Oceans". Academic Press, Sydney. 407pp.

Pearson, T.H. and R. Rosenberg (1978). Macrobenthic succession in relation to organic enrichment and pollution of the marine environment. Oceanography and Marine Biology Annual Review, **16**: 229-311.

4.1 Measurement of Ambient Environmental Parameters

Abstract

All surveys of living resources of soft-bottom ecosystems should include environmental parameters which will characterise the conditions at the site during data collection. The parameters included with the survey methods described in this manual have been selected because they are important to the 'health' of the community and they do not require expensive, sophisticated equipment. The environmental parameters that should be measured are: temperature, salinity, depth and sediment grain size. In addition, it is useful to measure the dissolved oxygen content and colour of sediment. The recommended equipment are easily obtained and will provide standardised measures in all countries.

Logistics

Equipment

❏ Mercury thermometer with an accuracy of ±0.5 degrees Celsius enclosed in a protective casing - used to measure temperature just beneath the surface of the water.

❏ Small plastic vials to collect surface salinity samples.

❏ A water sampler such as a Nansen bottle (Fig. 4.1), or a Niskin bottle (Fig. 4.2) - these bottles sample water from the desired depth.

❏ Reversing thermometer (optional) - used to measure temperature at depth with an accuracy of ±0.5 degrees Celsius. (Fig. 4.3).

❏ Refractometer - used to determine salinity (Fig. 2.1).

❏ Depth sounder or weighted shot line.

❏ Plastic bags or jars for sediment sample.

❏ A standard set of sieves for grain size analysis (see Table 3.1).

❏ An oxygen meter or handheld digital millivoltmeter with an oxygen electrode.

Maintenance

❏ Rinse all equipment with freshwater after use.

❏ Rinse the glass cell and cover of the refractometer carefully after use (with distilled water if possible) and then carefully blot dry with tissue paper.

❏ Store the refractometer in its protective box/bag when not in use.

Soft-Bottoms

❑ Store the oxygen electrode in its protective box when not in use.

❑ Remove soil particles from finer sieves by brushing both surfaces with a camel hair brush or air blowing.

General procedure

Temperature

❑ Read the surface temperature before commencing sampling using a thermometer placed 30 centimetres below the surface.

❑ Collect a sample of water from the bottom using a water sampler such as a Nansen bottle (Fig. 4.1) or a Niskin bottle (Fig. 4.2):

» Lower the bottle to the required depth on a shot line.

» Send the messenger down the line to close the bottle.

» Lift the water sample taken by the bottle back to the deck.

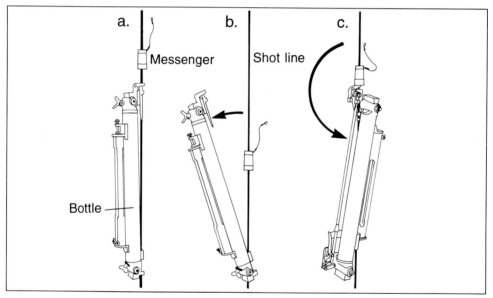

Figure 4.1   Nansen bottle shown before tripping (a), during tripping (b), and after tripping (c). The bottle is released by the messenger and overturns, trapping the water inside (after Ross 1970).

❑ Measure the temperature using a thermometer as soon as the sample is onboard the boat.

❑ If available, collect the bottom temperature using a reversing thermometer (Fig. 4.3). The thermometer may be attached to the water sampler, if not:

» Lower the thermometer on a line until it is close to the bottom.

» Allow approximately 7 minutes for the thermometer to stabilise.

» Send a messenger down the line to trigger the thermometer to reverse.

» Pull the thermometer to the surface and record the temperature.

Salinity

❑ Obtain water samples at the surface using small plastic vials.

❑ Use the water sample collected from the bottom by a Nansen bottle (Fig. 4.1) or a Niskin bottle (Fig. 4.2), as described above for the temperature reading.

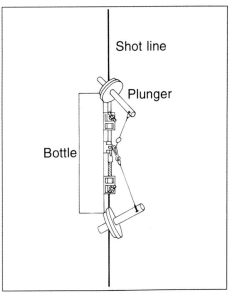

Figure 4.2   Niskin bottle - the messenger releases the plungers which close, trapping the water in the bottle.

Soft-Bottoms

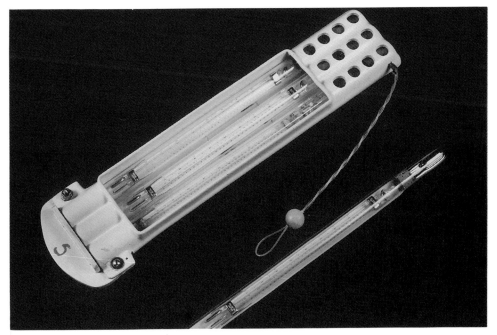

Figure 4.3   Reversing thermometer - the messenger releases the thermometer which turns, leaving a marker at the correct temperature.

❑ Put a drop or two of water under the cover of a refractometer (Fig. 2.1). Hold the cover down, and looking through the eyepiece, face the instrument to the light so that the salinity can be read.

❑ A series of salinity measurements should be made when transect areas are in close proximity to freshwater discharge so that the sphere of influence may be ascertained. Note that this is not accomodated in the database structure.

Oxygen

❑ Measure the dissolved oxygen concentration of the water samples taken from the surface and the bottom. See description of temperature and salinity readings for detail.

Depth

❑ Use a depth sounder on the boat or a drop line marked in metres.

Grain Size

❑ Take a grab sample to collect sediment from the sampling station (see section on grab sampling later in this chapter).

❑ Remove about 100 grams of sediment from the top of the grab sample and place it in a plastic bag or jar with a label.

❑ Analyse the grain size of the sample using the methods described in the section on soils in the Mangrove chapter (Section 3.1).

Data recording

❑ Record ambient environmental parameters for each station into field notebooks or data sheets.

Data processing

❑ Enter the data into the database using the data structure described at the end of this chapter (Section 4.5).

❑ Information about the sample is entered into the sample table (XXSBSAMP) and a unique sample identifier (SAMPLE_ID) is allocated. The type of data collected in the sample is described by the DATA_TYPE field, which for the ambient data is denoted by the letter "A".

❑ The ambient data are entered into the data table (XXSBADAT) using the sample identification allocated in the sample table.

❑ **Always check and verify data after entry.**

❑ Always backup data regularly.

4.2 Sampling Soft-Bottom Communities

Abstract

Survey methodologies described here include the sledge, grab, dredge and trawl. A sampling program including the **sledge** and **grab** are considered to be the minimum requirement for characterising nearshore habitats. The dredge is described as an alternative sampler to the sledge in areas which have very soft substratum. If sledge sampling indicates the presence of seagrass beds, beam trawling should be carried out to sample more mobile species (see Seagrass Communities, Chapter 5). Equipment has been selected specifically for small boat operation.

Logistics

Equipment
❑ Sledge, grab, dredge and trawl (see specifications with the description of the method).

❑ Marker buoys.

❑ Compass or GPS.

❑ Motorised boat.

❑ Motorised winch (optional).

❑ Sorting box (Fig. 4.4).

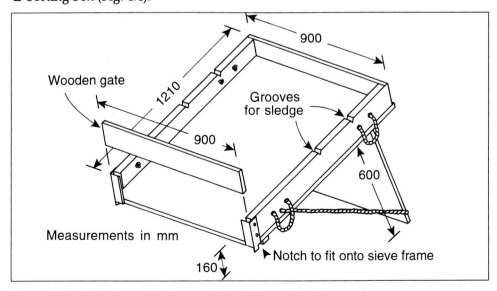

Figure 4.4   Wooden sorting box used for sledge and dredge samples.

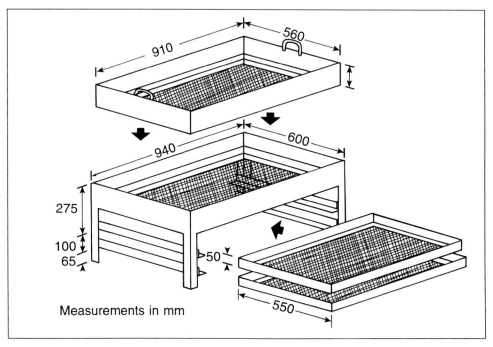

Measurements in mm

Figure 4.5 Wire-mesh sieves. Samples are gently washed through the set of sieves and the animals are removed from the mesh for identification.

❑ Wire-mesh sieves (5 mm, 3 mm, 2 mm, 1 mm and 0.5 mm) (Fig. 4.5). Sieves should be made from stainless steel or bronze gauze.

❑ Rope (12 millimetre) or cable (the warp) to tow or lift the equipment - length depends on the type of equipment and the depth of sampling.

❑ Pump for seawater (optional).

❑ Plastic specimen jars - various sizes.

❑ Preservatives - 10% buffered formalin; 70% alcohol.

❑ Waterproof labels and pencils. Preprinted labels ensure that all relevant information is recorded and speed up sample processing time on board. An example is given in Figure 4.6.

❑ Soft touch forceps.

Location ....

Site ....

Lat. .... Long. ....

Transect .... Station ....

Date .... Depth (m) ....

Gear type .... size ....

Habitat type ....

Mesh size .... Substrate ....

Figure 4.6 An example of a printed waterproof label for soft-bottom samples.

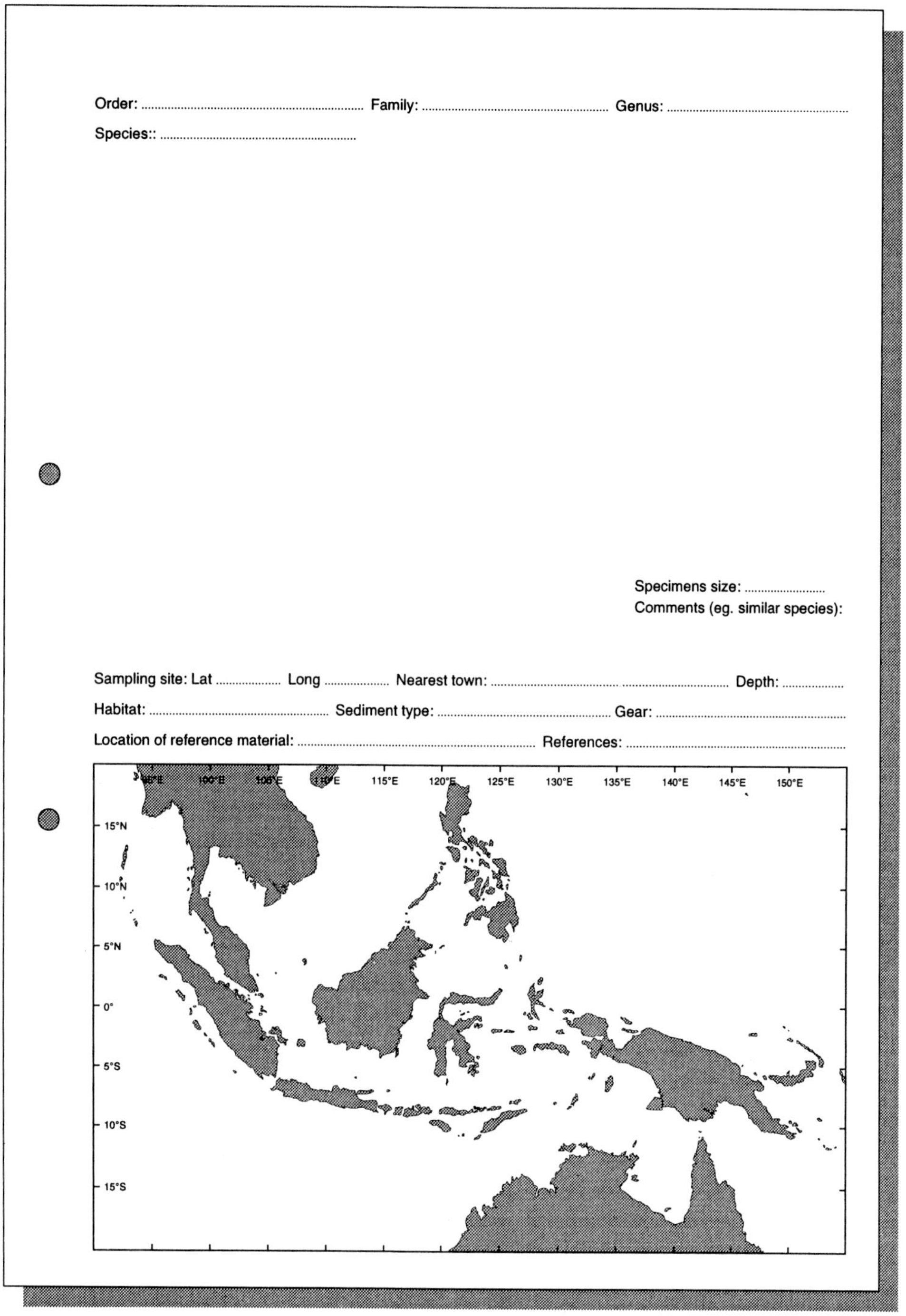

Order: .... Family: .... Genus: ....

Species:: ....

Specimens size: ....

Comments (eg. similar species):

Sampling site: Lat .... Long .... Nearest town: .... Depth: ....

Habitat: .... Sediment type: .... Gear: ....

Location of reference material: .... References: ....

Figure 4.7   Identification sheet to record the description of specimens collected.

❏ Dissecting and compound microscopes. A camera lucida and/or camera attachment is useful.

❏ Use standard identification sheets to document specimens collected (Fig. 4.7).

Maintenance
❏ Wash field equipment with freshwater after each trip.

Site selection

❏ The length of the transects, total number of transects, number of sampling stations and intensity of sampling will depend greatly on the width of the continental shelf, the primary objective of the study, and the facilities available (see Chapter 7 for discussion of the principles of experimental design).

❏ Transects should be perpendicular to the coast to maximise the gradient, and should be replicated (at least 2). See Chapter 7 for discussion of experimental design.

❏ A series of sampling stations should be established along the transects.

❏ It is advisable to have a greater number of sampling stations close to the coast where zonation patterns show the greatest gradient.

General procedure

❏ A preliminary survey, using sledge and grab sampling, should be done to characterise the area. The preliminary survey may take samples at regular intervals along the transect, e.g. 2-4 nautical miles. However, attention should be given to changes in depth and sediment type so that future sampling is refined to reflect zonation patterns.

❏ The Ockelmann sledge (0.5 metre gape) (Fig. 4.9) and Smith-McIntyre grab (0.05 square metres) (Fig. 4.11) are recommended. The minimum mesh sizes for sieving samples are 1 millimetre and 0.5 millimetre, respectively.

❏ All sampling runs of the sledge, trawl, or dredge should be perpendicular to the transect (i.e. parallel to the shore) at each station. This minimises changes in depth during the sample run, i.e. keeps the sample at the same depth gradient. The grab samples should be obtained from the stations along the transect.

❏ At least three replicate samples of each type of sampling gear should be done at each station.

❏ If sledge sampling indicates the presence of seagrass beds, beam trawling should be carried out to obtain the more vagile species, such as juvenile shrimps and fishes, that constitute an important part of such ecosystems (see Chapter 5).

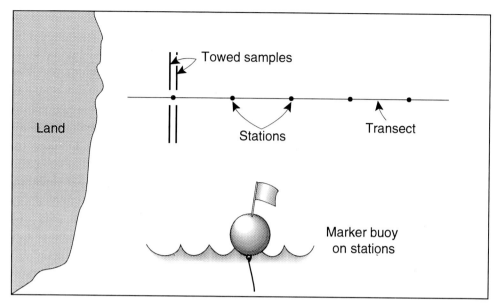

Figure 4.8   Diagrammatic representation showing a station (sampling position) marked on an imaginary transect which runs perpendicular to the shore.

❏ The position of each station established on the transect should be recorded at the beginning of sampling that station. A GPS (Global Positioning System) is very useful. Otherwise, use a handheld compass to determine the bearing with reference to at least 2 permanent landmarks established as reference points.

❏ Mark the station position with a radar reflector buoy, or if this is not available, a buoy (Fig. 4.8).

☞ *If specific sampling sites do not use transects, the principles must remain the same. Hence, for any site there should be a number of stations with replicate sledge and grab samples.*

4.2.1 The sledge

Abstract

Although the sledge provides only semi-quantitative sampling, it is an effective tool for sampling epifauna. Because these organisms are often highly persistent through time they are ideal for initial characterisation of an area.

Soft-Bottoms

Background

Sledges are designed to collect fauna resting on the seabed. Modifications of the design have been made to collect different types of fauna. For example, sledges have been deployed to collect demersal plankton (Myers 1942), newly settled benthic organisms (Ockelmann 1964), deep sampling (Hessler and Saunders 1967) and shallow intertidal zone sampling (Coleman and Seagrove 1955).

Advantages

❏ Collects a broad cross-section of benthic organisms, including larger (long-lived) but scattered organisms, which may show more stable long-term patterns.

Disadvantages

❏ Provides only semi-quantitative data.

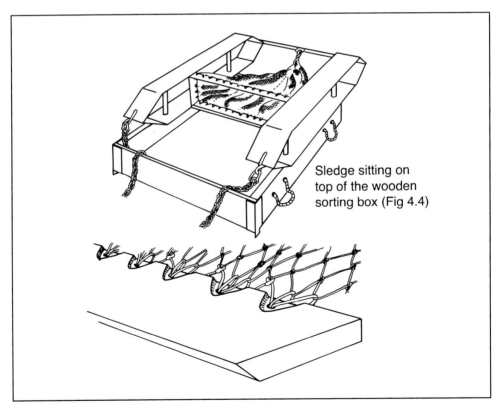

Sledge sitting on top of the wooden sorting box (Fig 4.4)

Figure 4.9   The Ockelmann sledge. Recommended size for operation in a small boat is 0.5 metre gape.

Equipment

❏ The recommended sledge is a 0.5 metre gape Ockelmann sledge (Fig. 4.9) with the net having a stretched mesh size of 1 centimetre. The sledge size has been selected to be easily handled by a minimum number of personnel operating from a small boat. If a larger boat is available, a 0.65 metre gape sledge could be used.

❏ A series of wire-mesh sieves (Fig. 4.5.). For sledge samples these should include: 5 mm, 3 mm, 2 mm, and 1 mm sieve mesh size.

❏ Other equipment is listed in the Introductory Section (4.2).

General Procedure for Sledge

❏ Determine the position of the station using a GPS or compass.

❏ Record the ambient parameters, location, date, time, depth, type of gear, replicate number and other data on a data sheet or field notebook.

❏ Tows are done perpendicular to the transect (i.e. parallel to the shore) (Fig. 4.8).

❏ At least 3 replicates should be done at each station.

❏ Lower the sledge on the towing wire or rope (the warp). The length of the warp should be at least 6 times the depth of the water at the sampling station. In very shallow water, the warp should be up to 15 times the depth of the water.

❏ Tow the sledge at a speed of 2 knots for 10 minutes parallel to the shore, or along a uniform depth gradient. Timing starts when the required length of wire is paid out along the sea floor.

❏ Set up a series of sieves of 5 mm, 3 mm, 2 mm and 1 mm mesh sizes (Fig. 4.5).

❏ Place the wooden sorting box (Fig. 4.4) flat on the deck.

❏ After a 10-minute tow, haul the sledge back to the boat.

❏ Stand the bar at the trailing edge of the sledge in the grooves on the wooden sorting box (Fig. 4.4).

❏ Empty the sample into the sorting box.

❏ Lift the wooden sorting box and place it onto the series of sieves. The notch of the sorting box should hook onto the sieves (Fig.4.4).

❏ Leave the wooden gate in place (Fig. 4.4), and hose the sample gently with seawater, picking out the larger animals. If there is excess water, be prepared to lift the gate slightly, releasing the water onto the sieves.

❏ Remove the wooden gate and wash the tailings through a series of sieves.

❏ Remove the smaller organisms remaining on the sieves using soft touch forceps.

Soft-Bottoms

❑ Preserve echinoderms, soft corals and sponges in alcohol, while all other specimens are to be preserved in 10% buffered formalin:

» Crinoids and ophiuroids should initially be preserved in undiluted alcohol to prevent fragmentation. Large holothurians should also be preserved in undiluted alcohol because of the large volume of coelomic fluid.

» Slit the body wall of large specimens or inject them with preservative.

» Store specimens in 70% alcohol.

» See Arnold and Birtles (1989) for further discussion of preservation and storage of invertebrate samples.

☞ *With large samples, care should be taken to ensure that there is sufficient preservative and that it is adequately mixed through the sample.*

❑ Label samples with the site, transect number, station number, position of the station, depth, type of gear, replicate number, time and date (Fig. 4.6). Further information such as tidal or weather conditions should be noted. The waterproof label should be placed inside the container and distinguishing details can be marked on the exterior for quick identification.

❑ All seived material can be kept in this condition until sorted out in the laboratory where specimens can be identified using taxonomic keys.

Standardisation

❑ Use the recommended equipment.

❑ Tow the sledge for the same length of time on all tows (10 minutes is recommended in this manual).

❑ The final (smallest) sieve mesh size should be 1 millimetre.

❑ Record the type of sledge used with particular reference to the dimensions and the mesh size.

Laboratory sorting

❑ The samples that have been collected and kept in formalin should be rinsed with water to facilitate sorting. Pour the formalin through a sieve to prevent possible loss of specimens, then rinse the sample with freshwater before pouring out into large sorting trays (preferably white).

☞ *Sorting of samples fixed in formalin should be carried out where there is good circulation of fresh air (ideally sorting is done in a fume hood).*

❑ Process the samples preserved in alcohol in the same manner.

❑ If possible, preservative solutions should be recycled.

☞ *Ensure that waste formalin is not poured down the sink - always dispose of formalin in a safe manner.*

❑ Sort the specimens into their respective groups and place larger species (e.g. macroalgae, sponges, and corals) in separate trays.

❑ Care should be exercised in sorting and picking small specimens (e.g. annelids and shrimps). The use of soft touch forceps to pick up specimens will help avoid crushing.

❑ Identification should be carried to at least the family level, and to species level if possible. If necessary send unknown species to experts for identification.

Data recording

❑ Record the ambient parameters, location and description of the station.

❑ Describe the equipment being used for collecting the samples, including dimensions and mesh size.

❑ Absolute counts should be done, except for colonial or uncountable groups like corals, sponges, bryozoans, algae for which wet weight will give some quantification. If wet weights are not measured then presence/absence data must be recorded.

❑ Identify fauna collected to at least the family level, and to species level if possible.

❑ Use standard identification sheets to document the species collected. An example of a completed sheet is given in Figure 4.10.

Data processing

❑ Enter the data into the database using the data structure described at the end of this chapter (Section 4.5).

❑ Information about the sample is entered into the sample table (XXSBSAMP) and a unique sample identifier (SAMPLE_ID) is allocated. The type of data collected in the sample is described by the DATA_TYPE field, which for the sledge data is denoted by the letter "S".

❑ The fauna data collected with the sledge are entered into the data table (XXSBFDAT) using the sample identification allocated in the sample table.

❑ When ambient environmental parameters are measured at the site another entry is made into the sample table and a unique sample identifier is allocated. The ambient parameters are denoted in the sample table by "A".

❑ **Always check and verify data after entry.**

❑ Always backup data regularly.

Soft-Bottoms

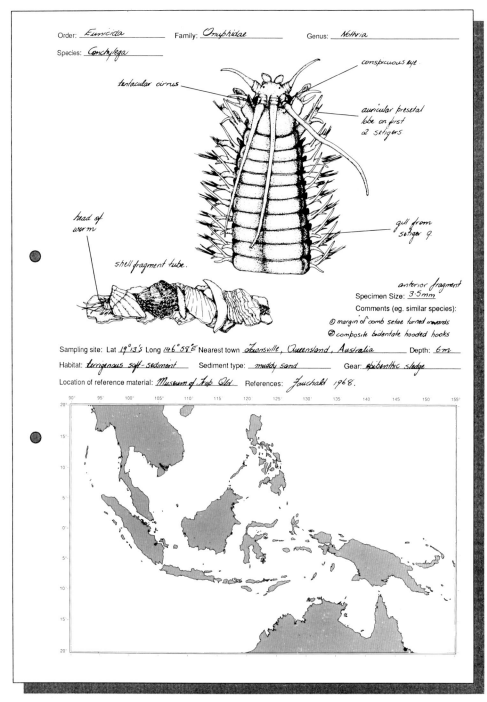

Figure 4.10 Completed identification sheet with map showing the location(s) where the samples were collected and drawing of the specimen detailing important characteristics.

4.2.2 The grab

Abstract

The grab is an effective device for collecting quantitative samples of organisms which inhabit the sediment, in particular the slow-moving and sedentary members of the epifauna and infauna. The grab is lowered vertically from a stationary boat to take a sample of sediment of a given surface area.

Background

Grabs have been used as sampling devices since early this century, when the Petersen grab was used in the study of the Danish fjords (Petersen and Boysen Jenson, 1911). Since then there have been many modifications and improvements on the Petersen design. In a discussion of macrofauna sampling techniques, Eleftheriou and Holme (1984) found only 3 grabs which collected a quantitative sample and were reasonably light, namely, the van Veen grab (van Veen, 1933), the Smith-McIntyre grab (Smith and McIntyre, 1954) and the Day grab. Of these the Smith-McIntyre grab, which was designed for working from a small boat in the open sea, was considered the best choice for more open sea conditions. Lighter grabs have more limited penetration into firm sediments, therefore, it is unlikely that deeper burrowers will be sampled. It is therefore advisable to use dredge samples to supplement information obtained by the grab.

Advantages

❏ Collects quantitative samples of slow-moving and sedentary members of the epifauna and infauna.

❏ Ease of handling and operation from a small boat.

Disadvantages

❏ Infauna collection is affected by depth and profile excavated by grab.

❏ Penetration depth is dependent on the type of substrate.

❏ Does not adequately sample scarce or fast-moving animals.

❏ Premature triggering of grab may occur.

❏ Jaws may not close completely, causing loss of samples.

❏ Profile of the bite gives unequal samples of different depths through the sediment.

Equipment

❑ A 0.05 metre^2 Smith-McIntyre grab (Fig. 4.11) is recommended since it can be easily handled with a minimum number of personnel using a small craft.

❑ A hopper with base (Fig. 4.12). Samples are put into the hopper which directs the washed sample into the seives.

❑ A series of wire mesh sieves (Fig. 4.5). For grab samples these should include: 5 mm, 2 mm, 1 mm and 0.5 mm sieve mesh.

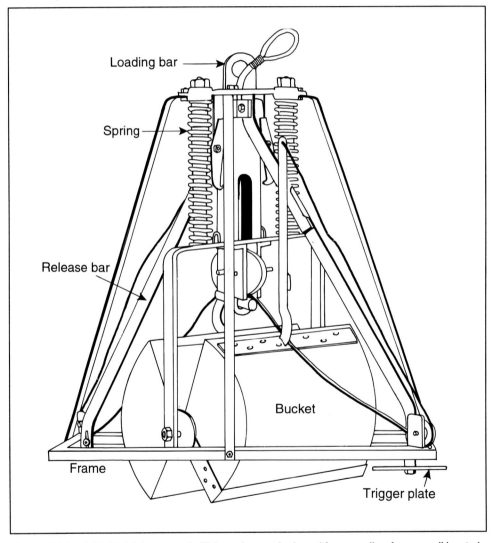

Figure 4.11   A Smith-McIntyre grab. This grab was designed for sampling from small boats in the open sea where conditions are often difficult. The size recommended covers an area of 0.05 m^2.

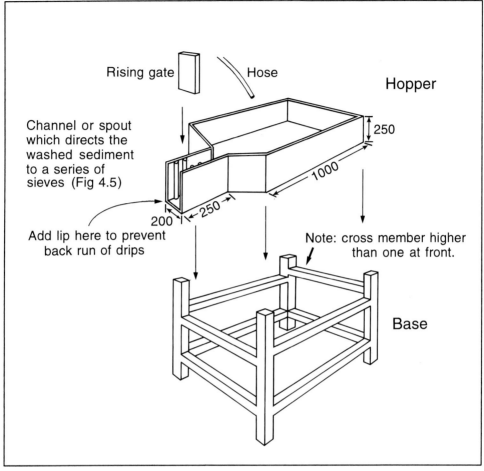

Rising gate   Hose   Hopper

Channel or spout
which directs the
washed sediment
to a series of
sieves (Fig 4.5)

250

1000

200   250

Add lip here to prevent
back run of drips

Note: cross member higher
than one at front.

Base

Soft-Bottoms

Figure 4.12   Hopper for treatment of sediment samples. Dimensions must be large enough to take the entire contents of the sampler, those shown on the diagram are approximate.

❏ Rose Bengal stain.

❏ Other equipment is listed in the Introductory Section (4.2).

❏ If the Smith-McIntyre grab is not available, use a van Veen grab (Fig. 4.13).

General procedure for grab sampling

❏ Determine the position of the station using a GPS or compass.

❏ Record the ambient parameters, location, transect number, date, time, depth, type of gear, replicate number and other data on a data sheet or field notebook.

❏ Take 5 replicate samples at each station.

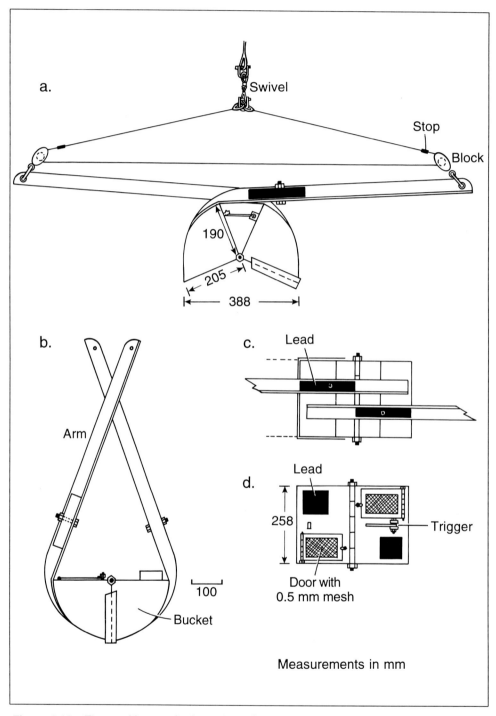

Figure 4.13   The van Veen grab, drawn to scale.

❑ Set up a series of seives (Fig. 4.5) of 5 mm, 2 mm, 1 mm and 0.5 mm mesh sizes.

❑ Place the hopper on its base with the spout positioned above the seives.

❑ Lower the grab vertically, at a slow and steady speed, to the seafloor from a stationary boat. Additional weight may be added to the grab when water currents are strong and when penetration of the sediment is difficult.

❑ Contact with the seabed triggers the buckets to close.

❑ After the grab is triggered, slowly pull it up onto the deck of the boat.

❑ Once on deck, place the sample on the hopper and hose down gently with running seawater.

❑ The run-off or tailings are directed through the series of sieves.

❑ Large organisms can be removed during the washing process and placed directly in properly labelled wide-mouthed preservation containers (preferably plastic).

❑ Preserve echinoderms, soft corals and sponges in 70% alcohol while all other specimens should be preserved in 10% buffered formalin. See Section 4.2.1 for detail.

☞ *With large samples, care should be taken to ensure that there is sufficient preservative and that it is adequately mixed through the sample.*

❑ Rose Bengal vital stain is recommended for staining the organisms in the samples.

❑ Label samples with the site, station number, position of the station, depth, type of gear, replicate number, time and date. Further information such as tidal and weather conditions should be noted. The waterproof label should be placed inside the container and distinguishing details can be marked on the exterior of the container for quick identification.

❑ All sieved material can be kept in this condition until it is sorted out in the laboratory where specimens can be identified using taxonomic keys.

Standardisation
❑ Use the recommended equipment.

❑ The final (smallest) sieve mesh size should be 0.5 millimetres.

❑ Record the type of grab used, with particular reference to the size of the grab and its depth penetration.

Laboratory sorting

❑ The samples that have been collected and kept in formalin should be rinsed with water to facilitate sorting. Pour the formalin through a sieve (0.5mm) to prevent possible loss of specimens, then rinse the sample with freshwater before pouring out into large sorting trays (preferably white).

Soft-Bottoms

☞ *Sorting of samples fixed in formalin should be carried out where there is good circulation of fresh air (ideally sorting is done in a fume hood).*

❑ Process the samples preserved in alcohol in the same manner.

❑ If possible, preservative solutions should be recycled.

☞ *Ensure that waste formalin is not poured down the sink - always dispose of formalin in a safe manner.*

❑ Put a subsample from the tray into a petri dish for examination under a low-powered dissecting microscope.

❑ Pick out all the specimens in the sample, separating into major classes first.

❑ Care should be exercised in sorting and picking small specimens (e.g. annelids). The use of soft touch forceps to pick up specimens will help avoid crushing.

❑ Put specimens into small labelled vials and add preservative (remembering to insert a waterproof label). Keep for sorting into family, genus and species (if possible).

❑ Continue this process until the whole sample (in the tray) has been sorted.

❑ Identify the specimens from each sample to at least family level using taxonomic keys. If necessary send unknown species to experts for identification.

Data recording

❑ Record the ambient parameters, location and description of the station.

❑ The equipment being used for collecting the samples must be described, including dimensions.

❑ Absolute counts should be done, except for colonial or uncountable groups like corals, sponges, bryozoans, algae for which wet weight will give some quantification. If wet weights are not measured then presence/absence data must be recorded.

❑ Identify fauna collected to at least the family level, and to species level if possible.

❑ Use standard identification sheets to document the species collected. An example of a completed sheet is given in Figure 4.10.

Data processing

❑ Enter the data into the database using the data structure described at the end of this chapter (Section 4.5).

❑ Information about the sample is entered into the sample table (XXSBSAMP) and a unique sample identifier (SAMPLE_ID) is allocated. The type of data collected in the sample is described by the DATA_TYPE field, which for the grab data is denoted by the letter "G".

❑ The fauna data collected with the grab are entered into the data table (XXSBFDAT) using the sample identification allocated in the sample table.

❑ When ambient environmental parameters are measured at the station another entry is made into the sample table and a unique sample identifier is allocated. The ambient parameters are denoted in the sample table by the letter "A".

❑ **Always check and verify data after entry.**

❑ Always backup data regularly.

4.2.3 The dredge

Abstract

The dredge is an invaluable tool in exploratory surveys for examination of the nature of the upper layer substrate and its fauna. Dredges have a heavy metal frame designed for variable penetration into the sediment and they can be used on a variety of sediment types. However, the dredge does not give quantitative samples. Despite this, the dredge gives a good overview of the community and is a reliable sampling device.

Background

Dredges have the longest history of use of any benthic sampler. Their design is determined by the purpose for which they are being used. This can vary between breaking off pieces of rock to limited penetration for collection in muddy sediments. For example, Nalwalk *et al.* (1962) used sturdy rock dredges for geological sampling, and Clarke (1972) used a heavy dredge for sampling mixed boulder and mud substrates. The Naturalists' or Rectangular dredge samples a shallow layer of substrate or can be used in very soft substrate. The heavier framed Charcot dredge and anchor dredges penetrate more deeply. See Eleftheriou and Holme (1984) for more detail.

Dredges should be towed using a weak link which will release if the dredge gets caught on the seabed.

Advantages

❏ Useful in broad area surveys and inventories.

❏ Samples deeper into the substrate.

❏ Simple design.

Disadvantages

❏ Provides, at best, semi-quantitative data.

❏ Opening can get clogged in certain substrates.

❏ Potential for uneven sampling of epifauna and infauna due to 'skipping' during the tow, if the warp is too short.

❏ Relatively small area/volume sampled.

❏ High-power boat required in soft substrates.

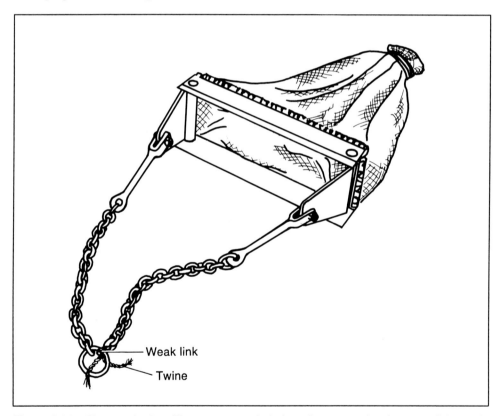

Figure 4.14 Charcot dredge. The recommended size when operating from small boats is 0.50 metre gape with a stretched mesh size of 2 centimetres. Note weak link of twine joining one side of the towing bridle to the ring.

Equipment

❏ A standard 0.5 metre Charcot dredge is recommended (Fig. 4.14) with a stretched mesh size of 2 centimetres. The mesh of the cod-end should be 60 ply.

❏ In areas where the substratum is very soft, use the lighter Naturalists' or Rectangular dredge with a net of stretched mesh size 2 centimetres.

❏ If the recommended dredges are not available, substitute any standard dredge which can be handled with a minimum number of personnel and can be operated from small boats.

❏ A weak link should be attached to one side of the dredge to minimise the loss of gear due to snagging.

❏ A swivel should be inserted between the towing rope and the dredge.

❏ A series of wire mesh sieves (Fig. 4.5). For dredge samples these should include: 5 mm, 3 mm and 2 mm sieve mesh size.

❏ Other equipment is listed in the Introductory Section (4.2).

General procedure for dredge sampling

❏ Determine the position of the station using a GPS or compass.

❏ Record the ambient parameters, location, date, transect number, time, depth, gear type, replicate number and other data on a data sheet or field notebook.

❏ Tows are done perpendicular to the transect (i.e. parallel to the shore) (Fig. 4.8).

❏ **At least** 2 replicate samples should to be taken at each station.

❏ Check that the cod-end is tied up.

❏ Lower the dredge with wire, or rope. The length of the warp should be at least 6 times the depth of the water at the sampling station, up to 15 times in very shallow water.

❏ Tow the dredge along the seafloor at a speed of 2 knots for 10 minutes parallel to the shore, or along a uniform depth gradient. Timing starts when the required length of wire (for towing at sampling depth) is paid out. If the dredge fills quickly, it may be necessary to reduce the tow time. Always record the time that tows start and finish with the data.

❏ Set up a series of sieves (Fig. 4.5) of 5 mm, 3 mm and 2 mm mesh sizes.

❏ Place the wooden sorting box (Fig. 4.4) flat on the deck.

❏ After 10 minutes of tow, haul the dredge back to the boat.

❏ Empty the sample into the sorting box.

❑ Lift the wooden sorting box and place it onto the series of sieves. The notch of the sorting box should hook onto the sieves (Fig.4.4).

❑ Leave the wooden gate in place (Fig. 4.4), and hose the sample gently with seawater, picking out the larger animals. If there is excess water, be prepared to lift the gate slightly, releasing the water onto the sieves.

❑ Remove the wooden gate and wash the tailings through a series of sieves.

❑ Remove the smaller organisms remaining on the sieves.

❑ Preserve echinoderms, soft corals and sponges in 70% alcohol while all other specimens are to be preserved in 10% buffered formalin. See Section 4.2.1 for detail.

❑ Label samples according to the station, position, replicate number, time and date. Further information such as tidal or weather conditions should be noted. The waterproof label should be placed inside the container and distinguishing details can be marked on the exterior for quick identification.

❑ All sieved material can be kept in this condition until it is sorted out in the laboratory, where specimens can be identified using taxonomic keys.

Standardisation

❑ Use the recommended equipment.

❑ Tow the dredge for the same length of time on all tows (10 minutes is recommended).

❑ The final (smallest) sieve mesh size used for dredge samples should be 2 millimetres.

❑ Record the type of dredge used with particular reference to the dimensions and the net mesh size.

Laboratory sorting

❑ The samples that have been collected and kept in formalin should be rinsed with water to facilitate sorting. Pour the formalin through a sieve (2 mm) to prevent possible loss of specimens, and then rinse the sample with freshwater before pouring out into large sorting trays (preferably white).

☞ *Sorting of samples fixed in formalin should be carried out where there is good circulation of fresh air (ideally sorting is done in a fume hood).*

❑ Process samples preserved in alcohol in the same manner.

❑ If possible, preservative solutions should be recycled.

☞ *Ensure that waste formalin is not poured down the sink - always dispose of formalin in a safe manner.*

❑ Sort the specimens into their respective groups and place larger species (e.g. macroalgae, sponges, and corals) in separate trays.

❑ Care should be exercised in sorting and picking small specimens (e.g. annelids and shrimps). The use of soft touch forceps to pick up specimens will help to avoid crushing.

❑ Identify the specimens from each sample to at least family level using taxonomic keys. If necessary send unknown species to experts for identification.

Data recording

❑ Record the ambient parameters, location and description of the station.

❑ Describe the equipment being used for collecting the samples, including dimensions and mesh size.

❑ Absolute counts should be done, except for colonial or uncountable groups like corals, sponges, bryozoans and algae, for which wet weight will give some quantification. If weights are not measured then presence/absence data must be recorded.

❑ Identify fauna collected to at least the family level, and to species level if possible.

❑ Use standard identification sheets to document the species collected. An example of a completed sheet is given in Figure 4.10.

Data processing

❑ Enter the data into the database at the end of each day using the data structure described at the end of this chapter (Section 4.5).

❑ Information about the sample is entered into the sample table (XXSBSAMP) and a unique sample identifier (SAMPLE_ID) is allocated. The type of data collected in the sample is described by the DATA_TYPE field, which for the dredge data is denoted by the letter "D".

❑ The fauna data collected with the dredge are entered into the data table (XXSBFDAT) using the sample identification allocated in the sample table.

❑ When ambient environmental parameters are measured at the site another entry is made into the sample table and a unique sample identifier is allocated. The ambient parameters are denoted in the sample table by the letter "A".

❑ **Always check and verify data after entry.**

❑ Always backup data regularly.

4.2.4 The trawl

Abstract

In order to get overall information about the soft-bottom community, the upper part of the community which includes the epifauna and that portion of the nekton living just above the bottom should be sampled. This includes fast-moving animals such as fish and squid, which are too mobile for the other sampling gear, but can be collected using a trawl net.

Background

Trawls such as the beam, Agassiz and Otter have been used for qualitative sampling of the epifauna. Otter trawls have also been effective for commercial fishing. Trawl sampling can effectively supplement information obtained by grab and sledge in benthic surveys.

Advantages

❏ The trawl can collect larger epifauna and demersal nekton to complement that collected by other gear.

❏ Collects fast moving animals.

❏ Useful for collecting the more scarce members of the epifauna.

Disadvantages

❏ Cannot collect quantitative data.

❏ The gear is large and requires heavy equipment (e.g. winches and booms) for operation.

❏ Requires a relatively large boat to operate.

❏ Collects relatively few animals in relation to the area swept by the net.

Equipment

❏ A 10 metre Otter trawl with 3 centimetre mesh is recommended (see Fig. 6.6 for commercial Otter trawl).

❏ Other equipment is listed in the Introductory Section (4.2).

General procedure for trawl sampling

❏ Determine the position of the station using a GPS or compass.

❏ Record the ambient parameters, location, date, transect number, time, depth, gear type, replicate number and other data on a data sheet or field notebook.

❏ Take at least 3 replicate samples at each station.

❏ Check that the cod-end of the net is tied up, as this can easily be forgotten.

❏ Lower the trawl with wire towing line (warp). The length of the warp on the trawl should be approximately 6 times the depth of the water at the station.

❏ Careful observation should be made when paying out the trawl. For example:

   » The otter boards should be set in order to widen the net.

   » The float or the headline should not be tangled with the bottom line.

   » The cod-end of the net should be spread out regularly.

❏ After the desired length of wire has been paid out, the time of trawling starts.

❏ Tow the trawl for 20 to 30 minutes at 2 knots boat speed, parallel to the shore.

❏ Carefully monitor the direction of the tow.

❏ After the net is retrieved, the contents of the cod-end should be washed onto a large sorting tray.

❏ Preserve the echinoderms, soft corals and sponges in 70% alcohol. Other specimens are to be preserved in 10% buffered formalin. See Section 4.2.1 for detail.

❏ Label samples according to the site, transect number, station number, position of the station, depth, type of gear, replicate number, time and date. Further information such as tidal or weather conditions should be noted. The waterproof label should be placed inside the container and distinguishing details can be marked on the exterior for quick identification.

❏ All material can be kept in this condition until it is sorted out in the laboratory where specimens can be identified using taxonomic keys.

Standardisation

❏ Use the recommended equipment.

❏ Tow the trawl for the same length of time on all tows.

❏ Record the type of trawl used, with particular reference to the dimensions and the mesh size.

Soft-Bottoms

Data recording

❏ The ambient parameters, location and description of the site must be recorded.

❏ The equipment being used for collecting the samples must be described.

❏ Use standard identification sheets to document the species collected. An example of a completed sheet is given in Figure 4.10.

❏ Identify fauna collected to at least the family level, and to species level if possible.

Data processing

❏ Enter the data into the database using the data structure described at the end of this chapter (Section 4.5).

❏ Information about the sample is entered into the sample table (XXSBSAMP) and a unique sample identifier (SAMPLE_ID) is allocated. The type of data collected in the sample is described by the DATA_TYPE field, which for the trawl data is denoted by the letter "T".

❏ The fauna data collected with the trawl are entered into the data table (XXSBFDAT) using the sample identification allocated in the sample table.

❏ When ambient environmental parameters are measured at the site another entry is made into the sample table and a unique sample identifier is allocated. The ambient parameters are denoted in the sample table by the letter "A".

❏ **Always check and verify data after entry.**

❏ Always backup data regularly.

4.3 Analysis of data

❑ Data collected using the sampling techniques discussed in this chapter provide a description of the soft-bottom communities of the area sampled. Species lists and densities of specimens caught give a good description of the communities sampled, their distribution and abundance.

❑ Diversity indices have been used widely as a means of integrating the complexity of a community into a single measure. The most commonly used diversity measures include:

» Shannon-Wiener index (H') - essentially a measure of how difficult it would be to correctly predict the species of the next individual collected from the community under study. It is a measure of uncertainty, so the larger the value, the greater the uncertainty. Values of the Shannon-Wiener index are dependent both on species richness (i.e. the number of species) and equitability (see below).

$$H' = -\sum_{i=1}^{s} pi\ (log_2\ pi)$$

Where pi is the proportion of the ith species.

For practical application the formula can be expanded to:

$$H' = C\ (log_{10} N - \frac{1}{N} \sum n_i\ log_{10}\ n_i)$$

Where N = total number of individuals;
n_i = number of individuals in the ith species;
C = conversion factor log_{10} to log_2.

» Rarefaction - allows comparison of diversity measurements from different surveys in which samples of different sizes were collected. This is done by using the shape of species abundance curves rather than the absolute number of species in the sample. Hurlebert has derived an analytical expression {$E(S_I)$} to enable calculation of the expected number of species in a 'rarified' sample.

$$E\ (S_I) = S - (\frac{I_c}{I})^{-1} \sum_{i=1}^{s} \frac{I_c - I_j}{I}$$

Soft-Bottoms

Where S_I = expected number of species in a sample of I individuals;
S = total number of species in original species;
I = total number of individuals in hypothetical sample;
I_c = total number of individuals in original sample;
I_j = number of individuals in species j of original species.

» Equitability (J) refers to the eveness with which individuals are distributed amongst species (Pielou 1966)

$$l = \frac{H'}{\log_2 S}$$

Where H' = measured Shannon-Weiner diversity;
S = total number of species.

» Margalef's species richness index (d) - is a measure of species richness which depends on the straight line relationship between species number and logarithm of area sampled.

$$d = \frac{s-1}{\log_e N}$$

Where d = diversity;
S = total number of species;
N = total number of individuals.

❑ Multivariate techniques of classification and ordination are useful for benthic monitoring studies. They allow consideration of the species identity, unlike diversity indices which are limited to a numerical expression of species abundance distributions.

4.4 References

Clarke, A.H. (1972). The arctic dredge, a benthic biological sampler for mixed boulder and mud substrates. Journal Fisheries Research Board Canada **29**: 1503-1505.

Colman, J.S. and F. Seagrove (1955). The tidal plankton over Stoupe Beck Sands, Robin Hoods's Bay (Yorkshire, North Riding). Journal of Animal Ecology, **24**: 445-462.

Eleftheriou, A. and N.A. Holme (1984). Macrofauna techniques. pp. 140-216. In: A.Holme and A.D. McIntyre (editors). "Methods for the Study of Marine Benthos," 2nd Edition. IBP Handbook 16. Blackwell Scientific Publications, Oxford. 387pp.

Myers, E.H. (1942). Rate of which Foraminifera are contributed to marine sediments. Journal of Sedimentary Petrology, **12**: 92-95.

Nalwalk, A.J., J.B. Hersey, J.S. Rectzel and H.E. Edgarton (1962). Improved techniques of deep sea rock dredging. Deep Sea Research **8**: 301-302.

Ockelmann, K.W. (1964). An improved detritus-sledge for collecting meiobenthos. Ophelia, **1**: 217-222.

Petersen, C.G.J. and P. Boysen Jenson (1911). "Valuation of the sea. I. Animal life of the sea bottom, its food and quantity". Report from the Danish Biological Station, **20**, 81pp.

Smith, W. and A.D. McIntyre (1954). A spring-loaded bottom-sampler. Journal of the Marine Biological Association. United Kingdom, **33**:257-264.

van Veen, J. (1933). Onderzoek naar het zandtransport von rivieren. De Ingenieur, **48**: 151-159.

Suggested reading

Arnold, P.W. and R.A. Birtles (1989). "Soft-Sediment Marine Invertebrates of Southeast Asia and Australia: A Guide to Identification". Australian Institute of Marine Science, Townsville. 272pp.

Hessler, R.R. and H.L. Sanders (1967). Faunal diversity in the deep sea. Deep Sea Research, **14**: 65-78.

Soft-Bottoms

Suggested References for Specimen Identification

The references suggested must be used with caution. None of the references, however good, can be a substitute for the primary literature and the experience of specialists in the various groups. In some phyla (e.g. sponges, bryozoans, ascidians) the references listed contain many species names which have been changed in the light of recent revisions. Monographs such as Day (1967) were designed for use in areas outside the Indo-West Pacific, and although very useful for identification to family (and often to genus), are unreliable for species identification. References for algae and fishes are given at the end of the chapter on sampling seagrass communities (see Section 5.2). The two references in the "General" section, while concentrating on coral reef-associated invertebrates, include examples from soft-bottom communities. They provide a good visual overview of tropical marine invertebrates. Finally, the list must be considered a selection of some of the more important references and is in no sense complete.

General

Colin, P.L. and C. Arneson (1995). "Tropical Pacific Invertebrates". Coral Reef Press, Beverley Hills, California. vii + 296pp.

Gosliner, T.M., D.W. Behrens and G.C. Williams (1996). "Coral Reef Animals of the Indo-Pacific". Sea Challengers, Monterey, California. vi + 314pp.

Foraminifera

Loeblich, A.R. Jr., and H. Tappan (1964). Sarcodina pp. 1-900. In: R.C. Moore (editor). "Treatise on Invertebrate Paleonotology". Part C 2(1,2). University Kansas Press, Lawrence (Kansas).

Sponges

Brien, P. et al. (editors) (1973). "Spongiaires". Traite de zoologie, volume 3(1). Masson and Cie Ed., Paris (in French). 716pp.

Hooper, J.N.A. and F. Wiedenmeyer (1994). "Zoological Catalogue of Australia. 12. Porifera". CSIRO Publication, Collingswood, Victoria. xiii + 624pp.

Lendenfeld, R. von (1889). "A monograph of the horny sponges". Trubner, London. 936pp.

Cnidaria

Bayer, F.M. et al. (1956). Coelenterata. pp. 1-498. In: R.C. Moore (editor). "Treatise on invertebrate paleontology. Part F." University of Kansas Press, Lawrence (Kansas).

Mather, P. and I. Bennett (editors) (1993). "A coral reef handbook", 3rd edition. Surrey Beatty and Sons Pty Ltd, Norton, NSW. 264pp.

Veron, J.E.N. and M. Pichon (1976). "Scleractinia of Eastern Australia (Part I)". Australian Institute of Marine Science Monograph Series, 1. Australian Government Publishing Service, Canberra. 86pp.

Veron, J.E.N. and M. Wijsman-Best (1977). "Scleractinia of Eastern Australia (Part II)". Australian Institute of Marine Science Monograph Series, 3. Australian Government Publishing Service, Canberra. 233pp.

Veron, J.E.N. and M. Pichon (1980). "Scleractinia of Eastern Australia (Part III)". Australian Institute of Marine Science Monograph Series, 4. Australian Government Publishing Service, Canberra. 422pp.

Veron, J.E.N. and M. Pichon (1982). "Scleractinia of Eastern Australia (Part IV)". Australian Institute of Marine Science Monograph Series, 5. Australian Government Publishing Service, Canberra. 159pp.

Veron, J.E.N. (1993). "Corals of Australia and the Indo-Pacific". Second Edition. University of Hawaii Press. 644pp.

Veron, J.E.N. (1992). "Hermatypic Corals of Japan". Australian Institute of Marine Science Monograph Series, 9. Australian Government Publishing Service, Canberra. 244pp.

Bryozoa

Canu, F. and R. Bassler (1929). "Bryozoa of the Philippines Region". Bulletin U.S. National Museum **100**(9): 685pp.

Gordon, D.P. (1984). The marine fauna of New Zealand: Bryozoa: Gymnolaemata from the Kermadec Ridge. New Zealand Oceanographic Institute Memoir **91**: 1-198.

Gordon, D.P. (1986). The marine fauna of New Zealand: Bryozoa: Gymnolaemata (Ctenostomata and Cheilostomata Anasca) from the western South Island continental shelf and slope. New Zealand Oceanographic Institute Memoir **95**: 1-121.

Gordon, D.P. (1989). The marine fauna of New Zealand: Bryozoa: Gymnolaemata (Cheilostomata Ascophorina) from the western South Island continental shelf and slope. New Zealand Oceanographic Institute Memoir **97**: 1-158.

Harmer, S.F. (1917-1957). "The polyzoa of the Siboga Expedition". Siboga Expedition Monograph 28. E.J. Brill, Leiden. 1148pp.

Hayward, P.J. and J.S. Ryland (1979). "British Ascophoran Bryozoans. Synopses of the British Fauna 12". Academic Press, London - New York. 312pp.

Ryland, J.S. and P.J. Hayward (1977). "British Anascan Bryozoans. Synopses of the British Fauna 10". Academic Press, London - New York. 188pp.

Soft-Bottoms

Mollusca

Abbott, R.T. and S.P. Dance (1986). "Compendium of Seashells". 3rd revised printing. American Malacologists Inc., Melbourne, Florida.

Cernohorsky, W.O. (1971). "Marine shells of the Pacific", revised edition. Pacific Publishing, Sydney. 248pp.

Cernohorsky, W.O. (1972). "Marine Shells of the Pacific". Volume 2. Pacific Publishing, Sydney. 411pp.

Cernohorsky, W.O. (1978). Tropical Pacific marine shells". Pacific Publishing, Sydney. 352pp.

Cox, L.R. et al. (1969). Mollusca 6: bivalvia. In: R.C. Moore (edtor). "Treatise on Invertebrate Paleontology". Part N, vol.(1,2). Univ. Kansas Press, Lawrence (Kansas). 951pp.

Habe, T. (1964). "Shells of the Western Pacific in Colour. Volume 2". Hoikusha Publishing Co. Ltd., Osaka. 233pp.

Habe, T., and S. Kosuge (1981). "Shells of the World in Colour, Volume 2. The Tropical Pacific". Hoikusha Publishing Co. Ltd., Osaka. 194pp.

Keen, A.M. (1971). "Sea Shells of Tropical West America". 2nd Edition. Stanford University Press, Stanford. 1064pp.

Kira, T. (1965). "Shells of the Western Pacific in Colour. Volume 1" (revised edition). Hoikusha Publishing Co. Ltd., Osaka. 224pp.

Lamprell, K. and T. Whitehead (1992). "Bivalves of Australia. Volume 1". Crawford House Press, Bathurst. xiii + 182pp.

Vaught, K.C. (1989). "A Classification of the Living Mollusca". American Malocologists Inc., Melbourne, Florida. 189pp.

Wilson, B., C. Wilson and P. Baker (1993). "Australian Marine Shells. Prosobranch Gastropods, Part One". Odyssey Publications, Kallaroo, Western Australia. 408pp.

Wilson, B., C. Wilson and P. Baker (1994). "Australian Marine Shells. Prosobranch Gastropods, Part Two". Odyssey Publications, Kallaroo, Western Australia. 370pp.

Crustaceans

Alcock, A. (1895-1900). Materials for a carcinological fauna of India, No. 1. The Brachyura Oxyrhyncha. Journal Asiatic Society, Bengal **64**: 157-291, 134-296, 67-233, 1-169, 279-456 (Reprint edition, Wheldon and Wesley Ltd., Codicote, Herts. 1968).

Alcock, A. (1905). "Catalogue of the Indian decapod Crustacea in the Collection of the Indian Museum. Part 2. Anomura. Fascicules 1. Pagurides". Calcutta. 197 pp.

Barnard, J.L. and G.S. Karaman (1991). The families and genera of marine Gammaridean Amphidoda. Parts 1 and 2. Records of the Australian Museum Supplement **13**: 1-866.

Chace, F.R. Jr. (1992). On the classification of the Caridea (Decapoda). Crustaceana, **63**: 70-80.

Chaitiamvong, S. and M. Supongpan (1992). "A Guide to Penaeoid Shrimps Found in Thai Waters". Australian Institute of Marine Science, Townsville, Australia. 77pp.

Holthius, L.B. (1991). FAO Species Catalogue, Volume 13. Marine lobsters of the world. FAO Fisheries Synopses **125**: 1-261.

Holthuis, L.B. (1993). "The Recent Genera of Caridean and Stenopodidean Shrimps (Crustacea, Decapoda): With an Appendix on the Order Amphionidacea". Natural History Museum, Lieden. 328pp.

Jones, D.S. and G.J Morgan (1994). "A Field Guide to Crustaceans of Australian Waters". Reed Publishers, Chatswood, NSW. 216pp.

Lovett, D.L. (1981). "A Guide to the Shrimps, Prawns, Lobsters and Crabs of Malaysia and Singapore". Universiti Pertanian Malaysia. 21pp.

Sakai, T. (1976). "Crabs of Japan and the Adjacent Seas". Kodansha Ltd., Tokyo, v. 1: 773 pp., v. 2: 16pp. + 251pl.

Phoronida

Emig, C.C. (1979). "British and other phoronids". Synopses of the British fauna (n.s.) 13. Academic Press, Sydney. 57pp.

Sipuncula

Edmonds, S.J. (1980). A revision of the systematics of Australian sipunculans (Sipuncula). Records South Australian Museum, **18**(1): 1-74.

Stephen, A.C. and S.J. Edmonds (1972). "The Phyla Sipuncula and Echiura". Publication 717 British Museum (Natural History), London. 528pp.

Polychaeta

Day, J.H. (1967). "A Monograph on the Polychaeta of Southern Africa. Part 1. Errantia. Part 2. Sedentaria". Publication 656, British Museum (Natural History), London 878pp.

Fauchald, K. (1977). "The Polychaete Worms. Definitions and Keys to the Orders, Families and Genera". Natural History Museum, Los Angeles County, Science Series 28: 188pp.

Soft-Bottoms

Echinoderms

Clark, A.M. and F.W.E. Rowe (1971). "Monograph of the Shallow-Water Indo-West Pacific Echinoderms". Publication 690, British Museum (Natural History), London. 238pp. + 31pl.

Fisher, K. (1919). Starfishes of the Philippine seas and adjacent waters. Bulletin U.S. National Museum, **100**(3): 712pp. +156pl.

Rowe, F.W.E. and J. Gates (1993). "Zoological Catalogue of Australia. 33. Echinodermata". CSIRO Publication, Collingswood, Victoria. xiii + 510pp.

Ascidians

Hastings, A. (1931). Tunicata. pp. 69-109, 3 pl. In: "Scientific Report Great Barrier Reef Expedition 1928-1929". Volume 4, Number 3. British Museum (Natural History), London.

Kott, P. (1985). The Australian Ascidiacea, Part 1. Phlebobranchia and Stolidobranchia. Memoirs of the Queensland Museum, **23**: 1-438

Kott, P. (1990). The Australian Ascidiacea, Part 2. Aplousibranchia (1). Memoirs of the Queensland Museum, **29**: 1-266.

Kott, P. (1992). The Australian Ascidiacea, Part 3. Aplousibranchia (2). Memoirs of the Queensland Museum, **32**: 375-620.

Kott, P. (1993). Subphylum Tunicata. pp. 168-178. In: P. Mather and I. Bennett (editors). "A Coral Reef Handbook", 3rd Edition. Australian Coral Reef Society, Brisbane.

Name, W. van (1918). "Ascidians from the Philippines and adjacent waters". Bulletin U.S. National Museum, **100** (1, pt.2): 49-174, pl. 23-33, I-III.

Cephalochordata

Whitley, G. 1933. The lancelets and lampreys of Australia. Australian Zoologist, **7**: 256-264, 13pl.

4.5 Soft-Bottom Database

Sample table

XXSBSAMP

Name	Type	Length/ Decimal	Description
SAMPLE_ID	C	9.0	The standard sample identification. This links the sample table to the data files. Use the format XXGGGNNNN where: XX = country code. See codes in Appendix 1. GGG = study group code NNNN = running number
LOCATION	C	30.0	Location name, e.g. Seribu Islands
SITE	N	3.0	Specific study area name
TRANSECT	N	1.0	Imaginary line extending from the shallow inshore to offshore.
STATION	N	2.0	Specific sampling points along the transect or at a site
DATE	D	8.0	Date when data were gathered (using the format MM/DD/YY)
LATITUDE	C	7.0	Latitude of station, in format AABBCCD AA = degrees BB = minutes CC = decimal seconds D = N (north) or S (south)
LONGITUDE	C	8.0	Longitude of station, in format AAABBCCD AAA = degrees BB = minutes CC = decimal seconds D = E (east) or W (west)
HABITAT	C	10.0	Description of habitat type (e.g. riverine, near-shore)
DATA_TYPE	C	1.0	Data code denoting the type of sample: A = ambient data; D = dredge data; G = grab data; S = sledge data; T = trawl data. Data file names are listed in the datacode table
DEPTH_M	N	5.2	Maximum depth of the sampling station, measured in metres
EQUIPTYP	C	20.0	Type of the equipment (e.g. Smith-McIntyre Grab,Naturalist's Dredge)
EQUIPSIZ	N	5.2	Size of equipment type used (e.g. $0.05m^2$)
MESHSIZ	N	2.0	Size of mesh in centimetres
TIME_START	C	4.0	Time sampling started, using the format HHMM (e.g. 1330 = 1:30 pm).
TIME_FINISH	C	4.0	Time sampling completed using the format HHMM (e.g. 1330 = 1:30 pm). This field is used for data type D (dredge), S (sledge) and T (trawl).
REMARKS	C	50.0	Relevant observations regarding the site and the data. This should include any other details that would further describe the equipment. For example, the depth penetration of the grab sample.

Soft-Bottoms

Ambient table
Filename: XXSBADAT.DBF

Name	Type	Length/ Decimal	Description
SAMPLE_ID	C	9.0	The standard sample identification. This links the data to the sample table. Format XXGGGNNNN.
TEMP_TOP	N	5.2	Temperature of water at the top (30cm below surface), measured in degrees Celsius
TEMP_BOT	N	5.2	Temperature of water at the bottom, measured in degrees Celsius
SALN_TOP	N	5.2	Salinity of water at the top, (30cm below surface) measured in ppt
SALN_BOT	N	5.2	Salinity of water at the bottom, measured in ppt.
OXY_TOP	N	5.2	Dissolved oxygen content from surface sample (30cm below surface), measured in ppm
OXY_BOT	N	5.2	Dissolved oxygen content from bottom sample, measured in ppm
GRAVEL	N	5.2	Gravel in sediment sample, recorded as a percentage
SAND	N	5.2	Sand in sediment sample, recorded as a percentage
MUD	N	5.2	Mud in sediment sample, recorded as a percentage

Fauna table
XXSBFDAT

Name	Type	Length/ Decimal	Description
SAMPLE_ID	C	9.0	The standard sample identification which links the data to the sample table. Format XXGGGNNNN
REPLICATE	N	1.0	Replicate number of sample taken at the station (e.g. 3 grab samples for each station)
FIELDCODE	C	40.0	Code assigned to the taxonomic entity by the field researchers. The code must uniquely link to one taxonomic entity. Description of the entity (i.e. binomial name) must be given to the database manager when a new code is created. This information is maintained in ALLTAXON
ABUNDANCE	N	4.0	Number of individuals sampled
WET_WEIGHT	N	7.1	Wet weight of colonial or uncountable organisms

Taxonomic Table
ALLTAXON

Name	Type	Length/Decimal	Description
FIELDCODE	C	40.0	Code assigned to the taxonomic entity by the field researchers. The code must link uniquely to one taxonomic entity. Description of the entity (binomial name) must be given to the database manager when a new code is created
TAXCODE	C	10	Unique code used to represent individual taxa. The codes are generated by the system manager. The TAXCODE ensures that the same kind of living things have the same code despite the fact that field researchers may give them different FIELDCODEs
SPECNAME	C	35	Species name (Latin binomial)
GENUSNAME	C	35	Genus name
FAMILYNAME	C	35	Family name
ORDERNAME	C	35	Order name
CLASSNAME	C	35	Class name
PHYLANAME	C	35	Phylum name
AUTHORITY	C	50	Name of authority, an organisation, or a system that was used as a reference to classify samples
REF_CODE	C	20	Reference code for samples which are stored in a reference collection, museum or herbarium. This allows researchers to look at an actual specimen which has been assigned this classification

Data code table
DATACODE

Field name	Data Value	Explanation
DATA_TYPE	A	Sample record refers to data in the ambient data file XXSBADAT
	D	Sample record refers to data in the data file XXSBFDAT collected using a dredge sampler
	G	Sample record refers to data in the data file XXSBFDAT collected using a grab sampler
	S	Sample record refers to data in the data file XXSBFDAT collected using a sledge sampler
	T	Sample record refers to data in the data file XXSBFDAT collected using a trawl sampler

Soft-Bottoms

SEAGRASS COMMUNITIES

General Introduction

Seagrass meadows occur in most shallow, sheltered soft-bottomed marine coastlines and estuaries of the world (Kirkman 1990). These meadows may be monospecific or may consist of multispecies communities of up to 12 species (Kirkman 1985). There are only 58 described species of seagrasses worldwide, within 12 genera, 4 families and 2 orders (Kuo and McComb 1989). However, the small number of species does not reflect the importance of seagrass ecosystems which provide a sheltered, nutrient-rich habitat for a diverse flora and fauna (Lanyon 1986).

Seagrass meadows physically help to reduce wave and current energy, help to filter suspended sediments from the water and stabilise bottom sediments (Fonseca and Cahalan 1992, Fonseca *et al.* 1982). The habitat complexity within seagrass meadows enhances the diversity and abundance of animals. Seagrasses on reef flats and near estuaries are also nutrient sinks, buffering or filtering nutrient and chemical inputs to the marine environment (Short and Short 1984). The high primary production rates of seagrasses are closely linked to the high production rates of associated fisheries. These plants support numerous herbivore- and detritivore-based food chains, and are considered as very productive pastures of the sea (McRoy and Helfferich 1980, Klumpp *et al.* 1989). The associated economic values of seagrass meadows are also very large, although not always easy to quantify (e.g. Watson *et al.* 1993).

In order to determine the importance of seagrass ecosystems and to detect changes that occur through perturbations (man-made and natural), we must first map the distribution and density of existing seagrass meadows. These maps must be monitored to determine natural variability in the extent of seagrasses (e.g. seasonal dieback) before estimates of loss or gain due to perturbation can be made. Coastal management agencies need to know what levels of change are likely to be ecologically or economically important, and sampling designs for baseline and monitoring surveys need to be sufficient to measure changes that are statistically significant (see Coles *et al.* 1995, Lee Long *et al.* 1996). Additional methods and issues for mapping seagrasses and sampling seagrass habitat parameters are also described elsewhere (UNESCO 1990, Kirkman 1996). The use of satellite imagery to map vast areas of coastline is a valuable management tool. However, this must be regularly verified by checks of recognisable sites on the satellite image by divers (ground truthing).

The methods in this manual will describe the community structure of a seagrass meadow and the associated fish and prawn species of commercial importance. Spatial and temporal changes in seagrass abundance and species composition must be measured and interpreted with respect to prevailing environmental conditions. These may need to be measured seasonally, monthly, or weekly, depending on the nature of their variability, and the aims of the study. Physical parameters important to seagrass growth and survival include light (turbidity, depth), sediment type and chemistry, and nutrient levels.

References

Coles, R. G., W.J. Lee Long and L.J. McKenzie (1995). A standard for seagrass resource mapping and monitoring in Australia. In: "Australian Marine Data Collection and Management Guidelines Workshop, 5-6th December 1995, CSIRO Marine Laboratories, Hobart, Tasmania". Environment Resources Information Network.
URL: http://www.erin.gov.au/sea/workshop/biology/biology.html

Fonseca, M.S. and J.A. Cahalan (1992). A preliminary evaluation of wave attenuation by four species of seagrass. Estuarine, Coastal and Shelf Science, 35: 565-576.

Fonseca, M.S., J.S. Fisher and J.C. Zieman (1982). Influence of the seagrass, *Zostera marina* L., on current flow. Estuarine, Coastal and Shelf Science, 15: 351-364.

Kirkman, H. (1985). Community structure in seagrasses in southern Western Australia. Aquatic Botany, 21: 363-375.

Kirkman, H. (1990). Seagrass distribution and mapping. pp: 19-25. In: R.C. Phillips and C.P. McRoy (editors). "Seagrass Research Methods". Unesco, France. 210pp.

Kirkman, H. (1996). Baseline and monitoring methods for seagrass meadows. Journal of Environmental Management, 47: 191-201.

Klumpp, D.W., R.K. Howard and D.A. Pollard (1989). Trophodynamics and nutritional ecology of seagrass communities. pp 394-457. In: A.W.D. Larkum, A.J. McComb and S.A. Shepherd (editors). "Biology of Seagrasses: A treatise on the biology of seagrasses with special reference to the Australian region". Elsevier, Amsterdam. 841pp.

Kuo, J. and A.J. McComb (1989). Seagrass taxonomy, structure and development. In: A.W.D. Larkum, A.J. McComb and S.A. Shepherd (editors). "Biology of Seagrasses: A treatise on the biology of seagrasses with special reference to the Australian region". Elsevier, Amsterdam. 841pp.

Lanyon, J. (1986). "Seagrasses of the Great Barrier Reef". Great Barrier Reef Marine Park Authority Special Publication Series (3). Townsville, Australia. 54pp.

Lee Long, W.J., L.J. McKenzie, M.A. Rasheed and R.G. Coles (1996). Monitoring seagrasses in tropical ports and harbours. In: J. Kuo, R.C. Phillips, D.I. Walker and H. Kirkman (editors). "Seagrass Biology: Proceedings of an International Workshop". Rottnest Island, Western Australia, 25-29 January, 1996. University of Western Australia. pp. 345-50.

McRoy, C.P. and C. Helfferich (1980). Applied aspects of seagrasses. pp. 297-342. In: R.C. Phillips and C.P. McRoy (editors). "Handbook of Seagrass Biology - An Ecological Approach". Garland Publications, New York.

Short, F.T. and C.A. Short (1984). Purification of estuarine and coastal waters. In: V.S. Kennedy (editor). "The Estuary as a Filter". Academic Press, New York.

UNESCO (1990). "Seagrass Research Methods". Monographs on oceanographic methodology 9. (Eds, R.C. Phillips and C.P. McRoy). UNESCO, Paris. 210 pp.

Watson, R.A., R.G. Coles and W.J. Lee Long (1993). Simulation estimates of annual yield and landed value for commercial penaeid prawns from a tropical seagrass habitat, north Queensland, Australia. Australian Journal of Marine and Freshwater Research, 44: 211-220.

Seagrasses

5.1 Measurement of Ambient Environmental Parameters

Abstract

All surveys of living resources of seagrass ecosystems should include environmental parameters, which will characterise the conditions existing at the site at the time of data collection. The parameters included with the survey methods described in this manual have been selected because they are important to the 'health' of the community and they do not require expensive, sophisticated equipment. The environmental parameters that should be measured are: temperature, salinity, turbidity, depth, redox potential (Eh) and sediment grain size. In addition, it is useful to measure the dissolved oxygen and to note the colour of sediment. The recommended equipment is easily obtained and will provide standardised measures in all countries.

Logistics

Equipment

❑ A camel hair brush.

❑ Depth gauge.

❑ A portable light meter - used to determine the turbidity and light penetration of water in the study area (Fig. 2.3). A model widely used for surveys conducted as part of the ASEAN-Australia project is the LICOR® 1000 quantum meter with an underwater quantum sensor.

❑ Mercury thermometer enclosed in a protective casing with an accuracy of ±0.5 degrees Celsius.

❑ A pH/millivoltmeter with a platinum electrode to measure Eh.

❑ Plastic bags or jars for sediment samples.

❑ 10 millilitre plastic vials/bottles (tight-sealing) - used to collect water samples for salinity measurements (when *in situ* measurements are not feasible).

❑ Refractometer - used to determine salinity (Fig 2.1).

❑ A water sampler such as a Nansen bottle (Fig. 4.1), or a Niskin bottle (Fig. 4.2) - these bottles sample water from the desired depth.

❑ Reversing thermometer (optional) - used to measure temperature at depth with an accuracy of ±0.5 degrees Celsius. (Fig. 4.3).

❏ 10% sulphuric acid - used to clean electode surfaces.

❏ Secchi disc (Fig. 2.2).

❏ A standard set of sieves for grain size analysis (see Table 3.1)

Maintenance

❏ Rinse all equipment with freshwater after use.

❏ Rinse the glass cell and cover of the refractometer carefully after use (with distilled water if possible) and carefully blot dry with tissue paper.

❏ Store the refractometer in its protective box/bag when not in use.

❏ Keep the platinum electrode surfaces of the pH/millivoltmeter well cleaned by overnight immersion in 10% sulphuric or chromic acids.

❏ Remove batteries and store the instrument in a cool dry place.

❏ Rinse the sieves with fresh water. Soil particles caught in the mesh of finer sieves can be removed by brushing both surfaces with a camel hair brush or air blowing.

General Procedure

Temperature

❏ Read the surface temperature using a thermometer placed 30 centimetres below the surface, before commencing sampling.

❏ Bottom temperature is read by:

    » the diver at transect depth in surveys of seagrass community structure (Section 5.2);

    » a reversing thermometer for trawl surveys (see Section 4.1).

Salinity

❏ Obtain water samples at the surface using small plastic vials.

❏ Collect water samples from the bottom (transect depth) using:

    » small plastic vials in surveys of seagrass community structure (Section 5.2);

    » a nisken bottle for trawl surveys. (see Section 4.1).

❏ Take these samples back to the boat, or to the shore, for measurement using a refractometer. Put a drop or two of water under the cover. Hold the cover down, and looking through the eyepiece, face the instrument to the light so that the salinity can be read (Fig. 2.1).

Seagrasses

❏ Make a series of salinity measurements when transect areas are in close proximity to freshwater discharge so that the sphere of influence may be ascertained.

Turbidity

❏ Use the Secchi disc to measure vertical visibility in deeper water. The disc is attached to a weighted rope which is marked at intervals along its length. Lower the disc until you can no longer see it, then pull it slowly back towards the surface until it is just visible. Record the distance to the disc from the marks on the rope (Fig. 2.2).

❏ Make the measurements with the Secchi disc on a clear day, within 2 hours before or after noon. If cloud cover does not allow measurement, then the cloud should be recorded in oktas (see Table 2.1, Fig. 2.12).

❏ In studies of seagrass community structure the diver can use a light meter to determine the amount of light penetration (at the depth of the transect) in situations when the Secchi disc is not appropriate, i.e. the water is shallow or visibility is very good (i.e. the water is clear). Take an underwater sensor to the desired depth and read the light level from the meter, which is in the boat (Fig. 2.3).

Depth

❏ In studies of seagrass community structure the diver measures the depth at each sampling station along the transect using a depth gauge (see section on Seagrass Community and Biomass). Convert the depths (measured in metres) to depth below mean sea-level using tidal phase tables.

❏ When working from a boat e.g. trawl samples, use a shot line or depth sounder to record the depth.

Redox

❏ A diver collects sediment samples from each sampling station along the transect. See Seagrass Community Structure and Biomass (Section 5.2) for details.

❏ Measure the redox potential (Eh) as soon as possible after collection (see Table 3.2).

❏ Use a handheld digital pH/millivoltmeter to measure electrical potential.

❏ Calibrate the electrodes with appropriate standards just before measurements are taken.

❏ Carefully insert the electrode into the sediment. Ensure that the contacts of the electrode are properly connected, then leave the probe in the sediment until the readings have stabilised (it may take several minutes for the electrodes to equilibrate).

❏ Correct the measured potentials to Eh (vs. a reference electrode) by addition of + 244 mV to the reading.

❏ Always carry out replicate determinations to obtain reproducible results.

Grain Size

❏ Take the sediment samples back to the laboratory for analysis.

❏ Analyse the grain size of the sample using the methods described in the section on soils in the Mangrove chapter (Section 3.1).

Data recording

❏ Measure a set of environmental parameters for each station. Record data onto data sheets at the study site. Include information about the exposure of the site. See Table 5.1 for codes.

Table 5.1   Codes used to describe the exposure of a site in the database.

Code	Type of exposure
1	Embayment
2	Protected by reef or island
3	Exposed

❏ Record the amounts of sand, silt and clay, as described in the Mangrove chapter (Section 3.1).

Data processing

❏ Enter the data into the database using the structure described at the end of the chapter (Secton 5.4).

❏ Enter information about the sample into the sample table (XXSGSAMP) and allocate a unique sample identifier (SAMPLE_ID). The type of data collected in the sample is described by the DATA_TYPE field, which for ambient data is indicated by the letter "A".

❏ Enter the ambient data into the data table (XXSGADAT) using the sample identification allocated in the sample table.

❏ **Always check and verify data after entry.**

❏ Always backup data regularly.

Seagrasses

5.2 Seagrass Community Structure and Biomass

Abstract

These methods assess the community structure of seagrass meadows along transects run perpendicular to the shore. The species composition, percentage cover and biomass are measured within replicate quadrats placed at regular intervals along the length of the transect. These subsamples are used to describe the whole seagrass meadow.

Background

Tropical seagrass communities tend to be characterised by complex mixed species stands (Poiner *et al.* 1989) which, like temperate communities, are dynamic on a variety of spatial and temporal scales. The rates of establishment, growth, death and reproduction of individual species within the community differ. The differences in response of these species to environmental parameters such as temperature, water turbidity, sediment stability and nutrient levels, result in change in species composition, density and biomass over time.

Detailed studies of changes in community structure of tropical seagrass communities are essential to understand the role of these communities and the effects of disturbance on their composition, structure and rate of recovery. Seagrass meadows should be mapped as a first step towards understanding these communities. This should include data on the cover of seagrass species and, wherever possible, estimates of biomass. Techniques for the study of seagrass communities are rapidly being developed. Estimates of coverage can be made using a technique developed by Saito and Atobe (1970) in studies of intertidal algal communities. This technique uses classes of dominance, which are converted to frequency and percent cover data.

Seagrass communities make significant contributions to coastal productivity. In addition, the abundance and diversity of animals associated with seagrass communities are strongly related to the species composition and biomass of the seagrass. In general, the more dense the seagrass bed, the greater the protection that is offered to macrofauna species. The structural attributes of the seagrass bed thus play an important role in determining the faunal community (Fortes 1990).

Exact measures of biomass require quantitative harvesting, which is a destructive technique. Limited sampling by harvesting will provide a useful description of the biomass of a community, and can provide relative measures of above- and below-ground components. However, detailed studies of seagrass biomass must consider the variability of the community, which may require sampling intensities which would be unacceptable in low density communities. Therefore, the manual includes a description of a visual technique developed by Mellors (1991) to estimate the above-ground biomass of seagrass (see description at the end of this section). In this technique, a limited number of samples (reference quadrats) are harvested to calibrate the estimates, thus reducing the volume of material collected.

Advantages

❏ The methods are simple and can be done with a minimum of personnel and facilities.

❏ The methods are reliable.

❏ Collection of shoots within a quadrat and sampling a core of sediment allows the characterisation of below-ground plant parts (e.g. rhizomes and flowering shoots).

Disadvantages

❏ Collection of vegetation for biomass estimates is destructive.

❏ Counting shoots can be time consuming underwater.

❏ It is dependent on the nature and distribution of the seagrass meadows.

Logistics

Personnel
❏ A team of at least 2 divers is required for these studies. If surveys are conducted from a boat an additional person is required in the boat.

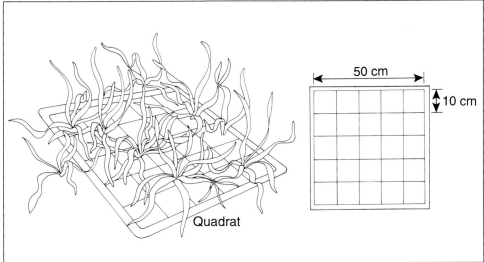

Figure 5.1 A quadrat divided into a grid for estimation of percent cover.

Equipment

Field eqiupment

❑ Small boat, with outboard motor and safety equipment.

❑ Quadrat (50 centimetre x 50 centimetre) with buoy (Fig. 5.1). The quadrat should be divided into a 10 centimetre x 10 centimetre grid. Brass or aluminium quadrats are recommended since they are light and durable.

❑ Preprinted data sheets on A4 size underwater paper are recommended. The sheets are attached to the slate and kept as a permanent record.

❑ Waterproof labels. Preprinted labels ensure that all required data are recorded for each sample. An example is given in Figure 5.2.

❑ Plastic bags (approximately 8 centimetres x 11 centimetres).

❑ 100 metre fibreglass measuring tapes.

❑ Dive knife.

❑ Mesh bags.

❑ Preservative - 5% solution of formalin in seawater.

❑ Ruler.

❑ SCUBA equipment.

❑ Depth guage.

❑ Slates and pencils.

❑ Small trowel to collect sediment samples.

❑ Underwater compass.

Location ....

Site ....

Date .... Time ....

Transect No. .... Station No. ....

Quadrat No. .... Depth ....

Remarks ....

....

Figure 5.2 Preprinted waterproof labels for seagrass vegetation samples.

Laboratory Equipment

❑ Laboratory balance.

❑ A handheld magnifying lens.

❑ 5% phosphoric acid - to remove epiphytes from the seagrass samples.

❑ Oven and muffle furnace.

❑ Crucibles.

Site Selection

❏ Aerial photographs will help identify the location and extent of seagrass meadows.

❏ A preliminary (general) visual survey of the area is required to map out, establish and adequately represent differences and the real extent of the seagrass meadows. Manta tows (see Section 2.2) are a useful method for general survey, but may not be suitable in areas with very poor visibility.

❏ Select the position for the transects (within each site) after the general survey of the seagrass meadow. The transects should be representative of the entire seagrass area chosen for survey and/or monitoring, and should be similar to each other (e.g. physical characteristics).

General Procedure

❏ Record the position of each transect. The start (inshore end) of the transect is the most useful reference.

❏ A GPS (Global Positioning System) can be very useful if available. Otherwise, use a handheld compass to determine the bearing, with reference to at least 2 permanent landmarks or markers established as reference points.

❏ Survey at least 3 replicate transects at each site. Swim the transects along a compass bearing, perpendicular to the shore. The length of the transect depends on the size of the seagrass meadows, and should extend to outer limits of the bed (where the seagrass disappears).

❏ The transects should be separated from each other by a reasonable distance (50 to 100 metres), and should be parallel to each other and perpendicular to the shore.

❏ Samples should be taken at regular intervals (usually 5 metres) along the transect (sampling stations), so that gradients in community structure are described.

☞ *In a large uniform (homogeneous) seagrass meadow which extends out from the shore for more than 100 metres, the sample interval may be every 15 to 20 metres. In heterogeneous communities, intervals may be less than 5 metres.*

❏ At least 4 replicate quadrats (50 centimetres x 50 centimetres) should be done at each sampling station (Fig. 5.3).

☞ *Safe diving practices should be used. When determining the length of the transect the depth of the transect must also be considered. As a general rule no decompression dives should be done while conducting surveys.*

❏ Record the ambient parameters for each station.

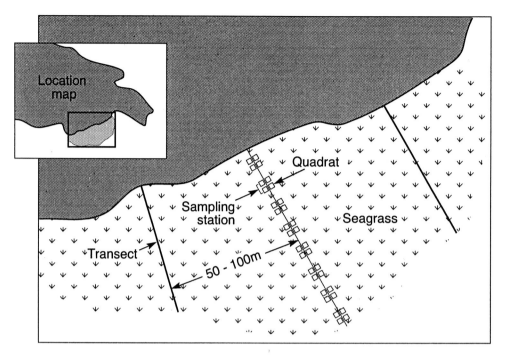

Figure 5.3   Schematic representation of sampling for baseline seagrass surveys.

❑ Estimate the percent cover of the plants (species/population) found in each replicate quadrat. Using the 10 centimetre grid on the quadrat, score each species in the grid using the categories developed by Saito and Atobe (1970) (Table 5.2).

❑ Record estimates onto the data sheet. See the worked example later in this chapter for a detailed description of estimates using the methods of Saito and Atobe (1970).

❑ Record the depth at each station where seagrass is sampled.

❑ Cut around the edge of the quadrat using a dive knife and then carefully loosen the vegetation inside the quadrat. Collect all the bottom vegetation inside the quadrat (including roots and rhizomes).

❑ Place the sample from each quadrat inside a separate plastic bag with a waterproof label identifying the sample.

☞ *More detailed studies of the seagrass community should include biomass estimates. The method developed by Mellors estimates above-ground biomass of seagrass visually, thus reducing the amount of plant material collected. The method could be adapted for use at each station by estimating 6 to 10 quadrats near the transect line.*

❑ Using a small trowel, collect 3 samples of sediment adjacent to the quadrats at each sampling station. Take each soil sample from the first 10 centimetres of the substratum. Approximately 500 grams of sediment should be collected (about half fill an 8 x 11 centimetre plastic bag).

❑ When diving is completed, add 5% formalin-seawater solution to each of the bagged seagrass samples, then seal the labelled bags.

❑ Take the seagrass and sediment samples back to the laboratory for analysis.

Laboratory Procedure

To determine species composition and percent cover

❑ Process individual quadrat samples.

❑ Rinse the plant sample from each quadrat in water. If possible, preservative solutions should be recycled.

☞ *Sorting of samples fixed in formalin should be carried out where there is good circulation of fresh air (ideally sorting is done in a fume hood).*

❑ Clean adhering debris off the samples.

☞ *If carbonates and encrusting epiphytic organisms cannot be removed by hand, then the sample should be placed in 5% phosphoric acid for 10 to 15 minutes (or until bubbling ceases), and then rinsed in tap water.*

❑ Sort the sample to species. Most of the gross morphological characters used can be seen with the naked eye. A hand lens is useful for some minute features.

❑ Count the total number of shoots per species, blot dry and weigh (wet weight in grams).

❑ Measure the shoot height (in centimetres) of at least 10 shoots for each species and calculate the mean.

To determine biomass

❑ Combine all materials of the same species from the 4 quadrat samples collected at each station.

❑ Subsample 50 shoots from each of the combined samples (each subsample now has only one species). In seagrass meadows, where the vegetation is sparse, the minimum sample is 10 shoots of each species in the sample.

❑ Take the subsample of shoots for each species, and separate into leaves, rhizomes and roots (Fig. 5.4), blot dry and weigh each portion (wet weight in grams).

❑ To obtain dry weight of each portion, place the separated shoots (leaves, rhizomes and roots) into labelled paper bags and dry in an oven at 40 to 50 °C to constant weight (dry weight in grams).

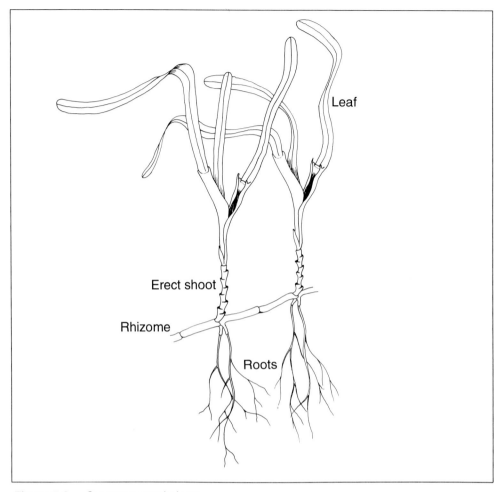

Figure 5.4   Seagrass morphology.

❑ Take 10 grams of the dried plant material. Put the subsample in a porcelain crucible and place in a muffle furnace at 555 °C for at least 5 hours to determine the biomass of the samples (in grams organic matter per square metre).

Sediment analysis
❑ Analysis of the soil samples is detailed in the Mangrove chapter (Section 3.1). Determine the Eh and the proportion of sand, silt and clay at each station (% content in sample).

Standardisation
❑ Make regular comparisons between divers to ensure consistent estimation of percent cover among observers. The variability between observers should be

checked at the beginning of each sampling trip. It is particularly important to test inexperienced observers against experienced team members.

❏ Set up a specimen collection for future reference. Put at least 3 complete and representative plants of each species inside wide-mouthed bottles containing 10% buffered formalin.

❏ Label reference samples with species (male/female), location, site, depth, substrate type, date and collector.

Data Recording

❏ Record the ambient parameters for every sampling station along the transect. Depth readings are later standardised by converting the measurements to depth below mean sea-level using local tide phase tables.

❏ Record the estimated cover for each quadrat using the 10 centimetre grid.

❏ Identify seagrass species using taxonomic guides.

❏ Divide samples into species and record the number of shoots, the mean shoot height and wet weight.

❏ Combine the species samples for each station (i.e. from the 4 quadrats) and record weight measurements (wet weight, dry weight and organic matter).

❏ Calculate the Eh and weight of sand, silt and clay material in the sediment samples using the techniques described in Section 3.1.

Processing Data

❏ At the end of each day, enter the data into the database using the structure described at the end of the chapter.

❏ Information about the sample is entered into the sample table (XXSGSAMP) and a unique sample identifier (SAMPLE_ID) is allocated. The type of data collected in the sample is described by the DATA_TYPE field, which for vegetation data is denoted by "V".

❏ Enter the seagrass cover data into the data table (XXSGVDAT) using the sample identification allocated in the sample table. Each species is entered into the database using the code shown in Section 5.5.

❏ Enter the biomass data, which is calculated for each sampling station, into the data table (XXSGVBDT) using the same SAMPLE_ID used for the vegetation cover data. Each species is entered into the database using the code shown in Section 5.4.

❏ The ambient data, including soil analysis and Eh, are entered into the data table (XXSGADAT) using the sample identification allocated in the sample table.

Seagrasses

❏ **Always check and verify data after entry, especially the species codes.**

❏ Always backup data regularly.

Data analysis

❏ The most commonly used way of expressing biomass or standing crop is dry weight in grams per square metre ($g\,m^{-2}$). If only wet weight can be determined routinely, at least one series of wet weight/dry weight (wwt/dwt) correlations should be made (Ott 1990).

❏ Root/shoot (R/S) ratios may be calculated on ash-free dry-weight data (Fonseca *et al.* 1990).

Comments

❏ Bare patches should **not** be avoided in the sampling of seagrass meadows since this may overestimate density. If transects are not used in sampling an area, then random sampling must be undertaken.

❏ Saito and Atobe (1970) developed a visual method for estimating cover. A detailed description of the method follows.

❏ Visual estimation of seagrass biomass can be undertaken using techniques similar to those developed in pasture research (Mellors 1991). A detailed description of the method follows.

Estimation of cover adapted from Saito and Atobe (1970)

❏ Place a 50 x 50 centimetre quadrat on the substratum. The quadrat should be subdivided into 25, 10 x 10 centimetre sectors (Fig. 5.1).

❏ Record the dominance of each species in each of the 25 sectors (10 x 10 centimetre) using the classes defined in Table 5.2. This process is repeated for each species in the quadrat.

❏ The coverage (C) of each species in each 50 x 50 centimetre quadrat is calculated as follows:

$$C = \frac{\sum(M_i \times f_i)}{\sum f} \tag{5-1}$$

where: M_i = mid point percentage of Class i:

f = frequency {number of sectors with the same class of dominance (i)}.

Table 5.2 Classes of dominance used to record cover.

Class	Amount of substratum covered	% substratum covered	Mid point % (M)
5	1/2 to all	50 - 100	75
4	1/4 to 1/2	25 - 50	37.5
3	1/8 to 1/4	12.5 - 25	18.75
2	1/16 to 1/8	6.25 - 12.5	9.38
1	less than 1/16	<6.25	3.13
0	absent	0	0

❏ An example of this method, using the species *Thalassia*, is outlined below. Estimates of dominance are made for each of the 25 sectors in the quadrat.

0	1	2	2	3
0	0	3	2	2
1	2	5	4	5
3	5	5	1	4
5	5	4	1	2

From the above example:

Class	Mid point % (M)	Frequency (f)	M x f
5	75	6	450
4	37.5	3	112.5
3	18.75	3	56.25
2	9.38	6	56.28
1	3.13	4	12.52
0	0	3	0
Total		25	687.55

❏ Therefore, using equation (5-1), the cover of *Thalassia* is:

$$C = \frac{687.55}{25} = 27.5\%$$

❏ Repeat for other species found within the quadrat.

Comments
❏ The maximum coverage that can be recorded for a species is 75%. Therefore, if the species being examined is more dominant than this, the method will be an underestimate.

Biomass estimates using the methods of Mellors (1991).

❏ This method visually estimates above-ground dry weight biomass. The method calibrates these standing crop estimates against a set of preselected quadrats which are harvested at the end of the sampling period. The visual technique is more precise than some traditional harvesting methods due to the larger number of replicates that can be taken.

❏ Select 5 reference quadrats at the start of each sampling period. The quadrats should represent the range of seagrass biomass (most to least) likely to be encountered during sampling.

❏ Rank the 5 reference quadrats on a linear scale, 1 (least) to 5 (most).

❏ Select the reference quadrats for Rank 1 and Rank 5 first, followed by Rank 3, and finally Rank 4 and Rank 2. See Table 5.3

Table 5.3 Ranks of estimated dry weight yield of above-ground biomass.

Rank	Estimate
0	nil
1	least
2	half-way between Ranks 1 and 3
3	half-way between Ranks 1 and 5
4	half-way between Ranks 3 and 5
5	most

❏ The reference quadrats must be agreed to by all observers.

❏ Leave the reference quadrats in place until sampling is completed.

❑ Observers swim along the transect recording the ranks in each quadrat. The number of quadrats estimated will depend on the variability of the seagrass density, but must be at least 4 at each station.

❑ Select 10 quadrats at the completion of the sampling period, to represent the ranks (1 to 5) encountered along the transect. These 10 reference quadrats cover the range of biomasses at the site.

❑ Collect all the seagrass from the 10 representative quadrats, for calibration of the rank estimates.

☞ *In seagrass beds of distinct species zonation (e.g. Halophila cf. Cymodocea), more than one set of calibration quadrats may be needed.*

❑ Calculate the dry weight as described earlier in this chapter.

❑ Establish calibration curves for each observer by regressing the above-ground dry weights against the corresponding rank for the 10 calibration quadrats. See Mellors (1991) for further information.

Standardisation

❑ Observers should undertake a training program before using this technique.

❑ In the laboratory, observers should weigh wet and dried samples of different species to become familiar with the moisture content of different species before sampling.

❑ Observers must be trained to estimate dry weight biomass and not percent cover. Observers must consider the area of bare ground between plants, plant height and the moisture content of each species.

❑ Laboratory training, weighing wet and dry samples of different species should be undertaken before field observations.

Comments

❑ The method is not applicable in turbid waters and does not provide an estimate of below-ground biomass.

References

Fonseca, M.S., G.W. Thayer and W.J. Kenworthy (1990). Root/shoot ratios. In: Phillips, R.C. and C.P. McRoy (editors.). "Seagrass Research Methods". Unesco, France. 210pp.

Fortes, M.D. (1990). "Seagrasses: A resource unknown in the ASEAN region". ICLARM Education Series 5, 46pp. International Centre for Living Aquatic Resource Management, Manila, Philippines.

Mellors, J.E. (1991). An evaluation of a rapid visual technique for estimating seagrass biomass. Aquatic Botany, **42**: 67-73.

Seagrasses

Ott, J.A. 1990. Biomass. In: Phillips, R.C. and C.P. McRoy (editors.). "Seagrass Research Methods". Unesco, France. 210pp.

Poiner, E.R., D.I. Walker and R.G. Coles (1989). Regional studies - seagrasses of tropical Australia. pp: 279-303. In: A.W.D. Larkum, A.J. McComb and S.A. Shepherd (editors). "Biology of Seagrasses: A treatise on the biology of seagrasses with special reference to the Australian region". Elsevier, Amsterdam. 841 pp.

Saito, Y. and S. Atobe (1970). Phytosociological study of intertidal marine algae. I. Usujiri Benten-Jima, Hokkaido. Bulletin of the Faculty of Fisheries, Hokkaido University, **21**: 37-69.

Suggested references for identification of algae and seagrasses

Christianson, I.G., M.N. Clayton, B.M. Allender (1981). "Seaweeds of Australia". A.H. and A.W. Reed Pty. Ltd. Adelaide. 112 pp.

Fortes, M.D. (1986). Taxonomy and Ecology of Philippine Seagrasses. PhD Dissertation. Univ. of the Philippines, Diliman, Q.C. Philippines. 245pp.

Gepp, A. and E.S. Gepp-Barton (1911). *Codiaceae*, including a monograph of *Flabellarieae* and *Udoteae*. pp. 1-150, 22 pl. In: M. Weber and L. deBeaufort (editors.). Siboga Expedition Report **62**(56).

Hartog, C. den. (1970). "The Seagrasses of the World". North-Holland Publishing Co. Amsterdam - London pp. 298.

Kuo, J. and A.J. McComb (1989). Seagrass taxonomy, structure and development. In: A.W.D. Larkum, A.J. McComb and S.A. Shepherd (editors.) "Biology of Seagrasses: A treatise on the biology of seagrasses with special reference to the Australian region". Elsevier, Amsterdam. 841pp.

Lanyon, J. (1986). "Seagrasses of the Great Barrier Reef". Great Barrier Reef Marine Park Authority Special Publication Series (3). Townsville, Australia. 54pp.

Tseng, C.K. (1983). "Seaweeds of China". Science Press, Beijing, China. 361pp.

5.3 Fish and Juvenile Prawn Survey in Seagrass Beds

Abstract

A beam trawl is towed behind a small boat to sample juvenile fish, prawn (shrimp) and crab species associated with seagrass meadows. Sampling is best conducted at night to increase the efficiency of catching nocturnal prawn species and other animals that use the seagrass at night. Initial sampling should be undertaken at least 4 times a year to provide information about the variability in abundance and diversity of species through space and time.

Background

Seagrasses provide important habitat for a variety of fauna. The shelter provided by the seagrass canopy and the high *in situ* primary production provide the base for very high faunal productivity (Howard *et al.* 1989). In addition to shelter, the seagrasses provide food both directly, and indirectly, through provision of habitat for planktonic and epifaunal crustaceans. Perhaps most significant from a fisheries perspective is their role as a nursery habitat for many species of commercially and recreationally important fish and crustaceans (Bell and Pollard 1989).

Many methods have been used to sample the mobile fauna associated with seagrasses, such as rotenone poisoning, beach seining and beam trawling. While a combination of these methods may be needed to describe the macrofaunal communities associated with seagrasses (see Chapter 6), beam trawling has been found to be the most effective and practical method for sampling seagrass at depths greater than 2 metres (Gray and Bell 1986).

Advantages

❏ The method is highly selective for juvenile prawns and fish.

❏ Net is easy to deploy.

❏ Many species are more vulnerable to trawling at night.

Disadvantages

❏ Net sampling can be biased by mesh size and net avoidance.

❏ Difficult to quantify.

Seagrasses

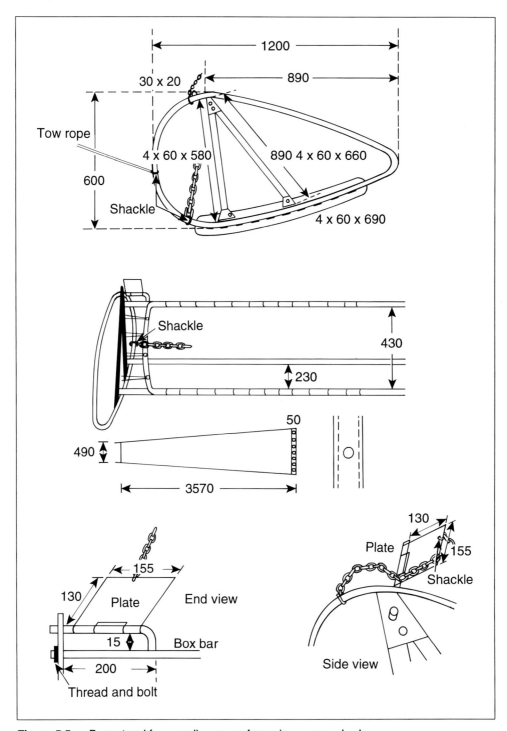

Figure 5.5   Beam trawl for sampling macrofauna in seagrass beds.

Equipment

❑ Small boat, with outboard motor and safety gear.

❑ A 'beam' trawl 1.5 m wide and 0.5 m high, constructed with a 1.25 centimetre diameter steel rod frame mounted on wooden shoes 12 centimetre wide and 47 centimetre long (Fig. 5.5). A cone-shaped, 2 millimetre mesh net, 6 metres long with a 1 metre long cod end.

❑ Waterproof lanterns.

❑ Plastic bags, buckets, pens, adhesive tapes, 5% formalin.

❑ Measuring board to measure fish (Fig. 5.6).

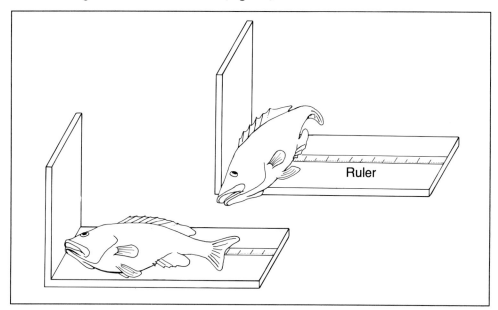

Figure 5.6   Board used to measure fish. Fish is held against the back of the board and measurements are read from the ruler set into the base.

❑ Calipers to measure crabs and prawns.

❑ Balance, measuring in milligrams.

❑ Binocular microscope and micrometer gauge.

❑ Preserving jars.

Site selection

❑ Aerial photographs will help identify the location and extent of seagrass meadows.

❑ Determine the extent of the seagrass meadow and map out the area.

❏ The tows should be representative of the entire seagrass area, and should be similar to each other (e.g. physical characteristics such as exposure, depth etc.).

General Procedure

❏ Take initial samples at least 4 times a year.

❏ Measure the ambient environmental factors for each trawl. These include temperature, salinity and depth. If sediment analysis is required, see description of grab sampling in Chapter 4.

❏ Determine the position of the site using a handheld compass to determine the bearing with reference to at least 2 permanent landmarks or markers established as reference points. A GPS is useful if available.

❏ At least 4 replicate trawls should be undertaken at each site.

❏ The trawls are allocated randomly within the site and do not overlap.

❏ Trawling is carried out after dark (to catch prawns).

❏ Lower the beam trawl on the towing wire or rope (the warp). The length of the warp should be 10 times the depth.

❏ Tow the beam trawl at approximately 1 knot for 2 minutes parallel to the shore, or along a uniform depth gradient. Timing starts when the required length of wire is paid out along the sea floor.

❏ Carefully monitor the direction of the tow.

☞ *An alternative to the timed method is to mark out the towing distance with buoys and then to make each replicate tow at a constant speed.*

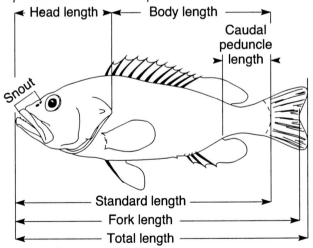

Figure 5.7   Standard fish measurements.

❑ Record the time at which trawling is started and the duration of the tow.

❑ All trawls are taken against tidal currents, when these are present.

❑ After 2 minutes, or when the distance has been towed, haul the net back to the boat.

❑ Wash the sample gently to the bottom of the cod end.

❑ Empty the cod end into a plastic bucket or tray and transfer to a large specimen jar.

❑ Label samples with the location, site, position (latitude and longitude), depth, date and time. Further information such as tidal or weather conditions should be noted. The waterproof label should be placed inside the container and distinguishing details can be marked on the exterior for quick identification.

❑ Preserve the catch with 5% formalin in seawater (add more formalin to large samples).

❑ Take samples back to the laboratory for identification using taxonomic keys.

❑ Measure (Figs. 5.7, 5.8 and 5.9) and weigh the samples.

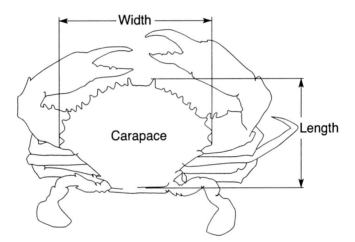

Figure 5.8 Standard length measurements for crabs.

Data Recording

❑ Record the following details onto sample labels species - location, site, date, time of collection, depth, nature of seagrass meadow and collector.

❑ If identification is not immediately possible, assign a reference code to each category (for later identification).

❑ Note the species, number of individuals present and if the organisms are adult or juvenile.

❑ Record the reproductive condition of crustacean (prawn and crab) samples.

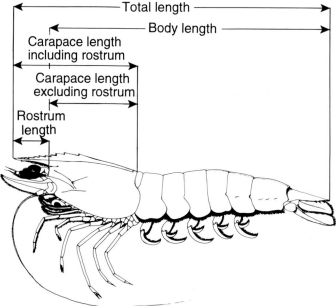

Figure 5.9   Standard length measurements for prawns or shrimp.

Data Processing

❏ Enter the data into the database using the structure described at the end of the chapter (Section 5.4).

❏ Information about the sample is entered into the sample table (XXSGSAMP) and a unique sample identifier (SAMPLE_ID) is allocated. The type of data collected in the sample is described by the DATA_TYPE field, which for seagrass fauna data is denoted by the letter "F".

❏ The seagrass fauna data are entered into the data table (XXSGFDAT) using the sample identification allocated in the sample table.

❏ When ambient environmental parameters are measured at the site another entry is made into the sample table and a unique sample identifier is allocated. The ambient parameters are denoted in the sample table by the letter "A".

❏ **Always check and verify data after entry.**

❏ Always backup data regularly.

References

Bell, J.D. and D.A. Pollard (1989). Ecology of fish assemblages and fisheries associated with seagrass. pp: 565-609. In: A.W.D. Larkum, A.J. McComb and S.A.

Shepherd (editors) "Biology of Seagrasses: A treatise on the biology of seagrasses with special reference to the Australian region". Elsevier, Amsterdam. 841pp.

Gray, C.A. and J.D. Bell (1986). Consequences of two common techniques for sampling vagile macrofauna associated with the seagrass *Zostera capricorni*. Marine Ecology Progress Series, **28**: 43-48.

Howard, R.K., G.J. Edgar and P.A. Hutchings (1989). Faunal assemblages of seagrass beds. pp: 536-564. In: A.W.D. Larkum, A.J. McComb and S.A. Shepherd (editors) "Biology of Seagrasses: A treatise on the biology of seagrasses with special reference to the Australian region". Elsevier, Amsterdam. 841pp.

Suggested reading for identification of fish

FAO (1974). "FAO Species Identification Sheets for Fishery Purposes". Food and Agriculture Organisation of the United Nations, Rome. Volumes III and IV.

Gloerfelt-Tarp, T. and P.J. Kailola (1984/85). "Trawled Fishes of Southern Indonesia and Northern Australia". Australian Development Assistance Bureau (ADAB), Directorate General of Fisheries - Indonesia and German Agency for Technical Cooperation. 406 pp.

Masuda, H., C. Araga and T. Yoshino (1980). Coastal fishes of Southern Japan (revised edition). Tokai University Press, Tokyo. 382 pp.

Masuda, H., K. Amaoka, C. Araga, T. Vyeno and T. Yoshiro (1984). "The Fishes of the Japanese Archipelago". 2 Volumes. Tokai University Press, Tokyo. 807pp.

Schroeder, R.E. (1980). "Philippine Shorefishes of the Western Sulu Sea". Bureau of Fisheries and Aquatic Resources and NMPC Books, Manila, Philippines. 266 pp.

Suggested reading for identification of prawns and crabs

Chaitiamvong, S. and M. Supongpan (1992). "A Guide to Penaeoid Shrimps Found in Thai Waters". Australian Institute of Marine Science, Townsville Australia. 77pp.

Grey D.L., W. Dall and A. Baker (1983). "A Guide to the Australian Penaeid Prawns". Northern Territory Government Printing Office, Australia. 140pp.

Holthuis, L.B. (1955). The recent genera of caridean and stenopodidean shrimps (Class Crustacea, Order Decapoda, Subsection Natantia) with keys for their determination. Zool. Verhandl, **26**: 1-157.

Lovett, D.L. (1981). "A Guide to the Shrimps, Prawns, Lobsters and Crabs of Malaysia and Singapore". Universiti Pertanian Malaysia. 21pp.

Sakai, T. (1976). "Crabs of Japan and the adjacent seas". 2 volumes. Kodansha Ltd., Tokyo. 773pp.

Seagrasses

5.4 Seagrass Communities Database

Seagrass sample data
XXSGSAMP

Name	Type	Length/Decimal	Description
SAMPLE_ID	C	9.0	The standard sample identification. This links the sample table to the data files. Format XXGGGNNNN XX = ISO country code. See codes in Appendix I GGG = study group code NNNN = running number
LOCATION	C	30.0	Location name e.g. Seribu Islands
SITE	C	30.0	Specific study area name
DATE	D	8.0	Date when data were gathered
TIME	C	4.0	Time of sampling using the format HHMM (e.g. 1330 = 1:30 pm)
LATITUDE	C	7.0	Latitude of site in format AABBCCD AA = degrees BB = minutes CC = decimal seconds D = N (north) or S (south)
LONGITUDE	C	8.0	Longitude of site in format AAABBCCD AAA = degrees BB = minutes CC = decimal seconds D = E (east) or W (west)
DATA_TYPE	C	1.0	Data code denoting the type of sample: A = ambient; F = Fauna; V = vegetation. Data file names are listed in the datacode table
EXPOSURE	N	2.0	Relative exposure of the site (see Table 5.1) 1 = Embayment 2 = Protected by reef or island 3 = Exposed
COLLECTORS	C	40.0	Name(s) of data collectors and their tasks
REMARKS	C	40.0	Relevant observations regarding the site and the data

Seagrass ambient data
XXSGADAT

Name	Type	Length/Decimal	Description
SAMPLE_ID	C	9.0	The standard sample identification. This links the sample table to the data files. Format XXGGGNNNN
REPLICATE	N	1.0	Replicate number of a transect (or trawl)
STATION_NO	N	2.0	Point along the transect where replicate quadrats are sampled for vegetation studies
DEPTH	N	5.0	Depth at which seagrass is sampled. Measured in metres
TEMP_TOP	N	5.2	Temperature reading at the top of the water column (30cm below surface), measured in degrees Celsius
TEMP_BOT	N	5.2	Temperature reading at transect depth, measured in degrees Celsius
SALN_TOP	N	5.2	Salinity reading at the top of the water column (30cm below surface), measured in ppt.
SALN_BOT	N	5.2	Salinity reading at transect depth, measured in ppt.
TURBIDITY	N	5.2	Visible depth of the standard secchi disc, measured in metres
LIGHT	N	6.0	Light penetration of the water measured with a portable light meter in μmoles/m^2/sec
SAND	N	5.2	Sand content in station sediment sample, measured in percentage
SILT	N	5.2	Silt content in station sediment sample, measured in percentage
CLAY	N	5.2	Clay content in station sediment sample measured in percentage
MEDGRAIN	N	6.4	Median grain size for the station, measured in millimetre
EH	N	8.2	Mean redox potential of sediment at the station

Seagrass vegetation (cover) data
XXSGVDAT

Name	Type	Length/Decimal	Description
SAMPLE_ID	C	9.0	The standard sample identification. This links the sample table to the data files. Format XXGGGNNNN
REPLICATE	N	1.0	Replicate number of a transect extending perpendicular from the shore to the outer extent of the seagrass meadow.
STATION_NO	N	2.0	Point along the transect where replicate quadrats are sampled
DEPTH	N	5.0	Depth at which seagrass is sampled. Measured in metres
QUAD_NO	N	1.0	Replicate quadrat number at the sampling station
FIELDCODE	C	10.0	Code assigned to the taxonomic entity by the field researcher (suggested codes listed in Section 5.5). The code must link uniquely to one taxonomic entity. Description of the entity (binomial name) must be given to the database manager when a new code is created. This information is maintained in ALLTAXON

Seagrasses

GRASSCVR	N	3.0	Seagrass cover, measured in percent for each species
TOT_SHOOT	N	7.2	Total number of shoots per species
WETWTSH	N	7.2	Wet weight of the shoots for a species, measured in grams
SHOOTHT	N	6.2	Shoot height for a species, measured in centimetres. Average of at least 10 shoots

Seagrass vegetation (biomass) data
XXSGVBDT

Name	Type	Length/ Decimal	Description
SAMPLE_ID	C	9.0	The standard sample identification. This links the sample table to the data files. Format XXGGGNNNN
REPLICATE	N	1.0	Replicate number of a transect extending perpendicular from the shore to the outer extent of the seagrass meadow.
STATION_NO	N	2.0	Point along the transect where replicate quadrats are sampled
DEPTH	N	5.0	Depth at which seagrass is sampled. Measured in metres
FIELDCODE	C	10.0	Code assigned to the taxonomic entity by the field researchers (see Section 5.5 for suggested codes). See XXSGVDAT for detail
WETWTLV	N	7.2	Wet weight of leaves for each species, measured in grams
WETWTRT	N	7.2	Wet weight of roots for each species, measured in grams
WETWTRHM	N	7.2	Wet weight of rhizomes for each species, measured in grams
DRYWTLV	N	7.2	Dry weight of leaves for each species, measured in grams
DRYWTRT	N	7.2	Dry weight of roots for each species, measured in grams
DRYWTRHM	N	7.2	Dry weight of rhizomes for each species, measured in grams
ORG_MATLV	N	3.0	Organic matter content of leaves for each species, measured in grams organic matter per m^2
ORG_MATRT	N	3.0	Organic matter content of roots for each species, measured in grams organic matter per m^2
ORG_MATRHM	N	3.0	Organic matter content of rhizomes for each species, measured in grams organic matter per m^2

Seagrass fauna data
XXSGFDAT

Name	Type	Length/Decimal	Description
SAMPLE_ID	C	9.0	The standard sample identification. This links the sample table to the data files. Format XXGGGNNNN
REPLICATE	N	2.0	Replicate number for each beam trawl
DEPTH	N	5.0	Depth of trawl. Measured in metres
TIME_START	N	4.0	Time at which trawl was begun. Format HHMM
TIME_FINISH	N	4.0	Time at which trawl was finished. Format HHMM
GROUP	C	1.0	Data code denoting the fauna group sampled in the tow: C = crab; F = fish; and P = prawn.
FIELDCODE	C	40.0	Code assigned to the taxonomic entity by the field researchers. The code must uniquely link to one taxonomic entity. Description of the entity (binomial name) must be given to the database manager when a new code is created. This information is maintained in ALLTAXON
TOT_LEN	N	6.2	Total length of fish/prawns (Fig. 5.7, 5.9). Measured in centimetres
STD_LEN	N	6.2	Standard length of fish (Fig. 5.7). Measured in centimetres
CARP_LEN	N	6.2	Carapace length of crabs (Fig. 5.8). Measured in centimetres
CARP_WID	N	6.2	Carapace width of crabs (Fig. 5.8). Measured in centimetres
WEIGHT_GRM	N	5.0	Weight in grams
GRAVID	C	1.0	Sexual maturity of individual: N = Not gravid (i.e. without eggs;) Y = Gravid (i.e. with eggs)
AGE_CLASS	C	1.0	Adult (A) or juvenile (J)
NOTES	C	20.0	Additional notes observed by the recorder e.g. if organisms are adult or juvenile

Seagrasses

Taxonomic Table
ALLTAXON

Name	Type	Length/Decimal	Description
FIELDCODE	C	40.0	Code assigned to the taxonomic entity by the field researchers. The code must link uniquely to one taxonomic entity. Description of the entity (binomial name) must be given to the database manager when a new code is created
TAXCODE	C	10	Unique code used to represent individual taxa. The codes are generated by the system manager. The TAXCODE ensures that the same kind of living things have the same code despite the fact that field researchers may give them different FIELDCODEs
SPECNAME	C	35	Species name (Latin binomial)
GENUSNAME	C	35	Genus name
FAMILYNAME	C	35	Family name
ORDERNAME	C	35	Order name
CLASSNAME	C	35	Class name
PHYLANAME	C	35	Phylum name
AUTHORITY	C	50	Name of authority, an organisation, or a system that was used as a reference to classify samples
REF_CODE	C	20	Reference code for samples which are stored in a reference collection, museum or herbarium. This allows researchers to look at an actual specimen which has been assigned this classification

Seagrass datacodes
DATACODE

Field name	Value	Explanation
AGE_CLASS	A	Adult
	J	Juvenile
DATA_TYPE	A	Sample record refers to data in the ambient data file XXSGADAT
	F	Sample record refers to data in the seagrass fauna data file XXSGFDAT
	V	Sample record refers to data in the seagrass vegetation data file XXSGVDAT and XXSGVBDT
EXPOSURE	1	Embayment
	2	Protected by reef or island
	3	Exposed
GRAVID	N	If not gravid (i.e. without eggs)
	Y	If gravid (i.e. with eggs)
GROUP	C	Crab fauna collected in trawl samples
	F	Fish fauna collected in trawl samples
	P	Prawn fauna collected in trawl samples

5.5 Seagrass Species Codes

Family Hydrocharitaceae

Enhalus acoroides	ENHA
Thalassia hemprichii	THAL
Thalassia testudinum	THAT
Halophila australis	HAUS
Halophila decipiens	HDEC
Halophila ovalis	HOVS
Halophila ovalis ssp. bullosa	HOBU
Halophila ovalis ssp. linearis	HOLI
Halophila minor	HMIN
Halophila hawaiina	HHAW
Halophila stipulacea	HSTI
Halophila johnsonii	HJON
Halophila beccarii	HBEC
Halophila spinulosa	HSPI
Halophila tricostata	HTRI
Halophila engelmanni	HENG
Halophila baillonis	HBAI

Family Posidoniaceae

Posidonia oceanica	POCE
Posidonia angustifolia	PANG
Posidonia australis	PAUS
Posidonia sinuosa	PSIN
Posidonia ostenfeldii	POST
Posidonia coriacea	PCOR
Posidonia denhartogii	PDEN
Posidonia kirkmanii	PKIR
Posidonia robertsonae	PROB

Family Cymodoceaceae

Syringodium isoetifolium	SYRI
Syringodium filiforme	SFIL
Halodule pinifolia	HDPI
Halodule uninervis	HDUN
Halodule beaufettei	HDBD
Halodule wrightii	HDWR
Halodule bermudensis	HDBE
Halodule ciliata	HDCI
Halodule brasiliense	HDBR
Cymodocea angustata	CYAN
Cymodocea rotundata	CYRO
Cymodocea nodosa	CYNO
Cymodocea serrulata	CYSE
Amphibolis antarctica	AMAN
Amphibolis griffithii	AMGR
Thalassodendron ciliatum	TCIL
Thalassodendron pachyrhizum	TPAC

Family Zosteraceae *

Zostera marina	ZMAR
Zostera caespitosa	ZCAE
Zostera caulescens	ZCAU
Zostera asiatica	ZASI
Zostera capricorni	ZCPR
Zostera mucronata	ZMUC
Zostera noltii	ZNOL
Zostera japonica	ZJAP
Heterozostera tasmanica	HETA
Phyllospadix torreyi	PYTO
Phyllospadix scouleri	PYSC
Phyllospadix serrulatus	PYSE
Phyllospadix iwatensis	PYIW
Phyllospadix japonicus	PYJA

Seagrasses

COASTAL FISHERIES

General Introduction

Many of the commercially important fisheries species, harvested on the continental shelves of tropical regions, have their nursery areas within the coastal zone (Dakin 1938; Kutkuhn 1966). Sampling within tropical coastal habitats throughout the world has shown that juvenile fish and shrimp (prawns) are often highly abundant in mangrove and seagrass habitats (Africa - Branford 1981, de Freitas 1986; Mexico - Edwards 1978; Puerto Rico - Stoner 1988; India - Achuthankutty and Nair 1980, Sambasivam 1985; Thailand - Boonruang and Janekaru 1985; Malaysia - Chong *et al.* 1990; New Guinea - Frusher 1983; and Australia - Staples *et al.* 1985, Robertson and Duke 1987).

Simultaneous sampling of a variety of inshore habitats has shown that the juvenile phase of several species of penaeid shrimp and fish are restricted entirely to mangrove associated water (Robertson 1988, Chong *et al.* 1990, Sasekumar *et al.* 1992), while some occur only in seagrass areas (Staples *et al.* 1985). Studies of penaeid shrimp within the forested areas of mangrove habitats has revealed great variation in the numbers of penaeids associated directly with this microhabitat. In Australia and Malaysia, high numbers of juveniles of *Penaeus merguiensis* have been recorded inhabiting mangrove forests at high tide (Robertson 1988, Chong *et al.* 1990), while in Florida, there are very few penaeids in *Rhizophora* prop-root habitats (Sheridan 1992).

The importance of mangrove and seagrass habitats to commercial fisheries has been demonstrated throughout the tropics. Despite this, these shallow water habitats are under threat from rapid economic development and growing populations in the coastal zones of all tropical countries. In order to ensure the economic viability of tropical fisheries, there is a pressing need to manage coastal habitats based on reliable scientific information about the use of these habitats by fish and prawns. This chapter describes some of the steps necessary to design a sampling program to survey fish and prawns in shallow coastal habitats. The emphasis is on sampling in mangrove habitats, but methods and approaches for other shallow soft-bottom habitats are also discussed (a more detailed discussion of sampling of fish and prawns in seagrass meadows is given in Chapter 5). The chapter stresses the importance of establishing the exact aims of any study to enable clear choices of sampling design and methodology. Appropriate environmental parameters should be measured during the sampling program, to allow further investigation of any established patterns of fish or prawn distribution (e.g. differences between habitats, or within a particular habitat at different times).

References

Achuthankutty, C.T. and S.R.S. Nair (1980). Penaeid prawn population and fry resources in a mangrove swamp of Goa, India. Symposium Series of the Marine Biological Association of India, **6**: 190-195.

Dakin, W.S. (1938). The habits and life-history of a penaeid prawn (*Penaeus plebejus*). Proceedings of the Zoological Society of London, **A 108**: 163-183.

Boonruang, P. and V. Janekaru (1985). Distribution and abundance of penaeid postlarvae in mangrove areas along the east coast of Phuket Island, Southern Thailand. Research Bulletin of the Phuket Marine Biological Centre No. 36, 29pp.

Branford, J.R. (1981). Sediment preferences and morphometric equations for *Penaeus monodon* and *Penaeus indicus* from creeks of the Red Sea. Estuarine, Coastal and Shelf Science, **13**: 473-476.

Chong, V.C., A. Sasekumar, M.U.C. Leh and R. D'Cruz (1990). The fish and prawn communities of a Malaysian coastal mangrove system, with comparisons to adjacent mudflats and inshore waters. Estuarine, Coastal and Shelf Science, **31**: 703-722.

de Freitas, A.J. (1986). Selection of nursery areas by six southeast African Penaeidae. Estuarine, Coastal and Shelf Science, **23**: 901-908.

Edwards, R.R.C. (1978). Ecology of a coastal lagoon complex in Mexico. Estuarine, Coastal and Shelf Science, **6**: 75-92.

Frusher, S.D. (1983). The ecology of juvenile penaeid prawns, mangrove crab (*Scylla serrata*) and the giant freshwater prawn (*Macrobrachium rosenbergii*) in the Purari Delta. pp.341-353. In: T. Petr (editor), "The Purari - Tropical Environment of a High Rainfall River Basin". Dr W Junk Publishers, The Hague.

Kutkuhn, J.H. (1966). The role of estuaries in the development and perpetuation of commercial shrimp resources. American Fisheries Society Special Publication, **3**: 16-36.

Robertson, A.I. (1988). Abundance, diet and predators of juvenile banana prawns, *Penaeus merguiensis* in a tropical mangrove estuary. Australian Journal of Marine and Freshwater Research, **39**: 467-478.

Robertson, A.I. and N.C. Duke (1987). Mangroves as nursery sites: comparisons of the abundance and species composition of fish and crustaceans in mangroves and other nearshore habitats in tropical Australia. Marine Biology, **96**: 193-205.

Sambasivam, S. (1985). Species composition and distribution of prawn juveniles in Pichavaran mangrove. pp. 481-491. In: L. Bhosale (editor), "The Mangroves". Shivaji University, Kolhapur.

Staples, D.J., D.J. Vance and D.S. Heales (1985). Habitat requirements of juvenile penaeid prawns and their relationship to offshore fisheries. pp. 47-54. In: P.C. Rothlisberg, B.J. Hill and B.J. Staples (editors), "Second Australian National Prawn Seminar". NPS2 Cleveland, Australia.

Sasekumar, A., V.C. Chong, M.U. Leh and R. D'Cruz (1992). Mangroves as habitat for fish and prawns. Hydrobiologia, **247**: 195-207.

Stoner, A.W. (1988). A nursery ground for four tropical *Penaeus* species: Laguna Joyuda, Puerto Rico. Marine Ecology Progress Series, **42**: 133-141.

Sheridan, P.F. (1992). Comparative habitat utilisation by estuarine macrofauna within the mangrove ecosystem of Rookery Bay, Florida. Bulletin of Marine Science, **50**: 21-39.

Coastal Fisheries

6.1 Measurement of Ambient Environmental Parameters

Abstract

All fisheries surveys should include environmental parameters, which will characterise the conditions existing at the site at the time of data collection. The parameters included with the survey methods described in this manual have been selected because they are important to the 'health' of the community and they do not require expensive, sophisticated equipment. The environment parameters that should be measured are: temperature, salinity, turbidity and oxygen concentration. The recommended equipment is easily obtained and will provide standardised measures in all countries.

Logistics

Equipment

❏ Mercury thermometer with an accuracy of ±0.5 degrees Celsius, enclosed in a protective casing - used to measure temperature just beneath the surface of the water.

❏ A water sampler such as a Nansen bottle or a Niskin bottle (Figs. 4.1, 4.2). These samplers are lowered to the required depth on a shot line. A messenger is sent down the line, closing the bottle which then contains water collected from the required depth.

❏ Reversing thermometer (optional) - used to measure temperature at depth with an accuracy of ±0.5 degrees Celsius. (Fig. 4.3).

❏ Refractometer - used to determine salinity (Fig 2.1).

❏ 10ml plastic vials/bottles (tight-sealing) - used to collect water samples for salinity measurements.

❏ A Secchi disc to measure turbidity. The Secchi disc is 30 centimetres in diameter and divided into 4 quarters alternating black and white in colour (Fig. 2.2).

❏ An oxygen meter or hand-held digital pH/millivoltmeter with an oxygen electrode to measure the oxygen concentration.

Maintenance

❏ Rinse all equipment with fresh water after use.

❏ Rinse the glass cell and cover of the refractometer carefully after use (with distilled water if possible) and then carefully blot dry with tissue paper.

❏ Store the refractometer in its protective box/bag when not in use.

General procedure

Temperature
❏ Take the readings before commencing sampling.

❏ Surface temperature is read using a thermometer placed in the water 30 centimetres below the surface.

❏ Collect a sample of water from the bottom using a water sampler such as a Nansen bottle (Fig. 4.1) or a Niskin bottle (Fig. 4.2). Take a temperature reading as soon as the sample is onboard the boat (see Section 4.1 for detail).

❏ If available, collect the bottom temperature using a reversing thermometer (Fig. 4.3). See Section 4.1 for detail.

Salinity
❏ Obtain water samples at the surface using small plastic vials. Salinity and oxygen concentration (see below) are measured for the samples.

❏ Collect water samples from the bottom using a water sampler, such as a Nansen bottle or Niskin bottle (see Section 4.1 for detail). Salinity and oxygen concentration (see below) are measured for the samples.

❏ Put a drop or two of water under the cover of a refractometer (Fig. 2.1). Hold the cover down, and looking through the eyepiece, face the instrument to the light so that the salinity can be read.

❏ A series of salinity measurements should be made when transect areas are in close proximity to freshwater discharge, so that the sphere of influence may be ascertained.

Turbidity
❏ Use the Secchi disc to measure vertical visibility. The disc is attached to a weighted rope which is marked at intervals along its length. Lower the disc until you can no longer see it, then pull it slowly back to the surface until it is just visible. Record the distance to the disc from the marks on the rope (Fig. 2.2).

❏ Make the measurements with the Secchi disc on a clear day, within ±2 hours before or after noon (Fig. 2.2).

Oxygen concentration
❏ Water samples from the surface and the bottom are collected, as described in the salinity section above.

❏ Measure the oxygen concentration of the samples using an oxygen meter or handheld digital pH/millivoltmeter with an oxygen electrode.

Coastal Fisheries

Data recording

❑ A set of environmental parameters are measured for each sample. Record data onto data sheets or into field notebooks.

❑ Additional environmental parameters recorded for each site include:

» Current speed and direction. Current vanes used as submerged droges can measure instantaneous currents in shallow tidal estuaries (Kjerfve and Medeiros 1989). They are inexpensive, reliable instruments which are designed for current measurements in the range 0.1 to 1.6 metres per second. The vanes are best suited for average current measurements in tidal situations, in the absence of wind waves.

» Tide - high, low or mid.

» Tidal phase - spring/neap, and ebb/flood.

» Climate data such as rainfall (mean annual and mean monthly), and monthly temperature (maximum and minimum).

» Index of 'human pressure' (see Table 3.4. and Table 3.5). Note fishing pressure (at least nil/medium/intense).

Data processing

❑ At the end of each day, enter the data into the database using the structure described in Section 6.3.

❑ Information about the sample is entered into the sample table (XXMFSAMP) and a unique sample identifier (SAMPLE_ID) is allocated. The type of data collected in the sample is described by the DATA_TYPE field, which for ambient data is indicated by the letter "A".

❑ Enter the ambient data into the data table (XXMFADAT) using the sample identification allocated in the sample table.

❑ Additional environmental parameters recorded for each site. Climate data are entered into the climate table (XXMFCDAT). The type of impact at a site is described by codes which are entered into the sample table (XXMFSAMP).

❑ Always check and verify data after entry.

❑ Always backup data regularly.

References

Kjerfve, B and C. Medeiros (1989). Current vanes for measuring tidal currents in estuaries. Estuarine, Coastal and Shelf Science, **28**: 87-93.

6.2 Sampling Techniques for Mangrove Fisheries

Abstract

This chapter focuses on the sampling methods required to answer the question, 'Which coastal habitats are important nursery areas for fish and prawn (shrimp)?'. To answer this question, we must collect information on the distribution, abundance (relative) and size structure of target species in **all** coastal habitats present in a study site. The methods presented emphasise habitats in, and adjacent to, mangrove forests.

Background

Mangrove ecosystems are important to the sustainable economic development of coastal fisheries. An understanding of their economic value is essential for the conservation of these important resources. Data obtained by surveying the fisheries potential of mangrove areas are needed to assess the economic value of mangrove ecosystems. The survey may have general resource survey objectives. However, if the project is to target only commercially important species, then significant effort in the planning stages of a project (approximately one month) must be devoted to surveys of artisanal and commercial catches. People working in subsistence and commercial fisheries not only know a great deal about fish/prawn behaviour, they also sample intensively most of the habitats in the coastal zone. The survey can usually be done by analysing subsamples of the catch which is returned to fisheries landing places each day and by questioning those working on the boats about the habitats they sampled.

Before beginning a major study (be it a general survey, or targeting some species), a pilot study should be done to establish the most appropriate sampling design. This study should focus on: **where** to sample; **when** to sample; and **what** to sample with. It is necessary to be aware of changes in the efficiency of gear being used in any sampling program, because gear types may vary in their effectiveness in capturing different taxa in different habitats, and at different periods during the tidal phase and time of day.

Many factors may be responsible for causing variation in fish/prawn catches. Appropriate environmental variables (to the taxa being studied), should be measured at the same times and places in which sampling occurs.

While the gear recommended for use in this manual has been selected to address the question of nursery habitats, the protocols described can be applied to other important questions related to the use of coastal habitats by fish and prawn species.

Coastal Fisheries

Advantages

❑ The advantages of using particular gear types in particular habitats are described in the "pros" section of Tables 6.1 and 6.2.

❑ The gear recommended is cheap and relatively easy to use.

Disadvantages

❑ The disadvantages of using particular gear types in particular habitats are described in the "cons" section of Tables 6.1 and 6.2.

Equipment

❑ Small boat with outboard motor and safety equipment.

❑ Measuring boards (Fig. 5.6) and calipers for fish and prawn.

❑ Scales for weighing fish, prawns and/or crabs.

❑ Data sheets, pencils and slates.

❑ Plastic bags and labels.

❑ 10% buffered formalin.

❑ Gear should be chosen from the following list:

» **Seine nets**: size 10 to 60 metres in length; meshes 5 mm or 20 mm with a 5 mm bag.

» **Otter trawl**: use commercially available gear.

» **Beam trawl**: 2 metres x 0.5 metres or 1 metre x 0.5 metres; 10 mm mesh with 5 mm cod-end.

» **Push nets**: use commercial gear.

» **Gill nets**: 30 to 60 metres in length; approximate mesh sizes 10 mm, 25 mm, 50 mm, or 75 mm.

» **Trap/Fyke/Bag net**: 20 metre wings; 5 mm mesh throughout.

❑ An extensive list of gear types and their attributes are described in Table 6.1 (active gear) and Table 6.2 (passive gear). The tables include descriptions of the habitats that the gear can be used in, and the advantages and disadvantages ("pros" and "cons") of using the gear. Definitions of potentially ambiguous terms used in these tables are included in the glossary.

Site selection

❑ Select sites that are representative of the region being studied.

Species selection

❏ Survey the artisanal and commercial catches to establish the species that are of greatest fisheries importance (catch and value).

❏ It is recommended that a minimum size limit be set for the study of some taxa because of taxonomic problems with small specimens. Penaeid shrimp are often difficult to identify accurately below 5 millimetres carapace length. Therefore, surveys should concentrate on prawn specimens between 5 to 15 millimetres carapace length (see Chapter 5 for taxonomic references).

General Procedure

Initial Survey

❏ This survey should be undertaken for approximately one month before sampling is done.

❏ Interview the local people associated with fishing and review the literature.

❏ Analyse subsamples of the catch, which is returned to fisheries landing places each day, and find out from the people on the boats where the catch was taken.

❏ Select target species based on survey data.

❏ Obtain the following information from fishery agencies.

» Total weight of catch for all species and gears.

» Weight of catch by species group.

» Price per kilo of each species.

Pilot Study

❏ After obtaining information on target species for study (based on fisheries survey data), design a pilot study to investigate the main sources of variation in the abundance of fish/shrimp in the coastal region.

❏ Sample all habitats in the study area. They should be chosen on prior knowledge of the taxon in question, and might also include habitats disturbed by humans.

❏ Sample over a period of 24 hours (diel sampling) to determine the best time of tide, or best time of day, to sample particular species. For studies focusing on shrimp, aim to sample every 3 hours. Fish sampling should be done at least every 6 hours to coincide with the tidal cycle.

❏ Conduct a 24-hour study every week for a month so that the interaction between tidal period and time of day can be examined.

❏ Use several gear types simultaneously in the pilot study. See the list of recommended gear, their dimensions and mesh sizes in the equipment listed above.

Coastal Fisheries

❏ Take at least 3 replicate samples with each gear, in each habitat, and for each sampling period, during the 24-hour study (this may not be feasible for all gear types).

❏ Repeat the pilot study during different seasons, if possible.

Sampling

❏ Measure the environmental variables for each site, and at each time that a sample is taken (see Section 6.1 in this chapter).

❏ Use several gear types simultaneously to sample fish and prawns, because different life history stages of most taxa occur in different habitats of the coastal zone.

❏ The selection of gear will be determined by the target species and habitats. While some passive gear types (see Table 6.1) integrate catches over time, species that have peaks in availability to samplers (e.g. penaeid shrimp), may have to be sampled with active gear types (see Table 6.2) if the focus of the study involves short-term changes in habitat use.

❏ Estimate what proportion of a target species in a habitat, are being collected by the gear i.e. the capture efficiencies, especially, if absolute abundance estimates (number metre^{-2}) are required. See Weinstein and Davis (1980) and Thayer *et. al* (1987).

☞ *It is important to assess the relative efficiency of the different gears used in any study because gear types may vary in their effectiveness in capturing different taxa in different habitats, during different phases of the tide and at different times of the day.*

❏ Along sharp boundaries between habitats, e.g. mangrove/seagrass/reef, use some nets parallel to the boundaries to sample movements of fish/shrimp between habitats. Such studies should be undertaken on a diel and tidal cycle basis.

❏ Write all details about the sample (including location, replicate number, gear type, time and date) onto a waterproof label.

❏ Place samples into plastic bags and preserve in 10% formalin. It is preferable to sort out big fishes from the sample and to store them in 20% formalin.

❏ Label samples by placing completed waterproof labels into the plastic bag with the preservative. If more than one bag is neccessary to hold the sample, make sure labels are completed for every sample bag.

❏ Identify species collected using taxonomic keys.

Data recording

❏ Record a full description of the net used i.e.type, size, mesh size.

❏ Record the weight by species of catch to the nearest gram (wet weight).

❏ Record fish length as standard length (Fig. 5.7).

❑ Measure crabs across the carapace (Fig. 5.8).

❑ Measure prawn lengths as carapace length in millimetres (Fig. 5.9).

Standardisation

❑ Surveys should concentrate on prawn specimens between 5 to 15 millimetres carapace length because of taxonomic problems with smaller specimens.

❑ Recommended texts for identification of species are given at the end of Chapter 5.

Processing data

❑ At the end of each day, enter the data into the database using the structure described at the end of this chapter (section 6.3).

❑ Information about the sample is entered into the sample table (XXMFSAMP) and a unique sample identifier (SAMPLE_ID) is allocated. The type of data collected in the sample is described by the DATA_TYPE field, which for fisheries data is indicated by the letter "F".

❑ When ambient parameters are measured at the site another entry is made into the sample table and a unique sample identifier is allocated. The ambient parameters are denoted in the sample table by the letter "A".

❑ The catch data are entered into the data table (XXMFDATA) using the sample identification allocated in the sample table.

❑ **Always check and verify data after entry.**

❑ Always backup data regularly.

Analysis

❑ Data from pilot studies are used to examine the relationships between catches and other covariates (for example, substrate, turbidity, temperature, salinity, oxygen concentration, and predator and prey abundance). This will indicate appropriate hypotheses for testing, with regard to causal connections between fish/prawn and habitats.

❑ Collections made using particular netting regimes (i.e. the same types of gear for the same duration) can be used to calculate a relative measure of abundance which is given by the biomass of the catch in the collection (catch per unit effort).

❑ Analysis of the species composition of the catch allows calculation of the catch per unit effort for each species.

Coastal Fisheries

Survey of commercial/artisanal catch

❑ Obtain total weight (all species) of catch from fishery agencies for each gear type (**Ai**):

gear 1, weight of total catch = A1

gear 2, weight of total catch = A2,

....

gear i, weight of total catch = Ai

❑ Obtain weight of catch by 'species group' (e.g. for Matang large white shrimp) and by all gear types. Calculate proportion of total (**Bi**):

$$Bi = \frac{weight\ of\ species\ group}{\Sigma\ weight\ of\ catch\ by\ gear\ i} = \frac{weight\ of\ species\ group}{A_i} \}$$

❑ Purchase a sample (at least 100 individuals) from each 'species group' and gear category, and sort to species and weigh. Calculate the proportion of each species by weight (**Ci**). Repeat for each species.

$$Ci = \frac{weight\ of\ species}{\Sigma\ weight\ of\ species\ group}$$

❑ Calculate the proportion of total catch for each species (**Di**).

$$Di = Ai \times Bi \times Ci$$

❑ Obtain the unit value (i.e. price per kilo of that species) information, calculate a value for each species and tabulate.

Species	Gear	Catch	Value ($/kg)	Total Value ($)

❑ Check fisheries statistical procedures by obtaining catch per unit effort data (raw data sheet) from the fisheries agencies for the month that sampling was conducted. Calculate the above catch and values using the information given in the fisheries data.

Comments

❑ Once a clear aim(s) has been established (see Chapter 7), investigators should consider whether the result of the study will provide the required management oriented information, before progressing to field work.

❑ The number of gear types will be determined by the focus of this study (i.e. how many species, what type of species, which habitats).

❏ Checklist for planning a study:

    1. What is the question?

    2. What are target species - fishery survey.

    3. Pilot study.

    4. Decisions on choice of gear, habitats, times.

    5. Decisions on covariates.

    6. Standardised sampling.

References

Thayer, G.W., D.R. Colby and W.F. Hettler (1987). Utilization of the red mangrove prop root habitat by fishes in south Florida. Marine Ecology Progress Series, **35**: 25-38.

Weinstein, M.P. and R.W. Davis (1980). Collection of seine and rotenone samples from tidal creeks, Cape Fear, N.C. Estuaries, **3**: 98-105.

Coastal Fisheries

Table 6.1 Active gear used for sampling in mangove, and adjacent, habitats.

GEAR	DESCRIPTION / USE	UNITS	PROS	CONS
MANGROVE FOREST:				
Scoop net (Fig.6.1)	Net on pole, mesh size 1 to 2mm. Manual scoop of fixed distance	N^o/m^2 g/m^3	Easy to use; used in inaccessible areas	Poor quantification; very selective; only used against banks
Tray net	Small square or round net scooped through the water column. Mesh size 1 to 2mm.	N^o/m^2 g/m^2	As above	As above
MANGROVE CREEK:				
Beam Trawl (research) (Fig. 6.2)	1m wide, mesh 3 to 10mm; 2m wide, mesh 10 to 20mm. Both with chains, rope; can have rollers or water jet. Pull by small boat, 10 to 70 hp. Speed of tow 1m/sec. Depressor in deep water; duration of tow depends on pilot study	N^o/m^2 g/m^2	Covers a range of habitats; integrating gear. Relatively easy to use	Special manufacture, selective for shrimp. Not good for most fish
Small seine net (Fig. 6.3)	<10m long, mesh 2 to 3mm, drop 2m, with pocket. Dragged a set distance along creek, extended across creek or pulled onto beach	N^o/m^2 g/m^2	Quantitative, less selective than other gears. Easy to use	Labour intensive. Many large (>10cm) fish and prawn escape

Table 6.1 (continued). Active gear used for sampling in mangove, and adjacent, habitats.

GEAR	DESCRIPTION / USE	UNITS	PROS	CONS
Push net (Fig. 6.4)	Manual or push by boat. Manual; mesh size 1mm, length 5m. Motorized; mesh size 25mm, length 18m.	N°/m^2 g/m^2	Easy to use; cheap to construct	Catches only small organisms, selective for shrimp only in waters < 1m deep.
Scoop net	As before			
Tray net	As before			
Cast net (Fig. 6.5)	Diameter when spread, 2 to 3m. Commercial, 10mm mesh. Thrown onto water by one person	N°/m^2 g/m^2	Good for confined areas and shallow waters. Easy to use.	Require skills and training; easily snagged; only for small fish, prawn; operators vary in efficiency
Drop net	Cylindrical, solid apron made of aluminium, fibre-glass etc.; top with mesh size 2mm, diameter 1m. Throw or place quickly on substrate, pushed in, and catch removed by pumping, scooping or closing	N°/m^2 g/m^2	Quantitative, useful for small spatial scale studies. Relatively easy to use	Small areas; labour intensisve
Lift net	2m x 2m, flat net with 2mm mesh. Place on substrate before sampling and then lift rapidly to surface. Use with light or bait to attract fish/shrimp	$N^{\circ}/lift$ $N^{\circ}/hour$	Specific, for rare species that must be concentrated. Relatively easy to use.	Non-quantitative
MANGROVE MAINSTREAM:				
Otter trawl (Fig. 6.6)	Trawl with otter boards to spread the mouth of net. Commercial nets 10 to 25mm mesh; research nets 3 to 12mm. Towed behind boats, 30 to 70 hp motors. Speed 1 to 2 m/s. Duration, variable and depends on pilot study. With current or across channel	N°/m^2 g/m^2	Covers a range of habitats; integrative; commercially available. Relatively easy to use.	Selective for species and size; needs experience to operate; mouth opening varies; catchability varies between species.
Purse seine	Mesh size 3mm. Needs boats. Encircle school and drag.	N°/m^2 N°/m^3	Samples pelagics	Selective; difficult to operate. Either use with an attractant of target schools. Biased.
Scoop net	In shallow region of mainstream; otherwise as before			
Cast net	In shallow region of mainstream; otherwise as before			

Table 6.1 (continued). Active gear used for sampling in mangove, and adjacent, habitats.

GEAR	DESCRIPTION / USE	UNITS	PROS	CONS
Beam trawl	As before			
Beach seine (Fig 6.7)	On accreting banks at edge of mainstream; 30 to 100m in length with a pocket; 3 to 25mm mesh. Set in semicircle and pull to shore	N^o/m^2 g/m^2	Quantitative; less selective than most gears. Relatively easy to use.	Labour intensive.
Push net (Fig. 6.8)	In shallow region of mainstream; otherwise as before			
SEAGRASS:				
Otter trawl	As before			May be destructive.
Beam trawl	As before			
Push net	As before			
Scoop net	As before			
Beach seine	As before			May ride up over dense seagrass.
Drop net	As before			
Spear fishing	Clear water, metal spears.	$N^o/hour$	Commercially available; useful in difficult areas; easy to use.	Skill required; selective; difficult to quantify.
MUDFLATS:				
Otter trawl	As before			
Beam trawl	As before			
Push net	As before			
Scoop net	As before			
Beach seine	As before			
Drop net	As before			
BEACHES:				
Beach seine	As before			
SHALLOW INSHORE:				
Otter trawl	As before			
Purse seine	As before			

Coastal Fisheries

Table 6.2 Passive gear used for sampling in mangove, and adjacent, habitats.

GEAR	DESCRIPTION/USE	UNIT	PROS	CONS
MANGROVE FOREST:				
Gill net - fish only (Fig. 6.9)	Cut lines through forest or choose open areas; various mesh sizes; leave for tidal period	N^o/m^2 net/hr g/m^2 net/hr	Easy to use	Relative abundances only
Encircling net (Fig. 6.10)	600m circumference recommended as minimum; mesh 10 to 20mm	N^o/m^2, g/m^2	Absolute values	Expensive; labour intensive; problem with edge effects if not big enough
Fish trap (Fig. 6.11)	Various designs and mesh sizes. Baited and left in water for predetermined period	N^o/trap/hr g/trap/hr	Easy to use	Species selective; small numbers.
Rotenone (fish poison)	Close off area about 100m^2, add poison then remove fish from surface with a scoop net as they come to the surface.	N^o/m^2, g/m^2	Absolute values	Only get fish and not shrimp; kills all fish - social considerations.
MANGROVE CREEK:				
Fyke, bag, trap nets (Fig. 6.12)	Mesh size 1.4cm (fish), 3mm (shrimp); if set on fringe of mangrove forest, wings should surround catchment area	N^o/m^2, g/m^2 or N^o/hr, g/hr	Absolute aereal values, if catchment size is known	Escape of fish from forest floor; only for well-defined catchment area.
Gill net (fish only)	Various width and mesh sizes; set for time determined in a pilot study.	N^o/m^2 net/hr g/m^2 net/hr	Easy to use	Relative abundances only
MANGROVE MAINSTREAM:				
Block net (fish only)	Block off portion of channel and gill net everything (fish to extinction); not <100m long with 5 gill nets.	N^o/m^2, g/m^2	Absolute values	Labour intensive; navigational hazards.
Bag net (Fig. 6.13)	Commercial fishery	catch per unit effort	Samples migrating animals	Relative abundances only
Gill net - fish only (Fig.6.14)	Various depth and mesh sizes; set for time determined in a pilot study	N^o/m^2 net/hr g/m^2 net/hr	Easy to use	Relative abundances only
Longline (Figs. 6.15 and 6.16)	Lines of hooks attached to a long rope line; layed out from boat	No./hook/hrg/ hook/hr	Catches larger fish	Not quantitative, selective.

Table 6.2 (continued). Passive gear used for sampling in mangove, and adjacent, habitats.

GEAR	DESCRIPTION/USE	UNIT	PROS	CONS
SEAGRASS:				
Gill net (Figs. 6.17 and 6.18)	Range of mesh sizes. In deeper waters set one on the surface and one on the bottom; 2hr intervals over 24hrs for tidal cycles	N^o/m^2net/hr g/m^2 net/hr	Easy to use	Relative abundances only.
Encircling net	As above (Mangrove Forest section) but smaller			
Fish corral (Fig. 6.19)	Use where available commercially	N^o/hr, g/hr	Migrating fish and shrimp; permanment structure	Navigational hazard, selective.
Rotenone	As above, Mangrove Forest section			
MUDFLATS:				
Barrier net / stake net (Fig. 6.20)	Set on mudflats; commercial fishery; closes known area.	N^o/m^2 g/m^2	Absolute values; easy to use.	Time consuming; labour intensive.
Gill net	As before			
Bag net	As before			
SHALLOW INSHORE:				
Gill net	As before, Mangrove Forest section			
Bag net	As before, Mangrove Mainstream section			
Fish trap	As before, Mangrove Forest section			
Longlines	As before, Mangrove Mainstream section			
BEACH:				
Gill net	As before, Mangrove Forest section			
Encircling net	As before, Seagrass section			
Fish trap	As before, Mangrove Forest section			

Coastal Fisheries

Table 6.2 (continued). Passive gear used for sampling in mangove, and adjacent, habitats.

GEAR	DESCRIPTION/USE	UNIT	PROS	CONS
EVERYWHERE:				
Longlines	As before, Mangrove Mainstream section			
Trammel nets (Fig. 6.21)	Different design for fish and shrimp	N^o/m^2 net/h g/m^2 net/h	Very effective.	Relative abundance only.
Drift nets	Shallow inshore	N^o/m^2 net/h g/m^2 net/h	Good for pelagics.	Not good in confined spaces eg. channels.

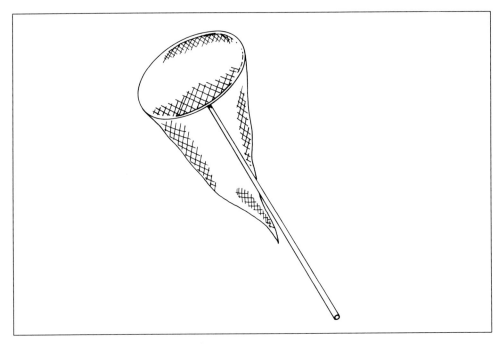

Figure 6.1   Scoop net (active gear)

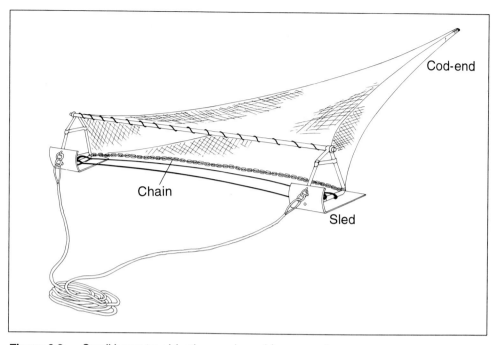

Figure 6.2   Small beam trawl (active gear) used for research.

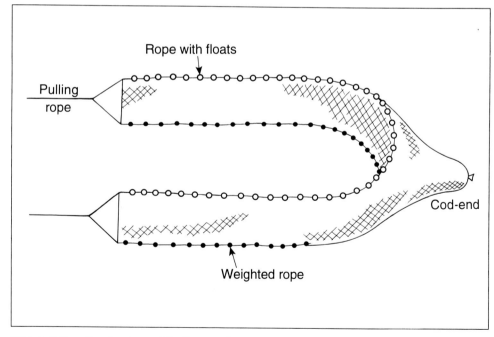

Figure 6.3   Small seine net (active gear).

Coastal Fisheries

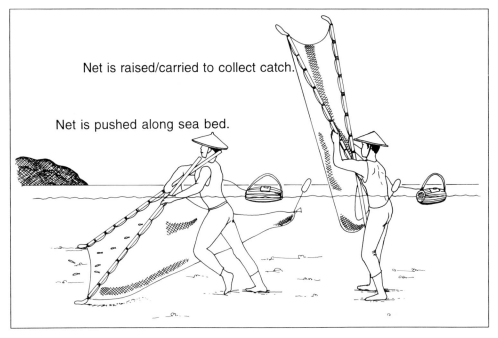

Figure 6.4   Push net (active gear), manual operation.

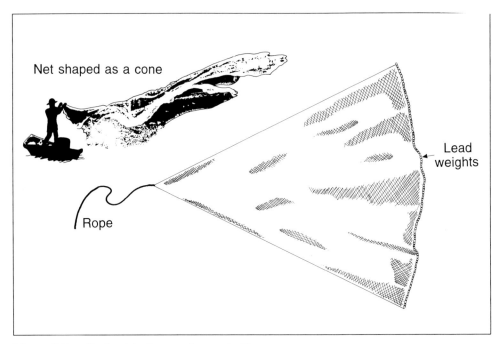

Figure 6.5   Cast net (active gear) operated by one person.

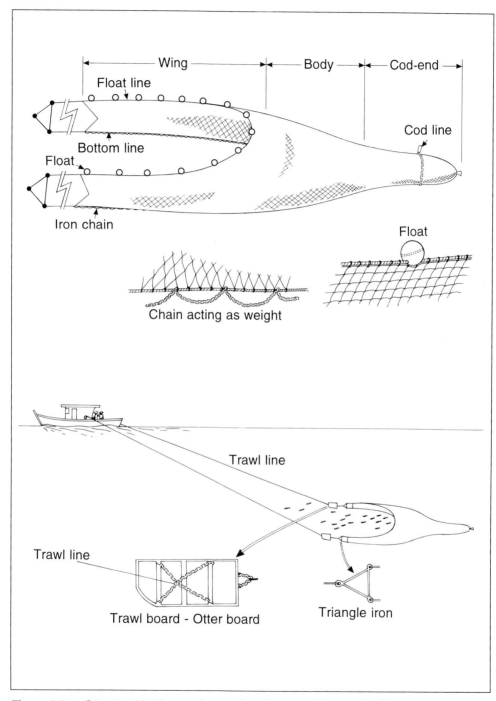

Figure 6.6 Otter trawl (active gear) - otter boards spread the mouth of the net.

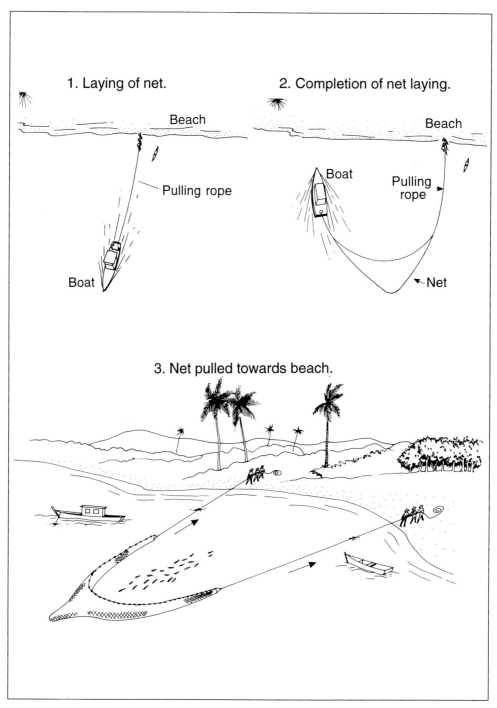

1. Laying of net.

2. Completion of net laying.

3. Net pulled towards beach.

Figure 6.7   Beach seine (active gear) - after setting the net in a semicircle it is pulled to shore.

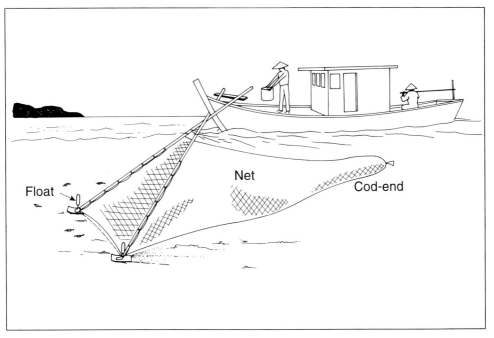

Figure 6.8   Push net (active gear) using a boat.

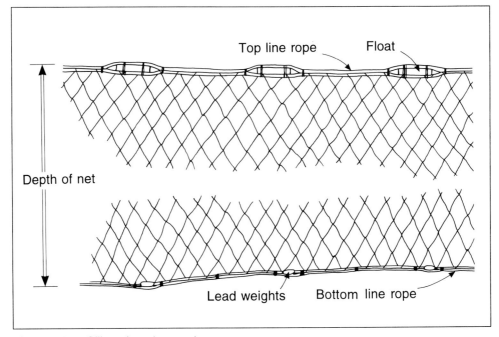

Figure 6.9   Gill net (passive gear).

Coastal Fisheries

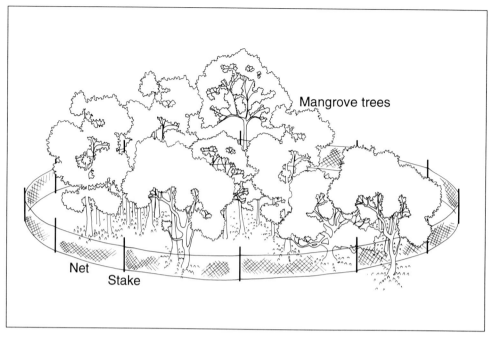

Figure 6.10 Encircling net (passive gear) set in the mangrove forest. The net is set on a high tide and emptied at low tide.

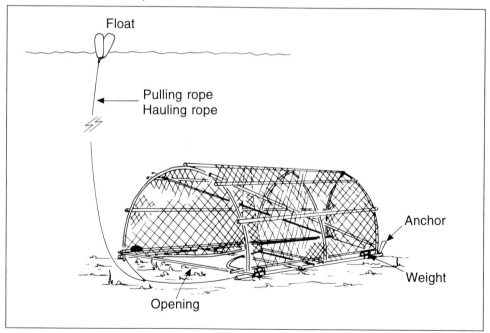

Figure 6.11 Fish trap (passive gear).

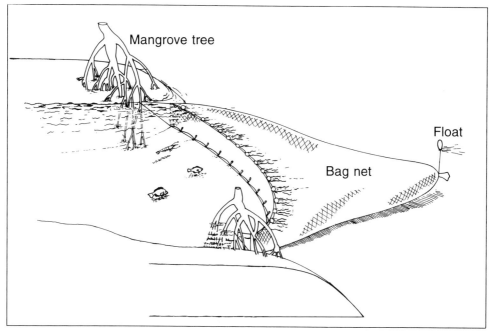

Figure 6.12 Bag net (passive gear). Set in the creek to catch contents of the creek on the ebb tide.

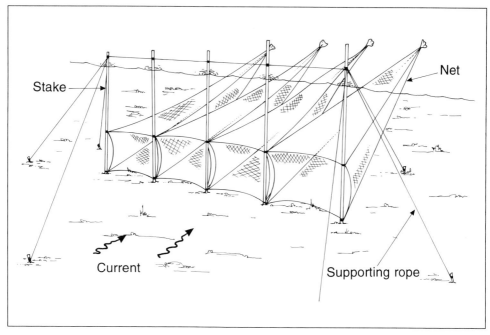

Figure 6.13 Bag net (passive gear). Commercial gear set in the mainstream.

Coastal Fisheries

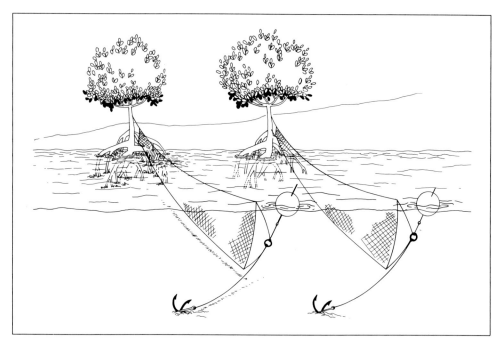

Figure 6.14   Gill net (passive gear) set out from the bank.

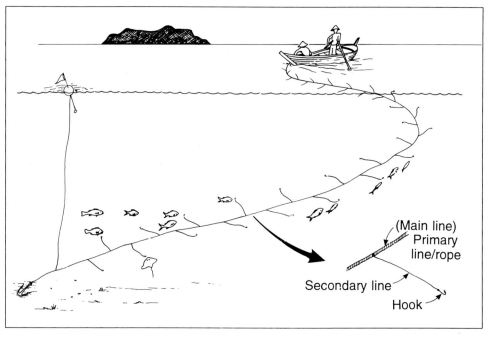

Figure 6.15   Longline (passive gear) set with baits.

Figure 6.16   Longline (passive gear) without baits.

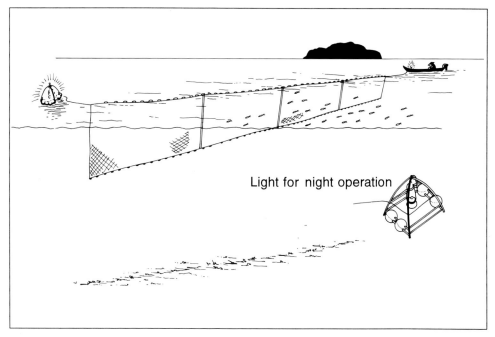

Light for night operation

Figure 6.17   Gill net (passive gear) set on the surface. Nets may be anchored or allowed to drift.

Coastal Fisheries

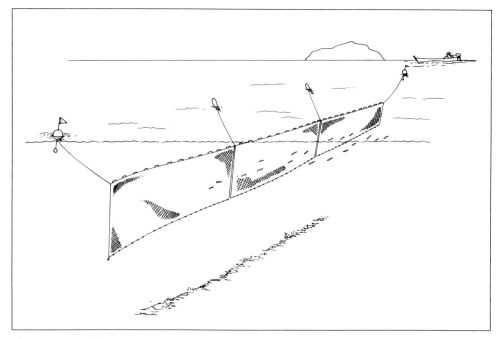

Figure 6.18 Gill net (passive gear) set in midwater. Nets may be anchored or allowed to drift.

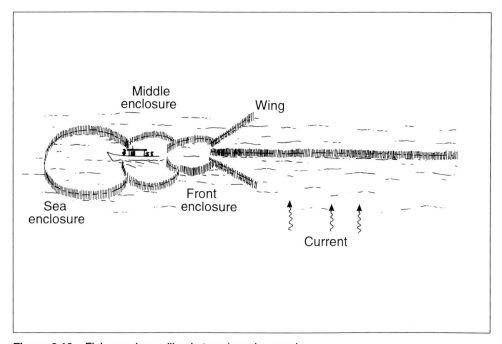

Figure 6.19 Fish corral or pallisade trap (passive gear).

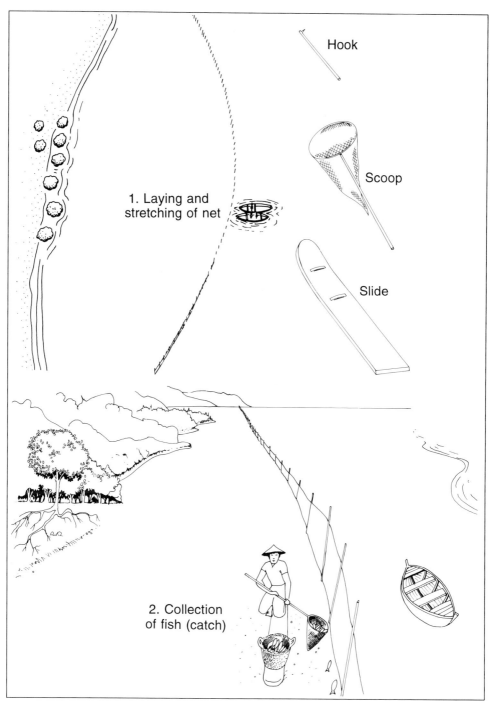

Hook

Scoop

Slide

1. Laying and stretching of net

2. Collection of fish (catch)

Figure 6.20 Barrier net (passive gear). Inset shows the equipment used to collect fish trapped by the net.

Coastal Fisheries

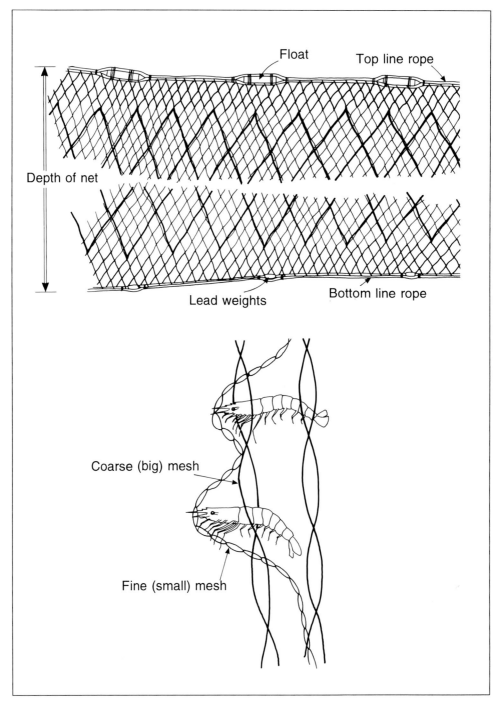

Figure 6.21 Trammel net (passive gear). Detail shows how shrimp are caught in the net.

6.3 Fisheries Database Structure

Sample table
XXMFSAMP

Name	Type	Length/Decimal	Description
SAMPLE_ID	C	9.0	The standard sample identification. This links the sample table to the data files. Format XXGGGNNNN: XX = ISO country code. See codes in Appendix I. GGG = study group code NNNN = running number
LOCATION	C	30.0	Location name e.g. Matang.
SITE	C	30.0	Specific study area (e.g. Sungai Selinsing in Matang, Malaysia).
DATE	D	8.0	Date when data were gathered (using the format MM/DD/YY).
LATITUDE	C	7.0	Latitude of the site in format AABBCCD AA = degrees BB = minutes CC = decimal seconds D = N (north) or S (south)
LONGITUDE	C	8.0	Longitude of the site in format AAABBCCD AAA = degrees BB = minutes CC = decimal seconds D = E (east) or W (west)
HABITAT	C	2.0	Habitat type at site. Codes are listed in DATACODE
EXPOSURE	N	1.0	Exposure of site (see Table 5.1)
DATA_TYPE	C	1.0	Data code denoting the nature of the study: A = ambient data; F = fisheries data. Data file names are listed in the datacode table
TIDE_PHASE	C	1.0	The phase of the tide: S = spring; N = neap.
TIDAL_RNGE	N	4.1	Tidal range at study site, measured in metres.
IMPCT_CODE	C	3.0	Impact code using the format abb, where: a is direct (D), indirect (I) or both direct and indirect (B); and bb is the type of impact (Table 3.4). Listed in datacode table.
IMPCT_ASSE	N	1.0	Assessment of impact on a scale 0 to 5 (Table 3.5), as listed in the datacode table
NET_TYPE	C	2.0	Net type as listed in the datacode table
NET_SIZE	C	10.0	Description or note on net dimensions (e.g. 5x1 metre), measured in metres.
MESH_SIZE	N	4.1	Net mesh size (stretched), measured in millimetres
REMARKS	C	50.0	Relevant observations regarding the site and the data

Coastal Fisheries

Climate data
XXMFCDAT

Name	Type	Length/ Decimal	Description
LOCATION	C	30.0	Location name e.g. Matang
RAINFALL	N	5.1	Mean annual rainfall at the location (if monthly values are not available). Measured in millimetres
MONTH	N	2.0	Month (1 to 12)
RAINFALL_M	N	5.1	Mean monthly rainfall at the location. Measured in millimetres
TEMP_MAX	N	3.1	Mean monthly maximum temperature. Measured in degrees Celsius
TEMP_MIN	N	3.1	Mean monthly minimum temperature. Measured in degrees Celsius

Ambient parameters table
XXMFADAT

Name	Type	Length/ Decimal	Description
SAMPLE_ID	C	9.0	The standard sample identification which will relate the sample records in all the data files to this file (using the format XXGGGNNNN).
REPLICATE	N	1.0	Number of the replicate sample
TEMP_TOP	N	8.0	Water temperature at the top of the water column (30cm below the surface), measured in degrees Celsius.
TEMP_BOT	N	5.2	Water temperature at the bottom of the water column, measured in degrees Celsius.
SALN_TOP	N	5.2	Salinity of water at the top (30 cm below the surface), measured in ppt.
SALN_BOT	N	5.2	Salinity of water at the bottom, measured in ppt.
OXY_TOP	N	5.2	Oxygen concentration of samples taken 30cm below the surface, measured in ppm
OXY_BOT	N	5.2	Oxygen concentration of samples taken from the bottom, measured in ppm
TURBIDITY	N	4.1	Turbidity of the water. Measured in metres using a Secchi disc

Fauna data table
XXMFDATA

Name	Type	Length/ Decimal	Description
SAMPLE_ID	C	9.0	The standard sample identification which will relate the sample records in all the data files to this file (using the format XXGGGNNNN).
REPLICATE	N	2.0	Number of replicates samples for each net type
TIME_START	C	4.0	Time sampling started using the format HHMM (e.g. 1330 = 1:30pm)

TIME_FINISH	C	4.0	Time sampling finished using the format HHMM (e.g. 1345 = 1:45pm)
TIDE	C	1.0	The state of the tide: H = high; M = between high and low; L = low
FIELDCODE	C	40.0	Code assigned to the taxonomic entity by the field researchers. The code must uniquely link to one taxonomic entity. Description of the entity (i.e. binomial name) must be given to the database manager when a new code is created. This information is maintained in ALLTAXON
WEIGHT_GRM	N	7.2	Weight of individual fish/prawn, measured in grams
TOT_LEN	N	6.2	Total length of individual fish/prawn (Fig. 5.7 and 5.9). Measured in centimetres.
STD_LEN	N	6.2	Standard length of individual fish/prawn (Fig. 5.7 and 5.9). Measured in centimetres.
CARP_LEN	N	6.2	Carapace length for crabs (Fig. 5.8). Measured in centimetres.
CARP_WID	N	6.2	Carapace width for crabs (Fig. 5.8). Measured in centimetres.

Taxonomic Table
ALLTAXON

Name	Type	Length/ Decimal	Description
FIELDCODE	C	40.0	Code assigned to the taxonomic entity by the field researchers. The code must link uniquely to one taxonomic entity. Description of the entity (binomial name) must be given to the database manager when a new code is created
TAXCODE	C	10	Unique code used to represent individual taxa. The codes are generated by the system manager. The TAXCODE ensures that the same kind of living things have the same code despite the fact that field researchers may give them different FIELDCODEs
SPECNAME	C	35	Species name (Latin binomial)
GENUSNAME	C	35	Genus name
FAMILYNAME	C	35	Family name
ORDERNAME	C	35	Order name
CLASSNAME	C	35	Class name
PHYLANAME	C	35	Phylum name
AUTHORITY	C	50	Name of authority, an organisation, or a system that was used as a reference to classify samples
REF_CODE	C	20	Reference code for samples which are stored in a reference collection, museum or herbarium. This allows researchers to look at an actual specimen which has been assigned this classification

Coastal Fisheries

Data codes table
DATACODE

Field name	Data Value	Explanation
DATA_TYPE	A	Sample record refers to data in the ambient data file XXMFADAT
	C	Sample record refers to data in the climate data field XXMFCDAT
	F	Sample record refers to data in the fisheries data file XXMFDATA
HABITAT	MF	Mangrove forest
	MC	Mangrove creek
	MM	Mangrove mainstream
	SG	Seagrass
	FL	Mudflat
	BE	Beach
	SI	Shallow inshore
IMPCT_ASSE	0	No impact
	1	Slight impact
	2	Moderate impact
	3	Rather high impact
	4	High impact
	5	Severe impact
IMPCT_CODE	###	Uses the format abb where
		where a = B (both direct and indirect impact)
		= D (direct impact)
		= I (indirect impact)
		where bb = BU (bunding for dyking)
		= CO (infrastructure including jetties, settlements etc - see Taable 3.4)
		= ER (erosion)
		= IC (illegal cutting)
		= MI (mining activities)
		= MU (multiple impact)
		= OT (others)
		= PP (prawn/fish ponds)
		= SC (shell collecting)
		= SS (severe storm)
NET_TYPE	B	Net type, B for beach seine net
	G	Net type, G for gill net
	P	Net type, P for trap net
	S	Net type, S for seine net
	T	Net type, T for trawl net
	BT	Net type, BT for beam trawl net
	PN	Net type, PN for push net
	BN	Net type, BN for bag net
TIDE	H	Tide code, H for sampling conducted during high tide
	L	Tide code, L for sampling conducted during low tide
	M	Tide code, M for sampling conducted between low and high tide
TIDE_PHASE	S	Spring tide
	N	Neap tide

SAMPLING DESIGN AND MONITORING

William G. Oxley
Australian Institute of Marine Science
Townsville, Queensland, Australia

Introduction

This chapter examines the reasons for monitoring coastal resources and discusses the importance of a sound sampling design. It builds on the broadscale monitoring described in previous chapters, and provides information on how projects can examine more specific questions about the systems being studied. The sampling rationale detailed in this chapter will enable confident conclusions and answers to be obtained in response to specific questions.

Many references are cited in the chapter to give an introduction to relevant literature for important topics. Where topics are particularly relevant to the sampling program, the reader should seek more detail from the literature.

Background

Quantitative tropical ecology developed at a time when the dominant belief about community ecology was that of systems in equilibrium, stabilised by competition for limited resources (Cody 1974, Pianka 1975, Schoener 1974). While allowing for the impact of occasional disturbances, communities were assumed to return to a similar structure when the external stresses were relaxed. During the last 20 years, many scientific studies have revealed that the frequency of natural disturbances is much higher than was previously thought, and environmental change can occur more rapidly than the system can return to an equilibrium following a perturbation (Connell 1978, Connell and Keough 1985, Weins 1984). One effect of this frequent change is that results from short-term studies are often misleading. Clearly, if data can be collected over longer periods of time, this natural variability can be identified and quantified. Long-term monitoring programs will also provide information helpful in determining the extent of human-induced (anthropogenic) impacts on tropical ecosystems, by allowing any impact to be measured against background levels of natural variability.

It is now widely accepted that ecosystems are constantly changing (Pickett and White 1985, Kolasa and Pickett 1991) and interest has focused on the processes behind these changes and the outcomes of such change (sessile benthos - Done 1992, in press; Hughes 1990: coral reef fish - Sale 1991). Ecological studies which seek to answer questions about the processes which control change and its implications, have therefore become increasingly important. Hence, a sampling program should seek to address not just the question of "Is there any change?", but rather - "What is the magnitude of change that is occurring; over what time-scales; and what are the processes behind these changes?" Questions such as these highlight the need for robust monitoring programs that provide unambiguous and interpretable results (Ward and Jacoby 1992).

The following steps should be observed in the design and implementation of a monitoring program:

❏ Determine the **objectives** of the project. Decide on **questions** you want to answer.

❏ Decide at which **scales** you wish to work. *This will be determined largely by the objectives of the study.*

❏ **Identify important sources of variation**. Decide which factors are important and of interest. Determine whether these can be realistically measured or controlled. *This will be helped by visiting the area you plan to study/monitor.*

❏ Formulate a design that has **replication** across all levels of interest. Use a **nested sampling design** to achieve this. Consider how the data will be analysed.

❏ Trial your design with a **pilot study**. Use this pilot study to gain valuable information on the feasibility of the design and to see which factors can reliably be taken into account.

❏ Consider how to enter and store the data. Develop a user friendly data collection sheet that will make data entry easy. Develop a protocol for data checking.

❏ **Analyse the pilot study data** and use these data to refine the design. Trial several software packages and determine which will be best suited for your analyses.

❏ Determine **who will undertake the monitoring**. Put in place a regular program of comparisons between observers.

❏ After starting data collection, examine data regularly to ensure quality and to look for anomalies. Do a full analysis every few years.

Objectives of a monitoring program

All monitoring programs should have defined objectives. Green (1979) states that "the interpretation of the results of a sampling exercise is only as clear as the statement of the **objectives** of the study." It is therefore worthwhile to define your objectives rather than measuring everything in the hope that some of the data may provide useful information.

The process of determining goals and objectives is usually iterative: research/sampling programs are generally restricted by funding and logistic constraints; and some hard decisions will have to be made about the intensity and extent of the program. A golden rule is that **it is much better to have a monitoring program that addresses fewer questions over a limited area and allows for repeated sampling over a number of years, rather than an extensive program which seeks to answer many questions over a large area with little replication.**

During the formulation of a monitoring program, it is extremely helpful to discuss the purpose of the study with others. This will help to clarify and refine the aims and objectives. If it is not possible to explain the objectives of the project to another person, then the objectives need refinement.

Scale of a monitoring program

There is increased awareness of the need for robust sampling designs in marine ecology, although the problems of sampling in the patchy marine environment are still not fully appreciated. A sampling design that does not account for a significant proportion of the variation in an ecosystem may provide a very poor picture of what is actually happening (Morrisey *et al.* 1992a, Morrisey 1993, Underwood 1993).

A balance must be found between sampling intensively at the scales of metres and kilometres, or 'spreading the effort' and sampling less intensively over 100's, or perhaps 1000's of kilometres to address spatial pattern. Similar decisions have to be made about the scale of temporal sampling. Only clearly defined questions and objectives will lead to to choice of an appropriate sampling strategy (Andrew and Mapstone 1987, Levin 1992). For example, data collected from one site on a reef will not provide information about the entire reef, and similarly, data from one reef will not provide information about all reefs in the region. The sampling effort needs to be spread throughout the area of interest if generalised statements and conclusions are to be made.

Sampling Design

The importance of replication and distribution of sampling effort

Tropical marine ecosystems are among the most variable environments in the world. Consequently, we need to take more than one sample at any place and any time, to understand the extent of this variability. These additional samples are called **replicates** and the use of replicate samples is known as **replication**. It is most important that there be replication across all levels of a sampling design. The more variable a system is, the more replicates needed to adequately describe the area being studied. These replicates should all be contained within an area that relates to the question you are asking. If questions are at the reef level, the replicates should be randomly distributed throughout the reef, and similarly, if questions are at a regional level then replicates should be spread throughout the region. Failure to replicate will mean that a sampling design is **confounded** and any conclusions drawn will be invalid.

Replication may be considered as insurance. The more replication we have, the greater the chance that the answer will be reliable, and little influenced by an unusually high or low density of whatever is being measured. A paper by Hurlbert (1984) is considered essential reading as it clearly explains the necessity for replication at all levels and the problems that arise without replication. Hurlbert also outlines the potential for false replication and refers to this as **pseudoreplication**. For example, five estimates of coral cover from one transect cannot be considered five replicate transects. Similarly, division of one long transect into five shorter transects does **not** make five replicates.

Identification of important sources of variation

Having decided on the scale of the project and the central questions you wish to ask, it is important to focus on other factors which may affect the data collected. A worthwhile step in this process is to list all the sources of variation that may affect the organisms to be studied. It will be useful at this stage to briefly visit the area(s) you plan to sample and take notes on any biological and physical factors which may affect the abundance of the animals or plants. For example, factors that produce a difference in fish abundances between places include: depth, time of day, state of tide, zone on reef (e.g. slope, flat), type of substratum, status of reef (e.g. marine reserve, tourism, fishing area), sea state, type of reef (e.g. fringing or patch), water temperature, salinity and visibility. Information from past studies on the organisms will provide clues and ideas on which physical and biological factors are most likely to affect abundance.

Having identified potential sources of variation, the next step is to decide which of these sources of variation are the most important and can be incorporated into your sampling design. For example, if a fish species is known to vary in abundance between shallow and deep zones on a reef, and you wish to consider both areas, then it is important to sample within both the shallow and the deep areas. This process is known as **stratification**. In this case you should randomly allocate replicates within each **stratum** (e.g. 3 replicates in the shallow area and 3 replicates in the deep area). However, if you wish to make generalised statements about fish abundances between shallow and deep areas, rather than on one particular reef, then you must sample shallow and deep populations from **at least** two reefs. The more reefs sampled the more generalised your conclusions will be. Alternatively, you can restrict the extent of sampling by considering only those fish that occur within a narrow depth range (e.g. 6 to 10 metres). It is important to realise that restricting the sampling will restrict the generality of your results: conclusions from sampling in shallow water may not apply at other depths. This sort of decision does reduce the amount of sampling that you have to undertake. It also offers logistic advantages - for example, increasing the amount of diving time available.

How to consider several levels of variation at the same time ('nesting')

Large-scale studies of the distribution of fauna and flora involve sampling across regions which are spaced wide apart (e.g. hundreds of kilometres). Within each of these regions, multiple (replicate) samples should be taken. However, there may be no prior knowledge of the scales of patchiness in the variables being measured. This means that patchiness at any of the spatial scales, between that of the sampling units (small-scale) and the regions (large-scale), will not be revealed by the sampling design. Consequently, any comparisons between regions would be suspect because the 'within region' variation is not adequately addressed by the replicate samples.

To solve this problem, sampling may be broken down into smaller components. This is known as a **nested** (or hierarchical) sampling design. Successively smaller spatial (or temporal) scales are nested within the scale above. As an example: a provincial authority wants coral cover compared between two regions of coastal fringing reef (each 20 kilometres long), separated by 500 kilometres of coastline, to help decide which area has a higher conservation potential (Fig. 7.1). In order to compare between the two regions, the coral cover has to be adequately determined **within** each region. Fringing coral reefs are known to be an extremely variable (patchy) and diverse habitat. Only by sampling from a significant portion of the 20 kilometre area of reef will the 'within region' coral cover be reliably determined. Because the whole area cannot be sampled, another approach must be used. A solution to this sampling problem is outlined in Figure 7.1. This design is able to consider a number of spatial scales at one time.

Sampling Design

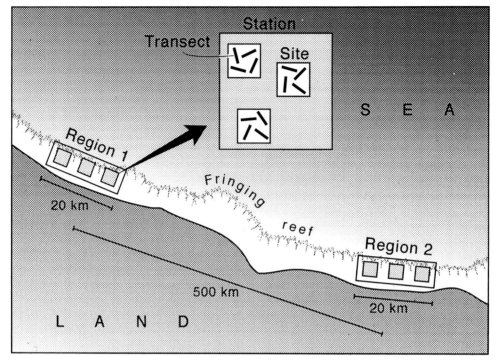

Figure 7.1   An example of a nested (hierarchical) sampling design. Regions are separated by 500 kilometres (provincial scale); stations are allocated within each region; sites are allocated randomly within each station; transects are randomly positioned within each site. This sampling design allows estimation of coral cover between 2 regions and provides estimates of how cover varies across 3 spatial scales. In this example a reliable estimate of coral cover at the provincial scale is not obtained because only 2 regions are sampled. In order to obtain a reliable estimate of coral cover at the provincial scale more regions would have to be sampled.

☞ *The numbers of replicates at each level of the designs shown in this chapter are examples only. The optimum number of stations, sites and transects chosen for any study should be determined by a pilot study and advice from a competent statistician.*

The example in Figure 7.1 may be taken further. Assume the fringing reef has two obvious zones, reef flat and reef slope, and that the provincial authority also asks whether coral cover is higher on the reef slope than the reef flat in the two regions. In order to answer this question, you should sample flats and slopes from all stations. The design shown in Figure 7.1 would need to be modified to show each station divided into reef flats and reef slopes with multiple sites on both the reef flat and the reef slope.

An example of what one station (Station X) would look like with three replicate sites in each zone, is shown in Figure 7.2. This extended sampling design will allow you to make a generalised statement about the relative abundance of coral between the two reef zones in the two regions. In this example, note the doubling in sampling effort required to answer the additional question about coral cover between zones (36 sites cf. 18). It is also important to realise that this design will allow you to make statements comparing coral cover between reef flats and reef slopes in the two regions sampled but you will not be able to make a generalised statement about reef flats versus reef slopes at the provincial scale (in this example approximately 500 km). You would have to sample from a number of reef flats and slopes throughout the province to make such a generalised statement.

Figure 7.2 also shows a variety of conclusions that could be reached when sampling differing numbers of sites within one station. In the scenarios outlined, four different conclusions are possible, depending on choice of sites. Replicate transects could have been sampled from only one site in each zone (flat/slope) and the data

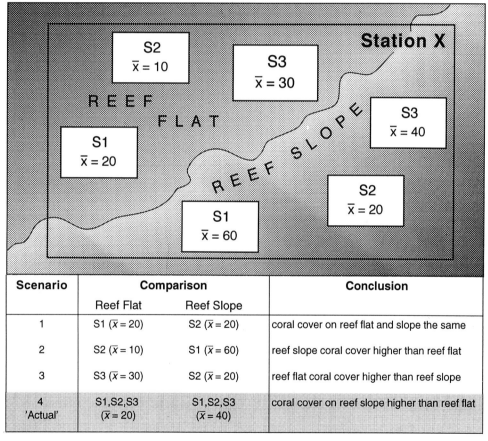

Scenario	Comparison		Conclusion
	Reef Flat	Reef Slope	
1	S1 ($\bar{x} = 20$)	S2 ($\bar{x} = 20$)	coral cover on reef flat and slope the same
2	S2 ($\bar{x} = 10$)	S1 ($\bar{x} = 60$)	reef slope coral cover higher than reef flat
3	S3 ($\bar{x} = 30$)	S2 ($\bar{x} = 20$)	reef flat coral cover higher than reef slope
4 'Actual'	S1,S2,S3 ($\bar{x} = 20$)	S1,S2,S3 ($\bar{x} = 40$)	coral cover on reef slope higher than reef flat

Figure 7.2 A schematic representation of Station X which has two habitats, reef flat and reef slope. There are 3 sites in each habitat. Percentage hard coral cover is estimated using replicate transects within each site. The mean cover for each site is shown. Scenario 4, which shows the mean of all sites in each habitat is the most reliable estimate.

analysed to determine whether a mean difference exists. Imagine you find the difference in scenario three: site three (flat) has higher coral cover than site two (slope). You have demonstrated that the sites have different coral cover, but you have no way of knowing whether this difference is because the sites are located in different zones. If only two sites are sampled, you will never be able to attribute differences to anything other than the fact that they are two different areas and you would be unable to answer the question posed. The large variation in the coral communities on both the reef flat and the reef slope means that one site within a zone will not be representative of that zone. A reliable estimate of coral cover, in the example shown, can only be obtained by sampling from all three sites within each zone (scenario four). This will provide a sound foundation for conclusions,

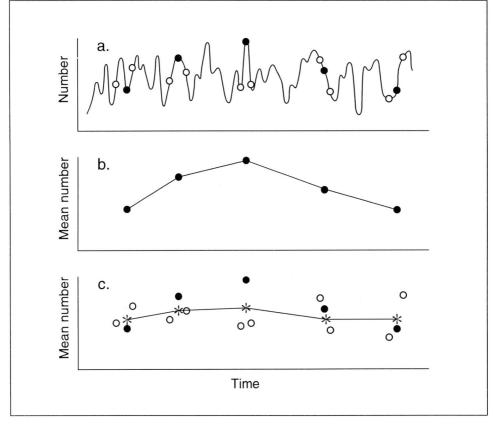

Figure 7.3   The effect of sampling (represented by closed and open dots) on the ability to detect temporal trends in abundance of a population. **a)** A fluctuating population showing no seasonal trend. Samples are taken at one time each season (●),or at 3 times (● and o) each season. b) When only one sample is taken in each season, data show an apparent seasonal trend. c) When 3 replicated times are sampled in each season, the mean abundance (*) shows no seasonal trend (after Underwood 1993).

that differences observed between reef flat and reef slope zones are due to differences between the two zones and not just between two sites. The more sites sampled within each zone the more confidence you will have in your answers and the more reliable your conclusions.

The same principles also apply to sampling over time (temporal scales). For example, if you wish to compare estimates of fish abundance over several sites and between years, it is necessary to have an estimate of how fish abundance varies over shorter time-scales. Otherwise, you will not know whether the differences observed, e.g. between Year 1 and Year 2, are due to a real shift in abundance, or whether the observed difference was due to sampling in two different months (Morrisey *et al.* 1992b, Underwood 1993) (Fig. 7.3).

The next step: a pilot study

All marine ecologists deal with problems of large spatial and temporal variation in populations. Completion of a pilot study will allow some questions to be examined on a small scale and allow consideration and quantification of many potential sources of variation. Pilot studies are a useful way to determine the optimal sampling design for the available resources.

By the end of a pilot study the following questions should be answered:

❏ What is the best balance between the ideals of the project and the reality of logistic constraints?

❏ Is the sampling design suitable?

❏ What is the appropriate sampling unit size?

❏ Can the sampling be repeated reliably? (i.e. Are the sites relocatable? Are the same observers available? etc.)

❏ Will the people chosen to carry out the project collect high quality data that are reliable and able to be analysed?

❏ What level of change is the project likely to be able to detect?

❏ Is the magnitude of change that is detectable consistent with the questions that were originally asked?

The pilot study should also provide important information about many of the logistic considerations. Some areas may be workable only at certain stages of the tide in fair weather conditions, or water clarity may affect the sampling technique. For example, visual fish census techniques along 50 x 5 metre transects are used on offshore coral reefs where underwater visibility is at least 15 metres. A pilot study may reveal that the visibility is often less than 3 metres in the coastal waters of your study area, indicating that this sampling unit is inappropriate.

Sampling Design

A pilot study should trial several sampling unit sizes to indicate the appropriate sample unit size for the organism/s under consideration. More detail about choice of sample unit size is in Sale and Sharp (1983), Downing and Anderson (1985) and an excellent review by Andrew and Mapstone (1987).

Once you have chosen a technique, continue to use it unless you have evidence that you can and should improve it. Too many long-term datasets are made more difficult (or impossible) to interpret because of frequent changes to the methodology. This manual provides detailed information on the techniques and protocols for a suite of methods that are suitable for assessment of tropical coastal systems, which were initially developed for use in the ASEAN region.

Statistical advice should be sought in these early stages, prior to the collection of large amounts of data, **not** six months (or six years) later. Delay in this process may result in a sampling design that is inappropriate and unable to answer the questions that you originally posed.

A **database management system** should be developed during the pilot phase of the project. Chapter 8 details the importance and advantages of a carefully designed database.

Who will undertake the monitoring?

It is important to standardise measurements between observers. The goal and success of any sampling project depends on obtaining high quality data. If person A identifies a species differently to person B, or if one consistently over or under-counts, the data quality is greatly reduced. Standardisation is achieved through regular training of team members and comparisons with known standards (e.g. specimen collection or slide/video reference material) and replicate counts. This will generally involve field trips dedicated to training and laboratory studies.

The most important consideration is to ensure that potential observer biases are not confounded with any other factors, i.e. if one observer surveys reef X and the other reef Y and the data are different, it may not be possible to separate whether the data are different because they are different reefs or because each observer counts differently.

Consider the case where two observers are collecting line intercept transect data, and wish to compare coral abundance on replicate transects, within several sites, between two reefs. In order to avoid confounding sites or reefs with observers, the two observers should sample alternate replicate transects within each site on both reefs. In this way any observer differences will cancel out at the site and reef level.

The analysis of the data collected

There is no point in just collecting data. Analysis of data allows interpretation of the changes that are occurring in the system and may provide a correlation between, for example, increasing nutrients and corresponding decreases in coral cover, **suggesting** effects which can then be tested using manipulative experiments. Information from data analyses allows for a review of the original design and consideration of its ability to answer the questions originally posed. The questions or the design can then be revised, if necessary. This should be an ongoing process, **not** one that begins after the first ten years of data collection.

There are many techniques available to analyse data. These can be broadly categorized into univariate and multivariate techniques. Univariate techniques consider one species or group of organisms at a time, while multivariate techniques examine relationships among multiple groups or species. Detailed discussion of these techniques is beyond the scope of this chapter. Several useful references include: univariate - Green 1993, Snedecor and Cochran 1989, Sokal and Rohlf 1995, Underwood 1981, Winer *et al.* 1991; multivariate - Clifford and Stephenson 1975, James and McCulloch 1990, Clarke 1993, Gray *et al.* 1992, Tabachnick and Fidell 1989.

Once the type of analysis has been decided, an appropriate statistical package needs to be chosen. There are a wide variety of statistical computer packages available. The following factors should be considered when deciding on the appropriate software:

❏ It should be able to do the intended analyses.

❏ Statistics software packages may limit the number of observations that can be included in each analysis.

❏ There should be adequate documentation detailing the way in which the package calculates and performs statistical tests (beware the 'default' setting - it may not be appropriate).

❏ The package should be appropriate for the computer hardware you are using (i.e. does the package require a Pentium with 32 Mb RAM and you have a 386 machine with 8 Mb RAM?).

❏ Consider software already in use at your institution since there will probably be expert users available to help.

The layout of field data sheets should consider the data entry format required by the database software. The data sheet should be designed to make data entry as easy as possible. The database software and the data analysis software should be compatible and allow transfer of data files.

Summary

There are no easy, recipe-type answers to sampling design. Each project requires careful consideration of the questions and objectives of the program, and subsequent design and implementation of a sampling scheme tailored to answer those questions.

Sampling Design

The importance of an appropriate and robust sampling design cannot be over-emphasised. Information on the abundance of organisms is often the only basis for ecological and management decisions. A well-designed sampling program will improve the quality of the data collected, thereby improving the capabilities for sound management decisions.

Time spent planning for a project is critical. Do not rush out and collect data without thorough planning. At least an equal amount of time should be allocated to deciding on the methodology used to collect the data, the way in which the samples will be collected (the sampling design), the format that data will be entered onto a database, and finally, the way that these data will be analysed. These issues should be considered before collecting any data. Time spent on careful planning will always save time, and probably money, in the long run.

References

Andrew, N.L. and B.D. Mapstone (1987). Sampling and the description of spatial pattern in marine ecology. Oceanography and Marine Biology Annual Review, **25**: 39-90.

Clarke, K.R. (1993). Non-Parametric multivariate analyses of changes in community structure. Australian Journal of Ecology, **18**: 117-143.

Clifford, H.T. and W. Stephenson (1975). "An Introduction to Numerical Classification". Academic Press, New York. 229pp.

Cody, M.L. (1974). "Competition and the structure of bird communities". Princetown University Press. 318pp.

Connell, J.H. (1978). Diversity in tropical rainforests and coral reefs. Science, **199**: 1302-1310.

Connell, J.H. and M.J. Keough. (1985). Disturbances and patch dynamics of subtidal marine animals on hard substrata. pp. 125-152. In: S.T.A. Pickett and P.S. White (editors) "The Ecology of Natural Disturbances and Patch Dynamics". Academic Press Inc., London. 472pp.

Done, T.J (1992). Constancy and change in the same Great Barrier Reef coral communities: 1980 - 1990. American Zoologist, **32**: 655-622.

Done, T.J. (in press). Decadal changes in reef building communities: Implications for reef growth and monitoring programs. Proceedings Eighth International Coral Reef Symposium, Panama. June 1996.

Downing, J.A. and M.R. Anderson (1985). Estimating the standing biomass of aquatic macrophytes. Canadian Journal of Fisheries and Aquatic Sciences, **42**: 1860-1869.

Gray, J.S., A.D. McIntyre and J. Stirn (1992). "Manual of Methods in Aquatic Environment Research. Part 11 - Biological assessment of marine pollution with particular reference to benthos". FAO Fisheries Technical Paper No 324 Rome, FAO. 49pp.

Green, R.H. (1979). "Sampling Design and Statistical Methods for Environmental Biologists". Wiley, New York. 257pp.

Green, R.H. (1993). Applications of repeated measures designs in environmental impact and monitoring studies. Australian Journal of Ecology, 18: 81-98.

Hughes, T.P. (1990). Recruitment limitation, mortality, and population regulation in open systems: A case study. Ecology, 71: 12-20.

Hurlbert, S.H. (1984). Pseudoreplication and the design of ecological field experiments. Ecological Monographs, 54: 187-211.

James, F.C. and C.E. McCulloch (1990). Multivariate analyses in ecology and systematics: Panacea or Pandora's box? Annual Review of Ecology and Systematics, 21: 129-166.

Kolasa, J. and S.T.A. Pickett (1991). "Ecological Heterogeneity". Springer Verlag, New York. 332pp.

Levin, S.A. (1992). The problem of pattern and scale in ecology. Ecology, 73: 1943-1967.

Morrisey, D.J., L. Howitt, A.J. Underwood and J.S. Stark (1992a). Spatial variation in soft-sediment benthos. Marine Ecology Progress Series, 81: 197-204.

Morrisey, D.J., A.J. Underwood, L. Howitt and J.S. Stark (1992b). Temporal variation in soft-sediment benthos. Journal of Experimental Marine Biology and Ecology, 164: 233-245.

Morrisey, D.J. (1993). Environmental Impact Assessment- a review of its aims and recent developments. Marine Pollution Bulletin, 26: 540-545.

Pianka, E. (1975). Niche relations of desert lizards. pp. 292-314 In: M.L. Cody and J.M. Diamond (editors) "Ecology and Evolution of Communities". Harvard University Press. 545pp.

Pickett, S.T.A. and P.S. White (1985). Patch dynamics: a synthesis. pp. 371-384. In: S.T.A. Pickett and P.S. White (editors) "The Ecology of Natural Disturbance and Patch Dynamics". Academic Press Inc., Sydney. 472pp.

Sale, P.F. (1991). "The Ecology of Fishes on Coral Reefs". Academic Press Inc., Sydney. 754 pp.

Sale, P.F. and B.J. Sharp. (1983). Correction for bias in visual transect censuses of coral reef fishes. Coral Reefs, 2: 37-42.

Sampling Design

Schoener, T.W. (1974). Resource partitioning in ecological communities. Science, **185**: 27-39.

Snedecor, G.W. and W.G. Cochran (1989). "Statistical Methods". 8th Edition. Iowa State University Press, Ames, Iowa. 503pp.

Sokal, R.R. and F.J. Rohlf (1995). "Biometry. The Principles and Practice of Statistics in Biological Research". 3rd Edition. W.H. Freeman and Co., San Francisco. 850pp.

Tabachnick, B.G. and L.S. Fidell (1989). "Using Multivariate Statistics". 2nd Edition. Harper Collins Publishers, New York. 746pp.

Underwood, A.J (1981). Techniques of analysis of variance in experimental marine biology and ecology. Oceanography and Marine Biology Annual Review, **19**: 513-615.

Underwood, A.J. (1993). The mechanics of spatially replicated sampling programmes to detect environmental impacts in a variable world. Australian Journal of Ecology, **18**: 99-116.

Ward, T.J. and C.A. Jacoby (1992). A strategy for assessment and management of marine ecosystems: baseline and monitoring studies in Jervis Bay, a temperate Australian embayment. Marine Pollution Bulletin, **25**: 163-171.

Weins, J.A. (1984). On understanding a non-equilibrium world: myth and reality in community patterns and processes. In: D.R. Strong, D. Simberloff, L.G. Abele, A.B. Thistle (editors) "Ecological Communities. Conceptual Issues and the Evidence". Princeton University Press, Princeton New Jersey. 613pp.

Winer, B.J., D.R. Brown and K.M. Michels (1991). "Statistical Principles in Experimental Design". 3rd Edition. McGraw-Hill, New York. 1057pp.

Suggested reading

Matson, P., C. Potvin and T. Travis Eds. (1993). Special Feature: Statistical Methods. Ecology **74**(6): 1615-1676.

Sullivan, K.M. and M. Chiappone (1993). Hierarchical methods and sampling design for conservation monitoring of tropical marine hard bottom communities. Aquatic Conservation: Marine and Freshwater Ecosystems, **3**: 169-187.

Rose K.A. and E.P. Smith (1992). Experimental design: the neglected aspect of environmental monitoring. Environmental Management, **16**: 691-700.

Schmitt, R.J. and C.W. Osenberg (1996). "Ecological Impact Assessment: Conceptual Issues and Application in Coastal Marine Habitats". University of California Press, Berkeley, California USA. 401pp.

DATABASE DESIGN AND OPERATION

Scott J. Bainbridge and Valonna J. Baker

Australian Institute of Marine Science
Townsville, Queensland, Australia

Introduction

This chapter describes the importance of using systematic methods for storing and retrieving data through the use of computer-based database management systems. The process of developing databases, as well as methods for handling the data and for ensuring data quality, are discussed.

In order to monitor complex ecosystems, such as coral reefs or mangroves, large amounts of data must be collected over long time periods. A database management system allows large amounts of data to be effectively organised and stored. When data are stored in an accurate reliable fashion, each new piece of information adds to the previous data in a consistent way. This accumulation of data becomes a tool that managers and scientists can use in understanding the complex ecosystems that exist along the coastal shelf.

The development of a database system involves a number of components, these include: the design and development of the database, developing set procedures for using the database, developing procedures for managing the data within the database, and setting standards and procedures for ensuring that the data are accurate and reliable.

The design of the database determines how easy it is to enter, manipulate and extract the data within the database. Procedures for using and managing the data help to set standards for data quality and ensure that the data in the database reflects the collected data. Standards for data quality, in turn, ensure that the data can be used with confidence and that the data retains its value.

A well-designed database, coupled with set procedures for data management and a high degree of confidence in the quality of the data, produces a dataset that can contribute to the understanding and management of environmental systems.

Database Design

Databases versus spreadsheets

Why use a database?

There are many reasons why a database should be an integral part of any monitoring program:

❑ **Data Consistency**: Databases, by enforcing a set structure, help to promote data consistency. The process of designing the database and defining the data within the database produces a set structure to which the data must conform. Datasets with the same structure can be easily joined, thereby allowing data collected at differing times or locations to be merged into one large database.

❑ **Efficiency**: Databases are very good at dealing with large amounts of data. Relational database systems, by reducing duplication of data, are very efficient in the way they store data.

❑ **Data Quality**: A number of features of databases help to ensure data quality. These include: data input screens that help inexperienced users; checking programs that check for errors in the data; and the underlying structure of the database that promotes data consistency.

❑ **Data Analysis**: Databases form a gateway to other packages, such as statistics and graphics software. Most software can use the data, either directly from the database, or from data files extracted from the database. This gives the user access to a range of statistical and presentation routines.

❑ **Data Integration**: The structure of the database forms the definition on which differing datasets can be joined. This allows individual datasets to be integrated into regional or international databases, building 'big picture' databases.

Why not use a spreadsheet ?

The flexibility and easy use of a spreadsheet often tempts people into using a spreadsheet rather than a true database for storing data. While there is no argument that a spreadsheet is initially quicker - you do not have to define tables, structures, and so on - a spreadsheet is inappropriate for large datasets and can lead to major problems in data consistency and integration. Some of the reasons for not using a spreadsheet include:

❑ **Data Consistency**: The very flexibility that makes a spreadsheet so easy to use also makes it difficult to maintain and enforce data consistency. For example, a spreadsheet will allow any mix of data types within the one column; numbers mixed with dates, mixed with character values. A database, by enforcing a set structure, will not allow this, and so gives greater protection against invalid values and allows for automatic checking of data input.

❑ **Data Integration**: The problems with maintaining data consistency in a spreadsheet makes it difficult to integrate datasets that are stored in spreadsheets. Databases encourage set structures, which act as the foundation for integrating different datasets into regional or international databases.

❑ **Speed**: Databases are very good at handling large amounts of data; they include functions such as indices and specialised searching algorithms to quickly find and display data. A spreadsheet has no such capability, making it cumbersome and slow for large amounts of data. Most modern databases will hold as much data as there is disc space, most spreadsheets have set limits on the amount of information they can hold.

❑ **Data Extraction**: The real strength of a database is in its ability to retrieve data based on often complex queries. Databases have in-built query languages and support structures, such as that of a Relational database, that allows complex queries to be performed, thus giving maximum access to the data. A spreadsheet has little to no querying ability.

❑ **Ability to Program**: Databases have powerful in-built programming languages that include complex querying languages. They also include routines for generating input screens and reports and often contain powerful in-built statistical routines. The macro capabilities of spreadsheets are less powerful and are designed for a range of tasks, the least of which is manipulating data.

Large datasets (such as those covering large spatial and temporal scales) require a computer database system. For these data, a database provides a means of storing large amounts of data easily and efficiently, they enable datasets to be integrated, and help to ensure data integrity and consistency.

Database design

Types of databases

A database is made up of data tables which contain *fields* and *records*. Using the example of a ledger book, the columns down a page are equivalent to the *fields* in a database table, the rows across represent *records* in the database. The *fields* contain the attributes of the object or event being recorded, each *record* holds a different set of observations about the object or event.

There are a number of different types of database design of which the *Flat File* and *Relational* models are the most common. The Flat File database is based on the structure of a card index, where each card holds all the information about an object or event. In the Relational model, the information is split across a number of cards which are related to each other by linking fields.

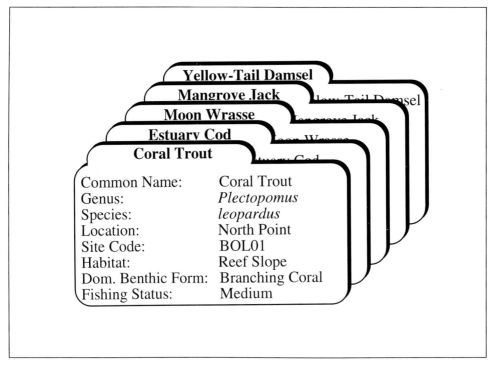

Figure 8.1   A card index showing fish species and habitat details.

As an example, you could have a card index with details of fish species at a number of sites around an area. You may want to record the species and details about the habitat. The card index may include: the common name; species details; the general location; the site number; and the current details of the site, such as: habitat type; dominant benthic form; and the fishing status of the area. The card index may look something like Figure 8.1. The information on the cards can be converted to a table where each item on a card (Common Name, Genus, Species, Location, and so on) becomes a *field* in the table and the information on each card becomes one *record* in the table. This results in a table that follows the structure of a Flat File system (Table 8.1).

The columns titled 'Common Name', 'Genus', 'Species' and so on, are the database *fields*; the rows starting 'Coral Trout', 'Estuary Cod' and so on, are the database *records*. The main problem with this system is that a lot of data are repeated, which makes it difficult to change and to keep up-to-date. Imagine that a storm had gone through the area and site 'BOL01' was now dominated by rubble, not by branching coral. In the Flat File system, and in the card index, each card or record with a site code of 'BOL01' would have to be updated, in this case three records would have to be updated.

Table 8.1 Tabular or Flat File version of the data shown in Fig. 8.1.

Common Name	Genus	Species	Location	Site Code	Habitat	Dominant Benthic Form	Fishing Status
Coral Trout	*Plectopomus*	*leopardus*	North Point	BOL01	Reef Slope	Branching Coral	Medium
Estuary Cod	*Epinephelus*	*tauvina*	South Corner	BOL06	Reef Bommie	Tabulate Coral	Low
Moon Wrasse	*Thalassoma*	*lunare*	North Point	BOL01	Reef Slope	Branching Coral	Medium
Mangrove Jack	*Lutjanus*	*argenti-maculatus*	South Shore	BOL34	Mud Flat	Seagrass	High
Yellow-tailed Damsel	*Pomacentrus*	*flavicauda*	North Point	BOL01	Reef Slope	Branching Coral	Medium

One way around this problem would be to split the data into two tables, one with the species details, the other with the site details. These two tables would have to be linked in some way so that the details from one table can be joined to the other. This type of structure, of many small linked tables, is called a Relational database. Tables 8.2 and 8.3 show the data from the Flat File system (Table 8.1) structured as a Relational database.

Table 8.2 Species Table.

Common Name	Genus	Species	Site Code
Coral Trout	*Plectopomus*	*leopardus*	BOL01
Estuary Cod	*Epinephelus*	*tauvina*	BOL06
Moon Wrasse	*Thalassoma*	*lunare*	BOL01
Mangrove Jack	*Lutjanus*	*argentimaculatus*	BOL34
Yellow-tailed Damsel	*Pomacentrus*	*flavicauda*	BOL01

Table 8.3 Site Table.

Site Code	Location	Habitat	Dom. Benthic Form	Fishing Status
BOL01	North Point	Reef Slope	Branching Coral	Medium
BOL06	South Corner	Reef Bommie	Tabulate Coral	Low
BOL34	South Shore	Mud Flat	Seagrass	High

Database Design

The two tables share one field, that of "site code". This field (SITE CODE) is the linking field and is often called the primary key. The SITE CODE field uniquely identifies each site, and so links the Species Table to the Site Table. As an example, to find the dominant benthic form where coral trout are found, you would first find the record for coral trout in the Species Table. The SITE CODE for coral trout ('BOL01') can then be used in the Site Table to find the dominant benthic form for that site ('Branching Coral').

Note that there is only one record for site 'BOL01' in the Site Table even though there are many fish species that occur at that site and are recorded in the Species Table. This sort of relationship is called a one-to-many relationship. If there were two records in the Site Table with a SITE_CODE of 'BOL01', then there would be no logical way of knowing which one should be matched to the Species Table. The SITE CODE must point from the Species Table to only one record in the Site Table for the join to work. This means the value in the SITE CODE field in the Site Table **must** be unique.

In the above example it may look as if the Relational structure has more data in it and is more complex than the Flat File structure. The difference between the structures is the extra field, SITE CODE, which is in both tables in the Relational structure, but only appears once in the Flat File structure. However, the Relational structure is actually more efficient, since the Site Table contains only three records. If you add up the total number of pieces of information, then for the **same** data, the Flat File structure has 40 entries {8 fields by 5 records} versus 35 for the Relational structure [Species Table (4 fields by 5 records) + Site Table (5 fields by 3 records)]. As the tables grow in size the savings become more apparent.

Some of the benefits of using a Relational structure over the Flat File structure are:

❑ More efficient data storage.
   Example: In the previous example, for a very simple and small table, the Flat File structure required 40 entries, for the **same** data, the Relational model required 35.

❑ Reduces data entry.
   Example: In the Flat File system (Table 8.1) to add a new species, 8 fields have to be added. In the Relational model (Tables 8.2. and 8.3) only 4 fields in the species table would need to be entered if the data were from an existing site. When data are collected from a new site, it is necessary to include a new record in the site table.

❑ Makes updating tables easier.
   Example: To change the fishing status for site 'BOL01' from medium to high in the Flat File structure (Table 8.1) requires updating each record where the SITE CODE is 'BOL01' - for this example this would mean updating three records. In the Relational structure only one record has to be changed in the Site Table no matter how many fish species were recorded for site 'BOL01'.

❏ Easier to alter the database structure.

Example: To add in a new column for the depth of a site in the Flat File structure, every record would have to be altered, in the Relational structure only the records in the Site Table would need to be altered. This makes it much easier to alter, expand, and manage the database.

The only negative in using a Relational database system over that of a Flat File system is that extra computational power is required to join the tables together to extract the data.

An example of a Relational database

The ASEAN-Australia Living Coastal Resources database is a good example of a well-designed database and may serve as an example of a biological database.

The basic design consists of three types of tables: a Sample or Master Table; the Data Tables; and Reference Tables. For each sample or observation that is taken, one record is entered into the Sample Table. The sample is given a unique code, called the SAMPLE_ID, which uniquely identifies that sample in the data tables. The Sample Table holds the details that describe the sample: what type of sample it was; the date; the location; the observer; and so on.

The actual data collected in the sample goes into a Data Table, with entries for every observation or reading. The entries in the Data Table are identified by the SAMPLE_ID, this field is the joining field between the Sample and Data Tables. The relationship between the records in the Sample Table and Data Table can be one-to-one, respectively, or one-to-many, respectively, but not many-to-one or many-to-many. The benefits of using a Relational database are most evident in one-to-many datasets. As an example, in the Manta Tow data, a sample would be the observations for a whole reef, with each 2-minute tow having one record in the Data Table, giving a one-to-many relationship.

If any codes are used in the Data Table (e.g. species, life forms, or other parameters) a full description is given in a Reference Table. The link between the Data and

Database Design

Table 8.4 Example of a Sample Table.

SAMPLE_ID	REEF_NAME	DATA_TYPE	LATITUDE	LONGITUDE	DATE	COLLECTORS	DEPTH_M
AUAIM0001	Myrmidon	T	1923·5S	14654·0W	11/22/91	Alan	9
AUAIM0002	Pandora	T	1901·6S	14621.0W	11/23/91	Mike	8
AUAIM0003	Lodestone	T	1905· 0S	14643.0W	11/23/91	Alan	10

Table 8.5 Example of a Data Table.

Table 8.6 Example of a Reference Table - Benthic Code Table.

SAMPLE_ID	BENTHOS	TRANSITION
AUAIM0002	ACB	45
AUAIM0002	SP	57
AUAIM0002	S	104
AUAIM0002	CB	153

BENTHOS	BENTHIC_DESCRIPTION
ACB	*Acropora* branching
ACT	*Acropora* tabulate
CB	Non-*Acropora* branching
SP	Sponge

Reference Tables will be the code used in the Data Table. This allows codes to be used in data collection and entry while retaining access to the full description.

This can be shown by an example using Line Intercept data:

The Site Table and Data Table are linked by the SAMPLE_ID field; the Data Table and Benthic Code Table are linked by the BENTHOS field.

Using the example above it is possible to show how these links work in joining the tables. Looking at the Data Table and the data with a SAMPLE_ID of 'AUAIM0002':

❏ The details of this sample can be found by looking for a record in the Sample Table with a SAMPLE_ID of 'AUAIM0002'. The Sample Table shows that these data were collected at Pandora Reef on the 11/23/91 by Mike. Note that the SAMPLE_ID is unique in the Sample Table so only one record has a SAMPLE_ID of 'AUAIM0002'.

❏ The details of the Benthos codes used in the Data Table can be found by linking to the Benthic Code Table. The first record in the Data Table has a BENTHOS code of 'ACB'. From the Benthic Code Table this can be translated to '*Acropora* branching'.

An example of a query may also help to show how the links are used: imagine that a user wanted to know the total length of *Acropora* branching coral at Pandora Reef. The query may look like:

```
<SHOW TOTAL LENGTH OF (Acropora branching) FROM (Pandora Reef)>
```

❏ The first step is to find the key items that have to be searched for; in this case it is for a BENTHIC_DESCRIPTION of '*Acropora* branching' and a REEF_NAME of 'Pandora'.

❏ The data required to calculate the total length of '*Acropora* branching' are in the Data Table but the query contains values (a BENTHIC_DESCRIPTION and a REEF_NAME) that are not in the Data Table. The system will need to use the data in the Sample Table and Benthic Code Table to find which records in the Data Table to process.

❏ The links between the tables are then found. These links are the SAMPLE_ID field that links the Data and Sample Tables, and the BENTHOS field that links the Data and Benthic Code Tables.

❏ Using the link between the Data and Sample Tables the database searches the Sample Table until a record where the REEF_NAME is 'Pandora' is found. The system then reads off the SAMPLE_ID for that record ('AUAIM0002').

❏ At the same time the database uses the link between the Data and Benthic Code Tables to find the record with a BENTHIC_DESCRIPTION of 'Acropora branching' and reads off the BENTHOS for that record ('ACB').

❏ The database now searches the Data Table for records where the SAMPLE_ID is 'AUAIM0002' and the BENTHOS is 'ACB' and calculates the result.

Principles of database design

The design of the database will influence both the way in which data can be manipulated within the database and the format in which data may be extracted. It is therefore important to have an understanding of the data to be collected, as well as the format required for output from the database (e.g. for further analysis).

Considerable time should be spent to ensure that the structure will allow the types of data extraction and formatting that will be required. There are no hard and fast rules about database design, except that of common sense and experience. There are a number of good books on database design and it is worth reading some of these (see suggested reading at the end of this chapter).

Some general principles include:

❏ Design the database using the relational model, even if the database software being used is not relational. If the project involves large datasets, or datasets that are to be combined into other datasets, the relational model provides a more robust structure for entering and extracting the data.

❏ Ensure that fields are correctly defined (e.g. numeric, character, etc.). Character fields sort differently to numeric fields, and character data sorts differently in upper case than in lower case. Where character data are being entered, ensure that all the data are in the same case (preferably uppercase), as some systems are case sensitive when querying the database.

❏ Where possible, formulate rules that define correct or acceptable values for each field. For example, water depths cannot be negative, dates have to be of correct format, and so on. These rules later form the basis for computer checking routines.

❏ Ensure that any variable required for data manipulation is included in the database. This may include dates, location, latitude and longitude, site, tidal phase, etc.

Database Design

❏ Ensure that linking or relational fields have a one-to-one or one-to-many relationship in the database (but **never** a many-to-many relationship). This means that a linking field **must** be unique in one of the tables (such as the SAMPLE_ID field in the Sample Table in the previous example).

❏ Ensure that replicates and duplicates are properly identified in the database so that the data can be extracted for each duplicate or summarised for all replicates or duplicates.

Steps in designing a database

The design of a database tends to be an evolutionary process. As the data are collected or the requirements of the data change, so does the database. A good design is one that can be built up to incorporate new data types or changes in the data being collected. Because of this there are no definitive procedures for designing a database. However, the basic steps can be outlined:

❏ The initial step is to try to familiarise yourself with the data being collected. This may involve understanding the sampling procedures, the experimental design (including the definition of samples, replicates and duplicates), the variables being collected, the sampling conditions and the types of analyses required. A trip into the field to observe data collection is very valuable.

❏ The next step is to design data sheets that will be used in the field and the database structure. These tend to be parallel steps, as the way in which data are collected will be reflected both in the field data sheets and in the database structure. Data sheets are used in the field to ensure that all required variables are collected, that the data are collected in a consistent way, to provide permanent record of the raw data, and to ensure that the data are available to other people at a later date. The following steps should be undertaken:

» Write down all the variables that need to be collected for any data type. This may include the date, time, observer and location as well as the main data being collected, such as readings from instruments or the field measurements.

» Arrange the variables to be collected into groups of related data. These often fall into the following groups: site location details; the main variables being collected; and reference datasets, such as species codes.

» Design the data sheets and database tables to reflect the data groupings identified above. Look for redundancy of data input, and check that the relationships between the tables are correct. Where possible use codes, as this makes data entry easier. This may require extra tables to hold the codes and the values they represent, and codes must be carefully checked but it is important to make data entry as efficient as possible, both on the field data sheets, and in the database.

❏ Define the type, length, and rules governing the values for each field. The field type will be usually Numeric, Character or Date. The length defines the maximum value that can be allowed. By defining rules for each field, it becomes possible to write checking programs within the database programing language. This can reduce errors in data input. Describe each data table giving the purpose of the table, and for each field, the field name, type, length and rules. This description becomes a simple Data Dictionary.

❏ Make sure that all the variables that are required for manipulating the data and for later analysis are in the database. If you wish to extract or sort by date, then this has to be in the database.

❏ Check that replicates are correctly identified in the database. Replicates must be identifiable within the database, both as groups of replicates from the one sample and as individual replicates. This allows for analysis of groups of replicates, and for between replicate analysis. Where a sample has both field and laboratory data, ensure that the data from the laboratory analysis can be matched to the corresponding field data for that sample.

❏ Data tables can now be constructed in the software package being used. A number of computer systems and software packages are suitable, as the same general principals apply to most database systems. Some recommendations are the Microsoft Acess™, dBase™ or Paradox™ database software running on IBM™ compatible computers. If the database is being used on more than one computer, ensure that the structure of each copy is identical.

❏ Data entry screens should be constructed so that inexperienced users can enter data into the database system. Where possible, data checking routines should be incorporated into the data entry programs using the data validation rules defined above. **Always check the data after they have been entered**; it is easier to highlight and fix errors at the data entry stage than at a later stage. Data entry programs can only test that values are valid, not that they are correct. While data entry programs are a critical component of data quality procedures, the data still need to be hand checked.

❏ Once data collection has commenced, modifications to the database may be required. This is a normal part of ensuring that the database reflects the data that are being collected. It is important to get feedback from the users, to identify sources of error, and to try and remove these.

❏ The best method of checking how a database is performing is to test it by extracting data as soon as possible. Problems are easier to identify and rectify early, with only a small amount of data in the database. This is also an important part in the feedback process and will help to identify problem areas in the database design, or in the data values.

Database Design

There are no simple rules for producing a working database system as it is very much a trial and error exercise. The time spent in designing the database is important in ensuring that the database will function as required.

Database operation

It is not sufficient to just input the data into a database system - the data must be managed. Data management includes procedures for ensuring that the data are entered correctly, that the database is described, and that the data are backed-up. There is no point spending thousands of dollars collecting data if the data in the database are not correct, or if nobody knows where it is or what it means.

The main principals of data management are:

❑ Allocation of **responsibility** for data management.

❑ Set procedures for **data collection.**

❑ Set procedures for all aspects of **data handling.**

❑ **Data quality** awareness.

❑ **Data description**.

❑ Archiving and storage of the **raw data**.

Responsibility

Defining responsibility for the various components of data management is as important as defining the procedures. By allocating responsibility for the various stages of data handling it is possible to enforce standards of data quality. The person who collects the data may be appointed as the person responsible for entering and checking the data, while the responsibility for backing-up and archiving data may go to people working in a computer centre.

Written procedures should be produced which fully describe all the steps for using and maintaining the database and detail the allocation of responsibility for each procedure. Having set procedures and responsibilities, and making people aware of their responsibilities, makes it easier to set and achieve data quality.

Data collection

The collection of the data is the most important step in any environmental monitoring program. Once the data are recorded on a data sheet it becomes the 'truth' about a particular measured variable at a particular time; all the steps after this are merely transcribing, manipulating, and analysing this 'truth'. Some factors to consider when collecting data are:

❑ Use of standard methods which should be documented.

❏ Training of collectors to ensure uniform recognition of species, life forms, etc.

❏ Use of data sheets to ensure all required variables are recorded in a consistent and uniform manner.

Data handling

The only way to ensure that the data from the field data sheets are transferred accurately to the database is to use set procedures for all stages of data handling.

Procedures should be set up for:

❏ Allocation of Sample identification codes.

❏ Data entry.

❏ Data checking and validation.

❏ Procedures for adding variables and tables.

❏ Backup and archiving of computer data.

❏ Storage (archiving) of the field data sheets and any collected specimens.

Each step of handling the data should be described in a written guide, such as a User Guide or Standard Operational Procedure (SOP). This should detail all the procedures for operating the database, the methods used for data checking, a list of any codes used in the database, how to backup and archive the data, and responsibilities for each step of data handling.

Data quality

Data quality is more than the sum of the data handling procedures. It also includes an idea of the accuracy, precision, repeatability of the field measurements, and an awareness of the quality of the data within the database. Data quality can be maintained by using set, written procedures for data handling, by being aware of sources of error, and by constant checking.

The following steps and procedures help ensure data quality:

❏ It is important to have an understanding of the data and the experimental design.

❏ The use of field data sheets increases the accuracy of the collected data by ensuring that all the data are collected and they are is collected and recorded in a uniform manner. Field data sheets also make it easier to go back to the raw data at a later date, if required.

❏ Data should be entered into the database as soon as possible after collection. This allows any ambiguities to be sorted out while people still remember, and can also allow missing data to be collected or sites to be resurveyed.

Database Design

❏ Data entry programs within the database ensure that the entered data fall within logical limits. Checks that can be built into a program include: range checks (so that values fall within reasonable ranges); so that dates are valid; so that codes are valid; and so that the reference data (such as species codes) exist for all data entered.

❏ Data checking is an essential part of data entry and forms a major component in ensuring data quality. The importance of checking the data once it is in the database cannot be overemphasised. The best method for doing this is as follows:

» Input the data into the database.

» Print out the data.

» Using two people, check the print out against the field data sheets (one person reads from the field data sheet, the other checks the printout).

» Mark the corrections onto the printout.

» Update the database with the corrections.

» File the raw data sheets and the corrected printout.

» Backup all data to a secure archive medium.

❏ When the data have been entered into the database, it is possible to run data checking programs to pick up any logic errors, any missing values or values out of range. For example, with all the data entered, you may be able to search for missing sites or transects. These routines form a third checking phase after the data entry and manual checking procedures.

❏ Data backup and archiving are important parts of maintaining the data. The data should be regularly backed-up onto disk or tape, these should be stored in a secure place away from the original data source. Remember the three rules of computing - backup, backup, and backup! There is no excuse for not having backup copies of the data. As well as backing-up the data, the original field data sheets and any specimens taken as part of the sampling, need to be stored securely.

❏ Finally, there is a need for a person to be responsible for data quality. By allocating responsibility directly to one person, it becomes possible to put in place many of the procedures for data quality, including written procedural manuals. By giving some authority to this person, they can ensure that other personnel fulfil their obligations with regard to data quality.

Data dictionary

Describing the database structure and operation is as important as developing it. A full description allows other users to understand the structure of the database, the experimental design, and the relationships between datasets. Descriptions allow databases to become universal, hence increasing the value of the data.

Some of the components of a full data description include:

❑ A full description of the project including the background, goals, and other details.

❑ A full description of the sampling methods used, or references to other material that detail the sampling methodologies.

❑ A description of the sampling design, including the definition of what constitutes a sample, a replicate or a duplicate, if used.

❑ A description of each table in the database and how each table is related to the other tables in the database.

❑ For each column in each table, a description detailing; the Field Name, Field Type, Field Length, Field Rules, and a short description of what data the field contains.

❑ A short description of any software used, full program listings of any programs used for data entry and validation, and a description of the computer systems used in the project.

Ideally, the data description would integrate into the general written procedures for the use and management of the database. The database description should be made available to other organisations.

Conclusion

A database is an essential component of any project that collects data over large temporal and spatial scales. Not only is a database essential as a way of storing large amounts of data, but by enforcing standards of data consistency, a database makes it easier to maintain and use the data. While tools such as spreadsheets may seem easier in the short-term they are, in fact, far more difficult to use effectively with large or complex datasets.

The design of the database is the most important step in developing database systems. A well-designed system allows for easy, efficient data entry and gives full retrieval access to the data. The design process is iterative - the database should be adapted to the requirements of the data collected and to the needs of the users.

Designing the database is only the first step, the major effort is spent on data management. A number of procedures can be defined to aid in data management.

Database Design

It is important that these procedures become formalised in a written document (Standard Operational Procedure) that details not only the procedures for data handling, but also the person(s) responsible for each procedure.

The final component of a database system is data quality. To utilise the data the users must have confidence in the accuracy and reliability of the data. The process of checking the data at all stages of handling, including the collection and entry of the data, cannot be overemphasised. The worth of a database system is reflected by the accuracy of the data within it.

The use of a computer database is not a trivial exercise, particularly where large or complex datasets are being collected. There is a requirement to develop expertise in database design and to put in place set procedures for all aspects of data handling and quality. The return is that the data are well-managed and in a form that will integrate into other datasets. This will build datasets that span projects, institutions and countries.

Suggested reading

Beynon-Davies, P. (1992) "Relational Database Design." Blackwell Scientific Publications, Oxford, England. ISBN 0 63203 318 5

Flemming, C. and B. Von Halle (1989). "Handbook of Relational Database Design." Addison-Wesley, Raefing Mass. USA. ISBN 0 20111 434 8

Hawryszkiewycz, I. T. and T. Igor (1990) "Relational Database Design: an Introduction." Prentice-Hall, New York, USA. ISBN 0 13771 791 1

Maciaszek, L. (1990) "Database Design and Implementation." Prentice-Hall, New York, USA. ISBN 0 72480 307 6

Pratt, P. and J. Adamski (1987) "Database Systems: Management and Design." Boston Boyd and Fraser Publishing Company. ISBN 0 87835 227 9

Wiederhold, G. (1983). "Database Design." 2nd Edition. McGraw-Hill, New York, USA. ISBN 0 07070 132 6

Wertz, C. (1993) "Relational Database Design: A Practicioner's Guide." Boca Raton, Fla Greenwich, CT CRC Press and Manning Publications. ISBN 0 84937 450 2

COUNTRY CODES

FULL NAME	SHORT NAME	CODES CMC	ISO
EUROPE	**Europe**	AY*	
EUROPEAN ECONOMIC COMMUNITY	E.E.C.	AZ*	
ALBANIA	Albania	BA	AL
ANDORRA	Andorra	BB	AD
AUSTRIA	Austria	BC	AT
BELGIUM	Belgium	BE	BE
BULGARIA	Bulgaria	BF	BG
CZECHOSLOVAKIA	Czechoslovakia	BI	CS
DENMARK	Denmark	BJ	DK
DENMARK - Faeroe Is	Faeroe Is	BK	FO
FINLAND	Finland	BL	FI
FRANCE	France	BM	FR
FRANCE - Corsica	Corsica	BH	FR
GERMAN DEMOCRATIC REPUBLIC	G.D.R.	BO	DD
GERMANY, FEDERAL REPUBLIC OF	F.R.G.	BN	DE
GREECE	Greece	BQ	GR
HUNGARY	Hungary	BR	HU
ICELAND	Iceland	BS	IS
IRELAND	Ireland	BT	IE
ITALY	Italy	BU *	IT
ITALY - Sardinia	Sardinia	CF	IT
ITALY - Sicily	Sicily	CE	IT
LIECHTENSTEIN	Liechtenstein	BV	LI
LUXEMBOURG	Luxembourg	BW	LU

Country Codes

FULL NAME	SHORT NAME	CODES CMC	ISO
MALTA	Malta	BX	MT
MONACO	Monaco	BY	MC
NETHERLANDS	Netherlands	BZ	NL
NORWAY	Norway	CA *	NO
NORWAY - Svalbard and Jan Meyen	Svalbard	CM	SJ
POLAND	Poland	CB	PL
PORTUGAL	Portugal	CC *	PT
ROMANIA	Romania	CD	RO
SAN MARINO	San Marino	CS	SM
SPAIN	Spain	CG *	ES
(Includes Alboran, not covered by Flora Europaea)			
SPAIN - Balearic Islands	Balearic Is.	BD	ES
SWEDEN	Sweden	CH	SE
SWITZERLAND	Switzerland	CI	CH
UNITED KINGDOM	U.K.	CJ *	GB
UNITED KINGDOM - Channel Islands	Channel Is.	BG	GB
UNITED KINGDOM - Alderney C.I.	Alderney	CN	GB
UNITED KINGDOM - Guernsey C.I.	Guernsey	CO	GB
UNITED KINGDOM - Herm C.I.	Herm	CP	GB
UNITED KINGDOM - Jersey C.I.	Jersey	CQ	GB
UNITED KINGDOM - Sark C.I.	Sark	CR	GB
UNITED KINGDOM - Gibraltar	Gibraltar	BP	GI
VATICAN CITY	Vatican City	CL	VA
YUGOSLAVIA	Yugoslavia	CK	YU
NORTH AFRICA and MIDDLE EAST	N.Afr. & Mid.E.	CZ *	
ALGERIA	Algeria	DA	DZ
BAHRAIN	Bahrain	DC	BH
CYPRUS	Cyprus	DE	CY
EGYPT	Egypt	DF	EG
ISRAEL	Israel	DG	IL
JORDAN	Jordan	DH	JO

FULL NAME	SHORT NAME	CODES	
		CMC	ISO
KUWAIT	Kuwait	DJ	KW
LEBANON	Lebanon	DK	LB
LIBYA	Libya	DL	LY
MOROCCO	Morocco	DN	MA
NEUTRAL ZONE (Saudi Arabia - Iraq)	Neutral Zone	DW	NT

(Included for conformity with ISO, however, we believe that this area no longer exists following the settlement of the dispute between the two countries)

OMAN	Oman	DP	OM
PORTUGAL - Azores	Azores	DB	PT
PORTUGAL - Madeira	Madeira	DM	PT
PORTUGAL - Salvage Islands	Salvage Islands	DR	PT
QATAR	Qatar	DQ	QA
SAUDI ARABIA	Saudi Arabia	DS	SA
SPAIN - Canary Islands	Canary Is	DD	ES
SYRIA	Syria	DT	SY
TUNISIA	Tunisia	DU	TN
TURKEY	Turkey	DV	TR
UNITED ARAB EMIRATES	U.A.E.	DX	AE

(Includes Abu Dhabi, Ajman, Dubai, Fujairah, Ras al Khaimah, Sharjah and Umm al Quaiwain)

YEMEN	N. Yemen	DY	YE
YEMEN, DEMOCRATIC	S. Yemen	DZ*	YD
TROPICAL AFRICA	Tropical Africa	OZ *	
ANGOLA	Angola	PA	AO
BURKINA FASO	Burkina Faso	QQ	BF
BURUNDI	Burundi	PC	BI
CAMEROON	Cameroon	PD	CM
CAPE VERDE ISLANDS	Cape Verde Is.	PE	CV
CENTRAL AFRICAN REPUBLIC	C. African Rep.	PF	CF
CHAD	Chad	PG	TD
CONGO	Congo	PH	CG

FULL NAME	SHORT NAME	CODES CMC	ISO
COTE D'IVOIRE	Cote D'ivoire	PS	CI
DJIBOUTI	Djibouti	PJ	DJ
EQUATORIAL GUINEA	Eq. Guinea	PK *	GQ
(includes Rio Muni, Corisco, Elobey Chico and Elobey Grande)			
EQUATORIAL GUINEA - Bioko (Fernando Po)	Bioko	PI	GQ
EQUATORIAL GUINEA - Pagalu	Pagalu *	PO	GQ
ETHIOPIA	Ethiopia	PL	ET
GABON	Gabon	PM	GA
GAMBIA	Gambia	PN	GM
GHANA	Ghana	PP	GH
GUINEA	Guinea	PQ	GN
GUINEA-Bissau	Guinea - Bissau	PR	GW
KENYA	Kenya	PT	KE
LIBERIA	Liberia	PU	LR
MALAWI	Malawi	PV	MW
MALI	Mali	PW	ML
MAURITANIA	Mauritania	PX	MR
MOZAMBIQUE	Mozambique	PY	MZ
NIGER	Niger	PZ	NE
NIGERIA	Nigeria	QA	NG
RWANDA	Rwanda	QC	RW
SAO TOME	Sao Tome	QD *	ST
SAO TOME - Principe	Principe	QB	ST
SENEGAL	Senegal	QE	SN
SIERRA LEONE	Sierra Leone	QF	SL
SOMALIA	Somalia	QG	SO
SUDAN	Sudan	QJ	SD
TANZANIA	Tanzania	QK *	TZ
TANZANIA - Pemba Island	Pemba Is.	QL	TZ
TANZANIA - Zanzibar	Zanzibar	QM	TZ
TOGO	Togo	QN	TG
UGANDA	Uganda	QP	UG

FULL NAME	SHORT NAME	CODES CMC	ISO
WESTERN SAHARA	Western Sahara	QH	EH
ZAIRE	Zaire	QR	ZR
ZAMBIA	Zambia	QS	ZM
ZIMBABWE	Zimbabwe	QT	ZW
SOUTHERN AFRICA	Southern Africa	RM *	
BOTSWANA	Botswana	RB	BW
LESOTHO	Lesotho	RD	LS
NAMIBIA	Namibia	RE	NA
SOUTH AFRICA	South Africa	RL *	ZA
SOUTH AFRICA - Bophuthatswana	Bophuthatswana	RA	ZA
SOUTH AFRICA - Cape Province	Cape Province	RC	ZA
SOUTH AFRICA - Ciskei	Ciskei	RI	ZA
SOUTH AFRICA - Natal	Natal	RF	ZA
SOUTH AFRICA - Orange Free State	Orange Free State	RG	ZA
SOUTH AFRICA - Transkei	Transkei	RJ	ZA
SOUTH AFRICA - Transvaal	Transvaal	RK	ZA
SOUTH AFRICA - Venda	Venda	QZ	ZA
SWAZILAND	Swaziland	RH	SZ
U.S.S.R., CHINA and MONGOLIA	USSR, China etc.	FJ *	
CHINA	China	EZ *	CN
CHINA - Anhui Province	Anhui	FA	CN
CHINA - Fujian Province	Fujian	FB	CN
CHINA - Gansu Province	Gansu	FC	CN
CHINA - Guangdong - Hainan Island	Hainan Island	EX	CN
CHINA - Guangdong Province	Guangdong	FD *	CN
CHINA - Guangxi Autonomous Region	Guangxi	FE	CN
CHINA - Guizhou Province	Guizhou	FF	CN
CHINA - Hebei Province	Hebei	FG	CN
CHINA - Heilongjiang Province	Heilongjiang	FH	CN
CHINA - Henan Province	Henan	FI	CN
CHINA - Hubei Province	Hubei	FK	CN

Country Codes

FULL NAME	SHORT NAME	CMC	ISO
CHINA - Hunan Province	Hunan	FL	CN
CHINA - Jiangsu Province	Jiangsu	FM	CN
CHINA - Jiangxi Province	Jiangxi	FN	CN
CHINA - Jilin Province	Jilin	FO	CN
CHINA - Liaoning Province	Liaoning	FP	CN
CHINA - Nei Monggol Zizhiqu A.R.	Nei Monggol	FQ	CN
CHINA - Ningxia Autonomous Region	Ningxia	FR	CN
CHINA - Qinghai Province	Qinghai	FS	CN
CHINA - Shaanxi Province	Shaanxi	FT	CN
CHINA - Shandong Province	Shandong	FU	CN
CHINA - Shanxi Province	Shanxi	FV	CN
CHINA - Sichuan Province	Sichuan	FW	CN
CHINA - Xinjiang Uygur Zizhiqu A.R.	Xinjiang Uygur	FY	CN
CHINA - Xizang Zizhiqu Autonomous Region	Xizang Zizhiqu	FZ	CN
CHINA - Yunnan Province	Yunnan	FX	CN
CHINA - Zhejiang Province	Zhejiang	GA	CN
MONGOLIA	Mongolia	EY	MN
UNION OF SOVIET SOCIALIST REPUBLICS	U.S.S.R.	EA *	SU
ARCTIC U.S.S.R.	Arctic USSR	ET *	SU
ASIATIC U.S.S.R	Asiatic U.S.S.R.	EC *	SU
EUROPEAN U.S.S.R.	European U.S.S.R.	EB *	SU
U.S.S.R. - Armenia S.S.R.	Armenia	ED	SU
U.S.S.R. - Azerbaydzhan S.S.R.	Azerbaydzhan	EF	SU
U.S.S.R. - Byelorussian S.S.R.	Byelorussian	EG	BY
U.S.S.R. - Estonia S.S.R.	Estonia	EH	SU
U.S.S.R. - Georgia S.S.R.	Georgia (USSR)	EI	SU
U.S.S.R. - Kazakhstan S.S.R.	Kazakhstan	EJ	SU
U.S.S.R. - Kirghizia S.S.R.	Kirghizia	EK	SU
U.S.S.R. - Kurilskye Islands	Kurilskye Is.	EU	SU
U.S.S.R. - Latvia S.S.R.	Latvia	EL	SU
U.S.S.R. - Lithuania S.S.R.	Lithuania	EM	SU
U.S.S.R. - Moldavia S.S.R.	Moldavia	EN	SU

FULL NAME	SHORT NAME	CODES	
		CMC	ISO
U.S.S.R. - R.S.F.S.R.	R.S.F.S.R.	EO	SU
U.S.S.R. - Sakhalin	Sakhalin	EV	SU
U.S.S.R. - Tadzhikistan S.S.R.	Tadzhikistan	EP	SU
U.S.S.R. - Turkmenistan S.S.R.	Turkmenistan	EQ	SU
U.S.S.R. - Ukranian S.S.R.	Ukraine	ER	UA
U.S.S.R. - Uzbekistan S.S.R.	Uzbekistan	ES	SU
MIDDLE ASIA to INDOCHINA and JAPAN	Middle Asia	GK *	
AFGHANISTAN	Afghanistan	GB	AF
BANGLADESH	Bangladesh	GC	BD
BHUTAN	Bhutan	GD	BT
BURMA - Myanmar	Burma	GE	BU
HONG KONG	Hong Kong	GF	HK
INDIA	India	GG	IN
INDIA - Andhra Pradesh State	Andhra Pradesh	IA	IN
INDIA - Arunachal Pradesh Union Terr	Arunachal Prad.	IB	IN
INDIA - Assam State	Assam	IC	IN
INDIA - Bihar State	Bihar	ID	IN
INDIA - Chandigarh Union Territory	Chandigarh	IZ	IN
INDIA - Dadra & Nagar Haveli Union Terr.	Dadra & Nagar H.	GH	IN
INDIA - Delhi Union Territory	Delhi	GI	IN
INDIA - Goa, Daman and Diu Union Terr.	Goa, Daman, Diu	IE	IN
INDIA - Gajarat State	Gajarat	IF	IN
INDIA - Haryana State	Haryana	IG	IN
INDIA - Himachal Pradesh State	Himachal Prad.	IH	IN
INDIA - Jammu and Kashmir State	Jammu & Kashmir	II	IN
INDIA - Karnataka State	Karnataka	IJ	IN
INDIA - Kerala State	Kerala	IK	IN
INDIA - Madhaya Pradesh State	Madhaya Pradesh	IL	IN
INDIA - Maharashtra State	Maharashtra	IM	IN
INDIA - Manipur State	Manipur	IN	IN
INDIA - Meghalaya State	Meghalaya	IO	IN

FULL NAME	SHORT NAME	CMC	ISO
		CODES	
INDIA - Mizoram Union Territory	Mizoram	IP	IN
INDIA - Nagaland State	Nagaland	IQ	IN
INDIA - Orissa State	Orissa	IR	IN
INDIA - Pondicherry Unin Territory	Pondicherry	GJ	IN
INDIA - Punjab State	Punjab	IS	IN
INDIA - Rajasthan State	Rajasthan	IT	IN
INDIA - Sikkim State	Sikkim	IU	SK
INDIA - Tamil Nadu State	Tamil Nadu	IV	IN
INDIA - Tripura State	Tripura	IW	IN
INDIA - Uttar Pradesh State	Uttar Pradesh	IX	IN
INDIA - West Bengal State	West Bengal	IY	IN
INDO-CHINA	Indo-China	EW	
(Comprises Kampuchea, Lao PDR, Thailand and Vietnam)			
IRAN (ISLAMIC REPUBLIC OF)	Iran	GL	IR
IRAQ	Iraq	GM	IQ
JAPAN	Japan	GN *	JP
JAPAN - Hokkaido	Hokkaido	OA	JP
JAPAN - Honshu	Honshu	OB	JP
JAPAN - Kyushu	Kyushu	OE	JP
JAPAN - Shikoku	Shikoku	OC	JP
JAPAN - Ryukyu Islands	Ryukyu Is.	GV	JP
(Includes Okinawa)			
KAMPUCHEA	Kampuchea	GO	KH
KOREA, DEMOCRATIC PEOPLES REPUBLIC OF	N. Korea	GQ	KP
KOREA, REPUBLIC OF	S. Korea	GR	KR
LAO PEOPLE'S DEMOCRATIC REPUBLIC	Laos	GS	LA
MACAO	Macao	GP	MO
NEPAL	Nepal	GT	NP
PAKISTAN	Pakistan	GU	PK
TAIWAN	Taiwan	GX	TW
THAILAND	Thailand	GY	TH
VIETNAM	Vietnam	GZ	VN

FULL NAME	SHORT NAME	CODES CMC ISO	
INDIAN OCEAN ISLANDS	Indian Oean Is.	LX *	
AUSTRALIA - Christmas Island	Christmas Is.	ME	CX
AUSTRALIA - Cocos (Keeling) Islands	Cocos Is.	MF	CC
CHAGOS ARCHIPELAGO (Brit. Indian Oc. Terr.)	Chagos Is.	MD	IO
(Includes Diego Garcia Is.)			
(BRITISH INDIAN OCEAN TERRITORY)			IO
COMORO ISLANDS	Comoro Islands	MX *	ZZ
(Comprises Mayotte and Comoros)			
COMOROS	Comoros	MG	KM
(Comprises Moheli, Grand Comore and Anjouan)			
FRANCE - Mayotte	Mayotte	MV	ZZ
FRANCE - Reunion	Reunion	MM *	RE
FRANCE - Reunion - Tromelin	Tromelin	MS	RE
INDIA - Andaman Islands	Andamans	MB	IN
INDIA - Lakshadweep Union Territory	Lakshadweep	MH	IN
(Includes Laccadive, Minicoy & Amindivi Islands)			
INDIA - Nicobar Islands	Nicobar	ML	IN
MADAGASCAR	Madagascar	MI *	MG
MADAGASCAR - Glorieuses Islands	Glorieuses Is.	MU	MG
MALDIVES	Maldives	MJ	MV
MAURITIUS	Mauritius	MK *	MU
MAURITIUS - Agalega Islands	Agalega Is.	MT	MU
MAURITIUS - Cargados Carajos	Cargados Carajos	MO	MU
MAURITIUS - Rodrigues	Rodrigues	MN	MU
SEYCHELLES	Seychelles	MP *	SC
SEYCHELLES - Coralline Islands	Seychelles: Cor.	MA	SC
(Includes Aldabra, Aldabra group, Amirante group, Alphonse group, Providence/ Farquhar group, Ile Vache de Mer, Denis Is., Coëtivy Is., Platte Is.)			
SEYCHELLES - Granitic Islands	Seychesses: Gra.	MW	SC
(Includes Mahe group, Praslin group, Silhouette group, Frigate group, Recif Is., Mamelle Is., The Brisans)			
SRI LANKA	Sri Lanka	MR	LK

Country Codes

FULL NAME	SHORT NAME	CODES CMC	ISO

YEMEN - SOCOTRA — Socotra — MQ — YD
    (Includes Abd al Kuri)

FULL NAME	SHORT NAME	CMC	ISO
SOUTH EAST ASIA to PAPUA NEW GUINEA	S.E. Asia to PNG	HW *	
BORNEO	Borneo	HH *	ZZ
BRUNEI DARUSSALAM	Brunei	HA	BN
EAST TIMOR	East Timor	HX	TP

(Included for conformity with ISO list, however, we understand that it no longer exists as a country in its own right, but has been subsumed within Indonesia (i.e. INDONESIA - Lesser Sunda Islands)

FULL NAME	SHORT NAME	CMC	ISO
INDONESIA	Indonesia	HB *	ID
INDONESIA - Irian Jaya	Irian Jaya	HK	ID
INDONESIA - Java	Java	HL	ID
INDONESIA - Kalimantan	Kalimantan	HM	ID
INDONESIA - Lesser Sunda Islands	Lesser Sunda Is.	HN	ID
INDONESIA - Moluccas	Moluccas	HP	ID
INDONESIA - Sulawesi	Sulawesi	HT	ID
INDONESIA - Sumatra	Sumatra	HU	ID
MALAYSIA	Malaysia	HC *	MY
MALAYSIA - Peninsular Malaysia	Pen. Malaysia	HQ	MY
MALAYSIA - Sabah	Sabah	HR	MY
MALAYSIA - Sarawak	Sarawak	HS	MY
PAPUA NEW GUINEA	P.N.G.	HD *	PG
PAPUA NEW GUINEA - Bismarck Archipelago	Bismarck Arch.	HG	PG
(Includes Admiralty Islands)			
PAPUA NEW GUINEA - Bougainville	Bougainville	HI	PG
PAPUA NEW GUINEA - D'entrecasteaux Is.	D'entrecasteaux	HJ	PG
PAPUA NEW GUINEA - Louisiade Archipelago	Louisiade Arch.	HO	PG
PAPUA NEW GUINEA - Trobriand Islands	Trobriand Is.	HV	PG
PHILIPPINES	Philippines	HE *	PH
PHILIPPINES - Bohol	Bohol	RN	PH
PHILIPPINES - Cebu	Cebu	RO	PH

FULL NAME	SHORT NAME	CODES	
		CMC	ISO
PHILIPPINES - Leyte	Leyte	RP	PH
PHILIPPINES - Luzon	Luzon	RQ	PH
PHILIPPINES - Masbate	Masbate	RR	PH
PHILIPPINES - Mindanao	Mindanao	RS	PH
PHILIPPINES - Mindoro	Mindoro	RT	PH
PHILIPPINES - Negros	Negros	RU	PH
PHILIPPINES - Palawan	Palawan	RV	PH
PHILIPPINES - Panay	Panay	RW	PH
PHILIPPINES - Samar	Samar	RX	PH
SINGAPORE	Singapore	HF	SG
AUSTRALIA and NEW ZEALAND	Australia, NZ	HZ *	
AUSTRALIA	Australia	JA *	AU
AUSTRALIA - Ashmore & Cartier Islands	Ashmore/Cartier	JO	AU
AUSTRALIA - Capital Territory	A.C.T.	JB	AU
AUSTRALIA - Coral Sea Islands Territory	Coral Sea Is.	JK	AU
AUSTRALIA - New South Wales	N.S.W.	JF *	AU
AUSTRALIA - NSW - Lord Howe Island	Lord Howe Is.	JE	AU
AUSTRALIA - Norfolk Island	Norfolk Is.	JH	NF
AUSTRALIA - Northern Territory	N Territory	JJ	AU
AUSTRALIA - Queensland	Queensland	JL	AU
AUSTRALIA - South Australia	S Australia	JM	AU
AUSTRALIA - Tasmania	Tasmania	JN *	AU
AUSTRALIA - Victoria	Victoria	JP	AU
AUSTRALIA - Western Australia	W. Australia	JQ	AU
NEW ZEALAND	New Zealand	JR *	NZ

(Includes offshore islands, e.g. Three Kings, Hen and Chicken Is., Great Barrier Is., The Snares)

NEW ZEALAND - North Island	N. Island (NZ)	JS	NZ
NEW ZEALAND - South Island	S. Island (NZ)	JT	NZ
NEW ZEALAND - Chatham Islands	Chatham I.s	JU	NZ
NEW ZEALAND - Kermadec Islands	Kermadec Is.	JV	NZ

Country Codes

FULL NAME	SHORT NAME	CODES	
		CMC	ISO

PACIFIC ISLANDS — Pacific Is. — JZ *

Island groups in the Pacific present a problem because geographical and political relationships overlap to a significant extent. Thus, these areas are presented as two lists - political and geographical.

Pacific Islands - political list: In this list CMC areas in the Pacific are listed in terms of their political status. The list is in two parts - areas that are political units (including island groups comprising a discreet political unit), and areas that are geographical units only (i.e. island groups that cross political frontiers). *Political units* that are subdivided by other CMC areas are in italics, with their subsets indented beneath.

Areas that are political units:

FULL NAME	SHORT NAME	CMC	ISO
CHILE - Easter Island	Easter Is.	KL	CL
CHILE - Islas Desventurados	Desventurados	KB	CL
CHILE - Juan Fernandez	Juan Fernandez	KE	CL
COLUMBIA - Isla Del Malpelo	I. Del Malpelo	KF	CO
COOK ISLANDS	Cook Is.	KK	CK
(Includes Raratonga)			
COSTA RICA - Isla Del Coco	I. Del Coco	KA	CR
ECUADOR - Galapagos	Galapagos	KC	EC
FIJI	Fiji	LQ	FJ
(Includes Rotuma, Conway Reef)			
FRANCE - Clipperton Island	Clipperton Is.	KJ	PF
FRANCE - French Polynesia	Fr Polynesia	KM *	PF
FRANCE - French Polynesia - Gambier Is.	Gambier Is.	KN	PF
FRANCE - French Polynesia - Marquesas Is.	Marquesas	KR	PF
FRANCE - French Polynesia - Society Is.	Society Is.	KW	PF
FRANCE - French Polynesia - Tuamotu Is.	Tuamotu Is.	KZ *	PF
FRANCE - French Polynesia - Tubuai Is.	Tubuai I.s	LA	PF
(Includes Austral Is.)			
FRANCE - New Caledonia	New Caledonia	LS	NC
FRANCE - Wallis and Futuna	Wallis & Futuna	LD	WF
HUNTER, MATTHEW AND WALPOLE ISLANDS	Walpole Group	LR	NC
JAPAN - Kazan Retto	Volcano Is.	LO	ZZ
JAPAN - Minama Tori Shima	Marcus Is.	LK	ZZ

FULL NAME	SHORT NAME	CODES	
		CMC	ISO
JAPAN - Ogasawara Shoto	Ogasawara Shoto	LG	JP
KIRIBATI	Kiribati	KQ *	KI
KIRIBATI - Banaba Island (Ocean I)	Banaba Is.	LF	KI
KIRIBATI - Gilbert Islands	Gilbert Islands	KI	KI
KIRIBATI - Line Islands	Kirib: Line Is.	JX	KI
(Includes Fanning I, Washington I, Christmas I)			
KIRIBATI - Phoenix Islands	Phoenix Is.	KU	KI
(Includes islands: Birnie, Gardner, Hull, McKean, Phoenix, Sydney,Canton and Enderbury)			
MEXICO - Guadelupe	Guadelupe	KD	MX
MEXICO - Revilla Gigedo	Revilla Gigedo	KG	MX
NAURU	Nauru	LM	NR
NEW ZEALAND - Tokelau	Tokelau	KX	TK
NIUE	Niue	KT	NU
PITCAIRN	Pitcairn	KV *	PN
PITCAIRN - Ducie Island	Ducie Is.	AA	PN
PITCAIRN - Henderson Island	Henderson Is.	AB	PN
PITCAIRN - Oeno	Oeno	AC	PN
PITCAIRN - Pitcairn Island	Pitcairn Is.	AD	PN
SOLOMON ISLANDS	Solomon Is.	LU	SB
(Includes Santo Cruz Is.)			
TONGA	Tonga	KY	TO
TRUST TERRITORY OF THE PACIFIC ISLANDS	Pac Trust Ter	LN *	ZZ
(This is apparently no longer a political entity, so use of this code should be avoided)			
FEDERATED STATES OF MICRONESIA	Micronesia	LV	FM
(Includes Caroline Is. [except Palau islands group], and includes Yap, Kosrae, Truk and Panape)			
MARSHALL ISLANDS	Marshall Is.	LL	MH
NORTH MARIANA ISLANDS	North Marianas	LY	MP
(Includes Mariana Is. except Guam)			
PALAU	Palau	LW	PW

Country Codes

FULL NAME	SHORT NAME	CODES CMC	ISO
TUVALU	Tuvalu	LB	TV
U.S. - American Samoa	American Samoa	KB	AS
U.S. - Guam	Guam	LI	GU
U.S. - Hawaii	Hawaiian Is.	KO	US
UNITED STATES MINOR OUTLYING ISLANDS	U.S. - Minor Is.	JC	UM
U.S. - Howland Island and Baker Island	Howland & Baker	LC	UM
U.S. - Johnston Island	Johnston Is.	KP	UM
U.S. - Line Islands	Us - Line Is.	JY	UM
(Includes Kingman Reef, Jarvis Island, and Palmyra Atoll			
U.S. - Midway Islands	Midway Is.	KS	UM
U.S. - Wake Island	Wake Island	LP	UM
VANUATU	Vanuatu	LT	BU
(Includes Banks Is. and Torres Is.)			
WESTERN SAMOA	Western Samoa	LE	WS

Areas that are not political units:

FULL NAME	SHORT NAME	CODES CMC	ISO
CAROLINE ISLANDS	Caroline Is.	LH *	PC
HAWAIIAN ISLANDS	Hawaiian Is.	LZ *	ZZ
LINE ISLANDS	Line Islands.	JW *	ZZ
MARIANA ISLANDS	Mariana Is.	LJ *	PC

Pacific Islands - geographical list: In this list CMC areas in the Pacific are listed in terms of their geographical rather than political relationships. It is a crude and arbitrary representation, as any list would have to be, but a map is available which has been annotated to show the CMC areas. Papua New Guinea has been included in the list for reference, because of the proximity of its eastern island groups to the Solomon Islands, although it is not part of the PACIFIC ISLANDS CMC area. However Australia, New Zealand, the Philippines and Japan are not included, although they could also be considered adjacent to some of these islands. Areas are listed in five bands running approximately N-S, following adjacent island chains. Island groups that are subdivided by other CMC areas are underlined, with their subsets indented beneath.

FULL NAME	SHORT NAME	CODES CMC	ISO
PACIFIC ISLANDS	Pacific Is.	JZ *	
First band:			
JAPAN - Ogasawara-Shoto	Ogasawara-Shoto	LG	JP
JAPAN - Kazan Retto	Volcano Is.	LO	ZZ
<u>MARIANA ISLANDS</u>	Mariana Is.	LJ *	ZZ
NORTH MARIANA ISLANDS	North Marianas	LY	MP
(Includes Mariana Is. except Guam)			
U.S. - Guam	Guam	LI	GU
<u>CAROLINE ISLANDS</u>	Caroline Is.	LH *	PC
FEDERATED STATES OF MICRONESIA	MICRONESIA	LV	FM
(Includes Caroline Is. [except Palau Islands group], and includes Yap, Kosrae, Truk and Panape)			
PALAU	Palau	LW	PW
<u>PAPUA NEW GUINEA</u>	P.N.G.	HD *	PG
PAPUA NEW GUINEA - Bismarck Archipelago	Bismarck Arch.	HG	PG
(Includes Admiralty Islands)			
PAPUA NEW GUINEA - Bougainville	Bougainville	HI	PG
PAPUA NEW GUINEA - Trobriand Islands	Trobriand Is.	HV	PG
PAPUA NEW GUINEA - D'entrecasteaux Is.	D'entrecasteaux	HJ	PG
PAPUA NEW GUINEA - Louisiade Archipelago	Louisiade Arch.	HO	PG
SOLOMON ISLANDS	Solomon Is.	LU	SB
(Includes Santo Crux Is.)			
AUSTRALIA - Coral Sea Islands Territory	Coral Sea Is.	JK	AU
FRANCE - New Caledonia	New Caledonia	LS	NC
VANUATU	Vanuatu	LT	VU
(Includes Banks Is. and Torres Is.)			
HUNTER, MATTHEW AND WALPOLE ISLANDS	Walpole Group	LR	NC
AUSTRALIA - NSW - Lord Howe Island	Lord Howe Is.	JE	AU
AUSTRALIA - Norfolk Island	Norfolk Is.	JH	NF

Country Codes

FULL NAME	SHORT NAME	CODES CMC	ISO

Second band:

FULL NAME	SHORT NAME	CMC	ISO
JAPAN - Minama Tori Shima	Marcus sI.	LK	ZZ
U.S. - Wake Island	Wake Island	LP	UM
MARSHALL ISLANDS	Marshall Is.	LL	MH
NAURU	Nauru	LM	NR
KIRIBATI - Banaba Island (Ocean Is.)	Banaba Is.	LF	KI
KIRIBATI - Gilbert Islands	Gilbert Islands	KI	KI
TUVALU	Tuvalu	LB	TV
FRANCE - Wallis And Futuna	Wallis & Futuna	LD	WF
FIJI (Includes Rotuma, Conway Reef)	Fiji	LQ	FJ
TONGA	Tonga	KY	TO
NEW ZEALAND - Kermadec Islands	Kermadec Is.	JV	NZ

Third band:

FULL NAME	SHORT NAME	CMC	ISO
U.S. - Howland Island And Baker Island	Howland & Baker	LC	UM
KIRIBATI - Phoenix Islands (Includes Islands: Birnie, Gardner, Hill, McKean, Phoenix, Sydney, Canton and Enderbury)	Phoenix Is.	KU	KI
NEW ZEALAND - Tokelau	Tokelau	KX	TK
WESTERN SAMOA	Western Samoa	LE	WS
U.S. - American Samoa	American Samoa	KH	AS
NIUE	Niue	KT	NU
COOK ISLANDS (Includes Rarotonga)	Cook Is.	KK	CK

Fourth Band:

FULL NAME	SHORT NAME	CMC	ISO
HAWAIIAN ISLANDS	Hawaiian Is.	LZ *	ZZ
U.S. - Midway Islands	Midway Is.	KS	UM
U.S. - Hawaii	Hawaiian Is.	KO	US
U.S. - Johnston Island	Johnston Is.	KP	UM

FULL NAME	SHORT NAME	CODES	
		CMC	ISO
<u>LINE ISLANDS</u>	Line Is.	JW *	ZZ
U.S. - Line Islands	US - Line Is.	JY	UM
(Includes Kingman Reef, Jarvis Island, and Palmyra Atoll)			
KIRIBATI - Line Islands	Kirib:Line Is.	JX	KI
(Includes Fanning I, Washington I, Christmas I)			
<u>FRANCE - FRENCH POLYNESIA</u>	Fr. Polynesia	KM *	PF
FRANCE - French Polynesia - Marquesas Is.	Marquesas	KR	PF
FRANCE - French Polynesia - <u>Tuamotu Is</u>.	Tuamotu Is.	KZ *	PF
FRANCE - French Polynesia - Gambier Is.	Gambier Is.	KN	PF
FRANCE - French Polynesia - Society Is.	Society Is.	KW	PF
FRANCE - French Polynesia - Tubai Is.	Tubai Is.	LA	PF
(Includes Austral Is.)			
PITCAIRN	Pitcairn	KV	PN
PITCAIRN - Ducie Island	Ducie Is.	AA	PN
PITCAIRN - Henderson Island	Henderson Is.	AB	PN
PITCAIRN - Oeno	Oeno	AC	PN
PITCAIRN - Pitcairn Island	Pitcairn Is.	AD	PN
CHILE - Easter Island	Easter Is.	KL	CL
CHILE - Islas Desventurados	Desventurados	KB	CL
CHILE - Juan Fernandez	Juan Fernandez	KE	CL
Fifth Band (American Coast):			
MEXICO - Guadelupe	Guadelupe	KD	MX
MEXICO - Revilla Gigedo	Revilla Gigedo	KG	MX
FRANCE - Clipperton Island	Clipperton Is.	KJ	PF
COSTA RICA - Isla Del Coco	I. Del Coco	KA	CR
COLOMBIA - Isla Del Malpelo	I. Del Malpelo	KF	CO
ECUADOR - Galapagos	Galapagos	KC	EC

Country Codes

FULL NAME	SHORT NAME	CODES	
		CMC	ISO

These areas cross geographical groupings (see political list):

FULL NAME	SHORT NAME	CMC	ISO
KIRIBATI	Kiribati	KQ *	KI
TRUST TERRITORY OF THE PACIFIC ISLANDS	Pac Trust Ter	LN *	ZZ

(This is apparently no longer a political entity, so this code should be used with caution)

FULL NAME	SHORT NAME	CMC	ISO
UNITED STATES MINOR OUTLYING ISLANDS	U.S. - Minor Is.	JC	UM
NORTH AMERICA	N. America	WT *	
CANADA	Canada	TA *	CA
CANADA - Alberta	Alberta	TB	CA
CANADA - British Columia	Brit. Columbia	TC	CA
CANADA - Manitoba	Manitoba	TD	CA
CANADA - New Brunswick	New Brunswick	TE	CA
CANADA - Newfoundland	Newfoundland	TF	CA
CANADA - Northwest Territories	NW Territories	TG	CA
CANADA - Nova Scotia	Nova Scotia	TH	CA
CANADA - Ontario	Ontario	TJ	CA
CANADA - Prince Edward Island	P.E.I. (Canada)	TK	CA
CANADA - Quebec	Quebec	TL	CA
CANADA - Saskatchewan	Saskatchewan	TM	CA
CANADA - Yukon Territory	Yukon Territory	TN	CA
CANADIAN ARCTIC	Canadian Arctic	TO *	CA
DENMARK - Greenland	Greenland	TP	GL
FRANCE - St Pierre And Miquelton	St Pierre	TR	PM
UNITED STATES OF AMERICA	U.S.	TT *	US
U.S. - Alabama	Alabama	TU	US
U.S. - Alaska	Alaska	UA	US
U.S. - Arizona	Arizona	UB	US
U.S. - Arkansas	Arkansas	UC	US
U.S. - California	California	UD	US
U.S. - Colorado	Colorado	UE	US
U.S. - Connecticut	Connecticut	UF	US

FULL NAME	SHORT NAME	CODES CMC	ISO
U.S. - Delaware	Delaware	UG	US
U.S. - District Of Columbia	DC	UH	US
U.S. - Florida	Florida	UI	US
U.S. - Georgia	Georgia (US)	UJ	US
U.S. - Idaho	Idaho	UK	US
U.S. - Illinois	Illinois	UL	US
U.S. - Indiana	Indiana	UM	US
U.S. - Iowa	Iowa	UN	US
U.S. - Kansas	Kansas	UO	US
U.S. - Kentucky	Kentucky	UP	US
U.S. - Louisiana	Louisiana	UQ	US
U.S. - Maine	Maine	UR	US
U.S. - Maryland	Maryland	UT	US
U.S. - Massachusetts	Massachusetts	UU	US
U.S. - Michigan	Michigan	UV	US
U.S. - Minnesota	Minnesota	UW	US
U.S. - Mississippi	Mississippi	UX	US
U.S. - Missouri	Missouri	UY	US
U.S. - Montana	Montana	UZ	US
U.S. - Nebraska	Nebraska	VA	US
U.S. - Nevada	Nevada	VB	US
U.S. - New Hampshire	New Hampshire	VC	US
U.S. - New Jersey	New Jersey	VD	US
U.S. - New Mexico	New Mexico	VE	US
U.S. - New York	New York	VF	US
U.S. - North Carolina	N Carolina	VG	US
U.S. - North Dakota	N Dakota	VH	US
U.S. - Ohio	Ohio	VI	US
U.S. - Oklahoma	Oklahoma	VJ	US
U.S. - Oregon	Oregon	VK	US
U.S. - Pennsylvania	Pennsylvania	VL	US
U.S. - Rhode Island	Rhode Island	VM	US

FULL NAME	SHORT NAME	CODES CMC	ISO
U.S. - South Carolina	S Carolina	VN	US
U.S. - South Dakota	S Dakota	VO	US
U.S. - Tennessee	Tennessee	VP	US
U.S. - Texas	Texas	VQ	US
U.S. - Utah	Utah	VR	US
U.S. - Vermont	Vermont	VS	US
U.S. - Virginia	Virginia	VT	US
U.S. - Washington	Washington	VU	US
U.S. - West Virginia	W Virginia	VV	US
U.S. - Wisconsin	Wisconsin	VW	US
U.S. - Wyoming	Wyoming	VX	US
CENTRAL AMERICA	Central America	WA *	
BELIZE	Belize	WB	BZ
COSTA RICA	Costa Rica	WC *	CR
EL SALVADOR	El Salvador	WD	SV
GUATEMALA	Guatemala	WE	GT
HONDURAS	Honduras	WF	HN
MEXICO	Mexico	WG *	MX
MEXICO - Aguascalientes	Aguascalientes	YA	MX
MEXICO - Baja California (Norte)	Baja Calif. (N)	WQ	MX
MEXICO - Baja California Sur	Baja Calif. Sur	WR	MX
MEXICO - Baja California Peninsula	Baja California	YB *	MX
(This is a region, not a state)			
MEXICO - Campeche	Campeche	YC	MX
MEXICO - Chiapas	Chiapas	YD	MX
MEXICO - Chihuahua	Chihuahua	YE	MX
MEXICO - Coahuila	Coahuila	YF	MX
MEXICO - Colima	Colima	YI	MX
MEXICO - Durango	Durango	YG	MX
MEXICO - Guanajuato	Guanajuato	YH	MX
MEXICO - Guerrero	Guerrero	YJ	MX

FULL NAME	SHORT NAME	CODES	
		CMC	ISO
MEXICO - Hidalgo	Hidalgo	YK	MX
MEXICO - Jalisco	Jalisco	YL	MX
MEXICO - Mexico D.F.	Mexico D.F.	WS	MX
MEXICO - Mexico State	Mexico State	YM	MX
MEXICO - Michoacan	Michoacan	YN	MX
MEXICO - Morelos	Morelos	YO	MX
MEXICO - Nayarit	Nayarit	YP	MX
MEXICO - Nuevo Leon	Nuevo Leon	YQ	MX
MEXICO - Oaxaca	Oaxaca	YR	MX
MEXICO - Puebla	Puebla	YS	MX
MEXICO - Queretaro	Queretaro	YT	MX
MEXICO - Quintana Roo	Quintana Roo	YU	MX
MEXICO - San Luis Potosi	San Luis Potosi	YV	MX
MEXICO - Sinaloa	Sinaloa	YW	MX
MEXICO - Sonora	Sonora	YX	MX
MEXICO - Tabasco	Tabasco	YY	MX
MEXICO - Tamaulipas	Tamaulipas	YZ	MX
MEXICO - Tlaxcala	Tlaxcala	WM	MX
MEXICO - Veracruz	Veracruz	WN	MX
MEXICO - Yucatan	Yucatan	WO	MX
MEXICO - Zacatecas	Zacatecas	WP	MX
NICARAGUA	Nicaragua	WH	NI
PANAMA	Panama	WK	PA
ISLANDS OF THE CARIBBEAN	Caribbean Is.	RZ *	
ANGUILLA	Anguilla	SO	AI
ANTIGUA AND BARBUDA	Antigua/Barbuda	SA	AG
(Includes Redonda)			
ARUBA	Aruba	RY	AW

FULL NAME	SHORT NAME	CODES	
		CMC	ISO
BAHAMAS	Bahamas	SB	BS
(Grand Bahama, Gt Abaco, Eleuthera Is., New Providence, Andros Is., Gt Exuma, Cat Is., San Salvador, Rum Cay, Long Is., Crooked Is., Acklins Is., Mayaguana Is., Gt Inagua, Little Inagua)			
BARBADOS	Barbados	SC	BB
BERMUDA	Bermuda	SD	BM
BRITISH VIRGIN ISLANDS	Brit Virgin Is.	WX	VG
CAYMAN ISLANDS	Cayman Is.	SE	KY
COLOMBIA - COLOMBIAN ISLANDS	Colombian Is.	SF	CO
(Including I. de Providencia and I. de San Andres)			
CUBA	Cuba	SG	CU
(Including Isla de Pinos)			
DOMINICA	Dominica	SH	DM
DOMINCAN REPUBLIC	Dominican Rep.	SI	DO
FRANCE - Guadeloupe	Guadeloupe	SL	GP
(Including Marie Galante, GrandeTerre, Basse-Terres, Iles des Saintes, Iles de la Petite-Terre, La Desirade)			
FRANCE - Martinique	Martinique	SQ	MQ
GRENADA	Grenada	SJ	GD
HAITI	Haiti	SM	HT
HISPANIOLA	Hispaniola	SN *	ZZ
JAMAICA	Jamaica	SP	JM
(Including Morant Cays and Pedro Cays)			
MONTSERRAT	Montserrat	SR	MS
NAVASSA ISLAND	Navassa Is.	SS	ZZ
NETHERLANDS ANTILLES	Neth. Antilles	ST *	AN
(Aruba, Bonaire, Curacao)			
NETHERLANDS LEEWARD ISLANDS	Neth. Leeward Is.	SU	AN
(Saba And St Eustatius)			
PUERTO RICO	Puerto Rico	SV	PR
(Includes Isla Mona, Vieques, Culebra)			
ST CHRISTOPHER - Nevis	St Kitts - Nevis	SW	KN
ST LUCIA	St Lucia	SX	LC

FULL NAME	SHORT NAME	CODES CMC	ISO
ST MARTIN AND ST BARTHELEMY	St Mart & St Bt	SY	GP
ST VINCENT	St Vincent	SZ	VC
THE GRENADINES	Grenadines	SK	VC
(Bequia, Mustique, Canouan, Union, Carriacou, Ronde)			
TRINIDAD AND TOBAGO	Trinidad/Tobago	WV	TT
TURKS AND CAICOS ISLANDS	Turks & Caicos	WW	TC
(North-, South-, West- and East-Caicos, Middle Caicos, Providenciales, Ambergris Cays, Big Sand Cay, Grand Turk, Salt Cay, Seal Cay)			
VENEZUELA - Venezuelan Islands	Venezuelan Is.	WZ	VE
(Los Monjes, Las Ave, Los Roques, La Orchila, La Tortuga, La Blanquilla, Los Hermanes, La Sola, Los Frailes, Margarita, Coche, Cutagua, Los Testigos, Patos, Isla de Aves (by Dominica))			
VIRGIN ISLANDS OF THE UNITED STATES	Virgin Is. (U.S.)	WY	VI
(Includes St Croiz)			
SOUTH AMERICA	South America	XA *	
ARGENTINA	Argentina	XB	AR
BOLIVIA	Bolivia	XC	BO
BRAZIL	Brazil	XD *	BR
BRAZIL - Acre State	Acre	XQ	BR
BRAZIL - Alagoas State	Alagoas State	XR	BR
BRAZIL - Amapa Federal Territory	Amapa	XS	BR
BRAZIL - Amazonas State	Amazonas	XT	BR
BRAZIL - Bahia State	Bahia	XU	BR
BRAZIL - Ceara State	Ceara	XV	BR
BRAZIL - Distrito Federal	Distrito Fed.	XW	BR
BRAZIL - Espirito Santo Staate	Espirito Santo	XX	BR
BRAZIL - Fernando De Noronha State	Fern. Noronha	XY	BR
BRAZIL - Goias State	Goias	XZ	BR
BRAZIL - Guanabara State	Guanabara	ZA	BR
BRAZIL - Maranhao State	Maranhao	ZB	BR
BRAZIL - Mato Grosso State	Mato Grosso	ZC	BR
BRAZIL - Mato Grosso do Sul State	Mato Grosso (S)	ZR	BR

Country Codes

FULL NAME	SHORT NAME	CODES CMC	ISO
BRAZIL - Minas Gerais State	Minas Gerais	ZD	BR
BRAZIL - Para State	Para	ZE	BR
BRAZIL - Paraiba State	Paraiba	ZF	BR
BRAZIL - Parana State	Parana	ZG	BR
BRAZIL - Pernambuco State	Pernambuco	ZH	BR
BRAZIL - Piaui State	Piaui	ZI	BR
BRAZIL - Rio Grande do Norte State	Rio Grande (N)	ZK	BR
BRAZIL - Rio Grande do Sul State	Rio Grande (S)	ZL	BR
BRAZIL - Rio de Janeiro State	Rio de Janeiro	ZJ	BR
BRAZIL - Rondonia Federal Territory	Rondonia	ZM	BR
BRAZIL - Roraima Federal Territory	Roriama	ZN	BR
BRAZIL - Santa Catarina State	Santa Catarina	ZO	BR
BRAZIL - Sao Paulo State	Sao Paulo	ZP	BR
BRAZIL - Sergipe State	Sergipe	ZQ	BR
CHILE	Chile	XE *	CL
COLOMBIA	Colombia	XF *	CO
ECUADOR	Ecuador	XG *	EC
FRANCE - French Guiana	French Guiana	XH	GF
GUYANA	Guyana	XJ	GY
PARAGUAY	Paraguay	XK	PY
PERU	Peru	XL	PE
SURINAME	Suriname	XM	SR
URUGUAY	Uruguay	XN	UY
VENEZUELA	Venezuela	XP *	VE

SOUTH ATLANTIC and SOUTHERN OCEAN IS.   S. Atlantic Is.   MY *

This is divided into the Antarctic Treaty Territory, and areas which are sovereign states or parts thereof.

ASCENSION ISLAND	Ascension Is.	NC	SH
AUSTRALIA - Heard And McDonald Islands	Heard Is.	NJ	HM
AUSTRALIA - Tasmania - Macquarie Island	Macquarie Is.	NL	AU

FULL NAME	SHORT NAME	CODES	
		CMC	ISO
BRAZIL - I. da Trindade	Trindade	NU	BR
FALKLAND ISLANDS	Falkland Is.	NI	FK
(Islas Malvinas)			
FRENCH SOUTHERN TERRITORIES	French S. Terrs.	NO *	TF
FRENCH SOUTHERN TERRITORIES - Ile Amsterdam	Amsterdam Is.	NA	TF
FRENCH SOUTHERN TERRITORIES - Iles Crozet	Crozet Is.	NH	TF
(includes Iles des Apotres, Ile aux Cochons, Ile da la Possession, Ile de la L'Est)			
FR SOUTHERN TERRITORIES - Iles Kerguelen	Kerguelen Is.	NK	TF
FRENCH SOUTHERN TERRITORIES - Ile St Paul	St Paul Is.	NP	TF
NEW ZEALAND - Antipodes Islands	Antipodes Is.	NB	NZ
NEW ZEALAND - Auckland Islands	Auckland Is.	ND	NZ
NEW ZEALAND - Bounty Islands	Bounty Is.	NE	NZ
NEW ZEALAND - Campbell Island	Campbell Is.	NG	NZ
NORWAY - Bouvet Island	Bouvet Is.	NF	BV
SOUTH AFRICA - Price Edward Islands	P.E. Is. (SA)	NM	ZA
SOUTH GEORGIA	South Georgia	NQ	FK
SOUTH SANDWICH ISLANDS	S. Sandwich Is.	NS	FK
ST HELENA	St Helena	NN	SH
TRISTAN DA CUNHA ISLANDS	Tristan da Cunha	NV	SH
ANTARCTIC TREATY TERRITORY	Antarctic T.T.	NX *	ZZ
comprises:			
ANTARCTICA	Antarctica	NW	AQ
ANTARCTIC ISLANDS	Antarctic Is.	NY *	ZZ
the latter includes:			
SOUTH ORKNEY ISLANDS	S. Orkney Is.	NR	BQ
SOUTH SHETLAND ISLANDS	S. Shetland Is.	NT	BQ
OCEANS AND SEAS			
ARCTIC OCEAN	Arctic Ocean	OS *	
NORTH ATLANTIC OCEAN	N. Atlantic	OG *	
SOUTH ATLANTIC OCEAN	S. Atlantic	OO *	

Country Codes

FULL NAME	SHORT NAME	CODES	
		CMC	ISO
CARIBBEAN SEA	Caribbean Sea	OK *	
MEDITERRANEAN SEA	Mediterranean Sea	OI *	
INDIAN OCEAN	Indian Ocean	OD *	
SOUTHERN OCEAN	Southern Ocean	OQ *	
NORTH PACIFIC OCEAN	N. Pacific	OU *	
SOUTH PACIFIC OCEAN	S. Pacific	OW *	
GENERAL CODES			
COUNTRY UNKNOWN	Country unknown	ZZ	ZZ
MANY COUNTRIES	Many countries	ZV *	
NEW WORLD	New World	ZW *	
OLD WORLD	Old World	ZX *	
PANTROPICAL	Pantropical	ZY *	

APPENDIX
II

Sampling Benthic Communities Using Video Transects

Katherine Osborne and William G. Oxley
Australian Institute of Marine Science
Townsville, Queensland, Australia

Abstract

Video transects may be used to assess a variety of sessile benthic communities including coral reefs, soft bottoms, sea grass beds, and rocky shores. The focus in this chapter is using video to assess coral reef benthic communities.

A 50 metre x 0.25 metre belt transect of the benthic community is videoed in the field. The video tape is then viewed and analysed in the laboratory, using a systematic point method, to estimate percent cover information of corals and other benthos. Lifeform categories are used to describe the community using morphological characteristics (see the Line Intercept Transect (LIT) method, Section 2.3). Where video recording and viewing equipment is available, the technique can be used in place of LIT to assess the sessile community of coral reefs. Consequently this chapter should be read in conjunction with Section 2.3 which describes the LIT technique.

Background

Video technology is applicable to answer a wide range of questions on the distribution and abundance of benthic organisms (seagrasses - Anderson 1994; corals - Carleton and Done 1995, Harriott *et al.* 1995; algae - Leonard and Clarke 1993).

Underwater video can be recorded in a variety of ways, including by snorkel, SCUBA or with a Remotely Operated Vehicle (ROV). The most common use of video in coral reef monitoring is to quantify percentage cover of reef benthic communities. The methods and data collected are therefore similar to those described for the Line Intercept method. Video transects are currently used in a large-scale long-term monitoring program looking at sessile benthos communities on the Great Barrier Reef (Christie *et al.* 1996, Osborne and Thompson in press, Ryan in press).

Video Transect

Advantages

❑ Field data can be collected by people not trained in lifeform identification.

❑ Provides a permanent record of the site.

❑ Reduces the time required for field data collection.

❑ Biota not in the original analysis can be sampled at a later date.

❑ Allows comparison between observers (correction for observer bias) at a later date.

Disadvantages

❑ Video equipment is expensive and requires regular maintenance.

❑ There must be ready access to a service center for spare parts and maintenance.

❑ There must be access to a laboratory with a stable power supply and good storage facilities for tapes (e.g. a data cabinet specially designed to house magnetic media).

❑ There is a risk of low quality or missing data since poor technique in using the video will result in inadequate images which may not be discovered until after the trip.

❑ Substrates with higher rugosity (roughness, corrugation) have lower resolution in a video image.

❑ Very complex substrates (many small or overlapping biota) have lower resolution in a video image.

❑ Separating lifeform categories consistently with a two dimensional image is not always possible. Therefore the power to detect temporal change of the percentage cover of individual lifeforms may be low in some environments.

❑ Taxonomic resolution on the video tape is less than that obtained by a skilled coral taxonomist underwater.

Logistics

Personnel

❑ A team of at least three personnel is required - 2 divers (1 to lay the tape - the 'tape layer'; and 1 to video the transects - the 'benthic observer'), and a person in the boat as surface support.

❑ The diver/observer who videos the transects must have had experience and training with the equipment prior to collecting data to ensure **quality** video images for analysis.

VIDEO POINT DATA

Location .... Sample ID ....

Reef name .... Reef zone .... Latitude ....

Date .... Time .... Wind .... Cloud .... Longitude ....

Turbidity .... Light .... Top .... Top ....

Temp. Bot. .... Salinity Bot. ....

Depth .... Sea .... Tide ....

Site N° .... Collector ....

Remarks ....

Replicate	Description / Notes	Time start	Time finish

Figure AII.1 Video point data sheet. This sheet is filmed at the beginning of each transect to identify the transect on the video tape.

Video Transect

Field equipment

❑ Small boat/s, with outboard motors and safety equipment.

❑ SCUBA equipment.

❑ Hand held Geographical Positioning System (GPS) - datum set to WGS-84.

❑ Underwater slate, pencil and data sheets.

❑ Video data sheets (Fig. AII.1).

❑ 6 fibreglass measuring tapes - 50 metres in length (see Figure 2.20).

❑ Hi-8 video camera and marine housing (including lenses) with instruction manuals.

❑ Appropriate colour filter - used to 'correct' the changes in colour absorption caused as light travels through water.

☞ *The best filter to use depends on the quantity and quality of available light. This is dependent on the angle of the sun, depth, and water clarity. Consult with the manufacturer of the video housing for the range of filters available.*

☞ *Lights may also be effective in correcting colour but they use a large amount of battery power.*

❑ Hi-8 professional metal particle video tapes (90 minutes).

❑ 4 battery packs.

❑ 2 battery chargers.

❑ Cleaning equipment for camera and housing, including O-ring kit and O-ring grease.

❑ Video head cleaning cassette.

Laboratory equipment

❑ Television monitor with 5 points arranged in a face-centred cube on the screen (Fig. AII.2).

❑ Hi-8 video cassette recorder/player with counter/timecode display and the ability to display a "jitter free" clear still picture when paused (e.g. Sony Video Cassette Recorder models EVO-9800P or EVO 9650P).

☞ *Domestic video players without "jitter free" stills may be used to view the videos but the speed of videoing transects in the field must be slower (i.e. for a 50m transect: 8 min. cf. 5 min.)*

❑ Personal computer (minimum 486 DX2/66 with 8Mb RAM).

❑ Database software for data entry. The structure of the database should conform to the structure detailed at the end of this chapter.

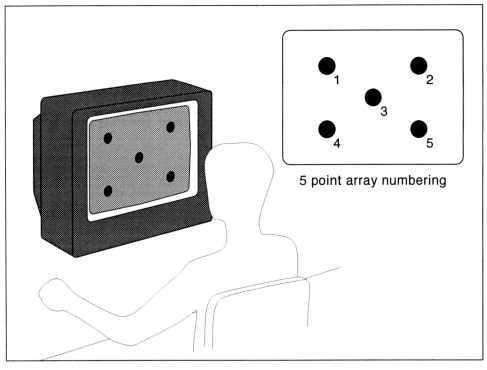

Figure AII.2 Television monitor showing the 5 sampling points arranged in a face-centred cube. The 5 points are always labelled as shown in the figure i.e. top left = 1, top right = 2, middle = 3, bottom left = 4 and bottom right = 5.

Maintenance

❑ Wash camera housing and fibreglass tapes in fresh water immediately after use.

❑ Store camera and housing in a dry, salt free environment.

❑ Discharge batteries before storage of camera equipment and before recharging for use.

❑ Replace O-rings on underwater housing at least once per year.

❑ Batteries will need to be replaced every second year.

☞ *Develop a routine of maintenance before and after each trip. Write this procedure down and ensure that all personnel know the routine.*

Site selection

❑ Read Chapter 7 Sampling Design and Monitoring.

❑ Draw up a preliminary sampling design and determine criteria (e.g. depth range, exposure, visibility, use status) for site selection.

Video Transect

❑ Use aerial photographs, charts and hold discussions with people familiar with the area to aid in selecting potential sites.

❑ Visit these sites to ensure that your pre-determined criteria are met and that the sites are suitable. Manta towing is a useful technique for site selection (see Section 2.2).

☞ *It may not be possible to find sites that match your pre-determined criteria. In this situation you should determine whether your objectives and/or design need revision. Do not just ignore your original criteria without considering the consequences.*

❑ The precise location of the sites should be recorded while at the site, noting landforms and unique reef features which might be useful in relocating the site (e.g. bays, indentations, channels) and GPS coordinates.

❑ For each site at least 5 transects of 50 metres length should be selected.

☞ *The sampling unit recommended in this manual is a 50 metre x 0.25 metre belt transect and the calculations in the chapter are based on this length. Shorter or longer video transects may be used to suit the habitats being surveyed. The appropriate length of transect can be determined in a pilot study.*

❑ If you wish to use permanent transects, then mark the transects on the site. Metal stakes, such as angle iron or star-pickets, should be hammered deep into the substratum (at least 0.5 metres). Place markers every 10 metres along the transect.

General procedure

Preparation of equipment

❑ Charge batteries - charging takes 4 to 8 hours.

❑ Clean and grease O-ring seals on camera housing.

❑ Insert blank tape and test all camera functions:

 » on/off

 » manual/autofocus

 » standby/record

 » wide angle /zoom

❑ Additionally, if you do not have a sophisticated video player which can display timecode on the screen, then setup the video camera so that "time of day" is displayed. This can be used later to pause the tape at regular intervals when analysing it.

❑ Place the video in the camera housing, attach the cables and close housing.

❑ Test all camera housing functions.

In the field

❏ Record videos between the hours of 0830 and 1530 for best lighting conditions (Great Barrier Reef, Australia). These times can be adjusted, depending on day length and water clarity.

☞*Avoid recording videos in the early morning and late afternoon. Diffraction of light by the water at these times reduces the available light and may make interpretation of video images difficult.*

❏ Locate the general area of the site from the surface using a GPS and/or past knowledge of reef topography. The precise location of the beginning of the first transect (if fixed transects are used) can be determined using snorkel.

❏ Anchor the boat slightly away from the site so that the anchor does not damage the coral on the transects.

❏ Collect ambient data (if required) and enter information onto the data sheet (Fig AII.1).

❏ Record location, date, site number, transect number, and the benthic observer's name onto the data sheet.

❏ Discuss the dive plan and ensure that conditions are safe for diving before divers enter the water.

❏ The dive team consists of the 'tape layer' and the 'benthic observer'.

❏ The 'tape layer' should have a 50 metre tape for **each** transect.

❏ The 'benthic observer' should have the video camera, filter and a slate with a pencil and the data sheet (Fig. AII.1).

Underwater procedure

The Role of the Tape Layer

❏ The 'tape layer' should stay clear of the 'benthic observer' until he/she has finished videoing a panorama. This panorama shot is videoed at the beginning of each transect.

❏ After the panorama has been completed:

» Attach the tape to the marker (e.g. star-picket) at the beginning of the transect.

» Swim along the transect wrapping the tape once around each marker until the end is reached.

» Ensure that the tape follows the contours of the reef as much as possible.

☞*This procedure describes sampling permanently marked transects. If transects are not marked, then secure the tape using coral, or other suitable 'anchors', at regular intervals.*

Video Transect

❏ Wait until the 'benthic observer' finishes recording before laying the next transect to ensure that divers do not become separated.

❏ Repeat the procedure until all transects are completed.

The role of the benthic observer

❏ Check the housing for leaks at the beginning of the dive and ensure that the equipment is functioning correctly.

❏ At the transect depth determine if a filter is necessary. For depths between 6 to 12 metres:

» If the visibility is greater than 8 metres fit an amber filter to the housing lens.

» If the visibility is less than 8 metres do not use a filter.

❏ Set the zoom function to wide angle.

❏ Set the camera to automatic focus.

❏ Record replicate transect number on the data sheet and video the completed data sheet to help identify the transects when analysing the videos in the laboratory.

☞ *To get best results when videoing panoramas with the video camera, move slowly, holding the video camera as steady as possible. Avoid sudden changes in the distances from video camera to subject which will cause the image to be blurred (due to the time lag for the automatic focus to adjust).*

❏ Video a panorama of the reef environment from a position at the start of the transect. The panorama should represent the reef area showing the general structure of the reef.

» Press RECORD.

» Start recording at the beginning of the transect.

» Turn in a clockwise direction, to record the reef slope.

» Avoid recording open water or a small area of the reef (< 5 metre radius) beneath you as this may not represent the reef area.

» Finish recording at the initial view (approximately 30 seconds).

» Put camera on STANDBY.

❏ Record the time code or counter, visible in the camera view finder, onto the data sheet (e.g. 00:00:30).

❏ Set the camera focus for the video transect as follows:

» Position the camera so the lens is 25 centimetres from an object.

» Set the camera to MANUAL focus.

☞ *If you are in shallow water, ripples on the surface of the water may be reflected onto the object you are focusing on. This ripple effect overrides the auto focus mechanism and results in a blurred image when MANUAL focus is selected. In these circumstances place the object you are focusing on in shadow using your body, aim the camera at the object, and then set the camera to MANUAL focus.*

❏ Keep the camera lens parallel to the substratum and a distance of 25 centimetres above it (Fig. AII.3). This films a belt 0.25 metres wide.

Figure AII.3   Diver recording the benthic community using a video camera.

❏ Record the video transect:

» Press RECORD.

» Video the base of the marker at the beginning of the transect for several seconds.

» Move approximately 50 centimetres to the right of the marker (perpendicular to the transect tape) then move forward parallel to the tape: the path videoed is 50 centimetres to the right of the transect tape.

☞ *The 'video path' is set to the side of the tape because the reflective nature of the fibreglass tape can adversely affect the exposure of the video camera.*

» Maintain a constant speed while swimming along the transect. Speed along a transect can be determined by checking the video counter.

☞ *If you are analysing the videos with a player that has a "jitter free" pause, then each transect should take approximately 5 minutes to video. Otherwise, a 50m transect should*

Video Transect

take approximately 8 minutes to video. Topographic complexity, surge and water currents may also cause some variation in the time required to complete the 50 metre transect.

☞ *Unless urgent, DO NOT video something other than the desired path (e.g. new coral species off transect or large fish) while in the process of videoing a transect. If it is urgent then video the item of interest, return to the beginning of the transect and redo the entire transect.*

> » If the tape does not follow the contour of the substratum (e.g. when there is a crevice in the reef), it may be necessary to move away from the preferred videoing path. When this is necessary, select a direction which requires the **least** deviation from the tape path (not more than 3 metres).

> » **Always try to maintain a constant distance of 25 centimetres between the camera lens and the substratum.**

> » At the end of the transect move towards the final marker and record it for several seconds (to indicate the end of the transect on the video tape).

> » Stop recording and leave the camera on standby.

❑ Record the time code or counter, visible in the camera view finder, onto the data sheet e.g. 00:05:30. The data sheet will now show for Transect 1 both the starting and final counters (e.g. Transect 1, 00:00:30-:00:05:30). This information allows easy calculation of the time interval for tape analysis in the laboratory.

❑ Record any irregularities in videoing onto the data sheet and make notes to aid analysis.

❑ Swim to the next transect with the 'tape layer' and repeat the procedure until all transects are completed.

After completing the transects

❑ It may aid later analysis of the tapes to video 'close ups' of abundant and/or different lifeforms and substrate types and note these on the data sheet while returning along the transects to the boat.

❑ The 'tape layer' should roll up the tapes as the divers return to the boat.

Laboratory procedure

❑ After returning to the laboratory or a safe dry place, rewind the video tape.

❑ Label both the video tape and its case with a description of the information on the tape including date, location, site and transect numbers and any irregularities during recording.

❑ Turn the copy protect switch on the video tape to "ON".

Number of sample points

❏ The video tape is sampled by stopping the tape at fixed time intervals. Each time the tape is stopped the observer identifies the benthos occurring under points arranged on the screen of the monitor (Fig. AII.2).

❏ A pilot study is recommended to determine the number of points required to sample the video. As a conservative guide two sampling studies (Ryan and Davidson in prep, Davidson in prep) have suggested that 40 to 80 pauses (200 to 400 points) result in good levels of precision when estimating total hard coral cover from 50 metre transects on the Great Barrier Reef.

❏ Calculate the time interval for sampling by dividing the time taken to video the transect (in seconds) by the number of tape pauses considered necessary (calculated during pilot study).

$$\textit{Time interval for sampling (secs)} = \frac{\textit{Time taken to video transect (secs)}}{\textit{Number of pauses required to sample video}}$$

For example:

» The time taken to video the transect was five minutes (300 seconds).

» Require 350 sample points for statistical analysis.

» 5 points are sampled at each stop - therefore need 70 pauses.

» Therefore the tape should be paused every

$$\textit{Time interval for sampling} = \frac{300}{70}$$

$$= 4.3 \ \textit{seconds}$$

Data recording and processing

❏ Open database on computer and prepare for data entry.

❏ Enter the information from the data sheet (Fig. AII.2) into the database structure described at the end of this appendix. Note that this structure is consistent with Coral Reef Database Structure (Section 2.9). Information about the sample is entered into the sample table and a unique sample identifier (SAMPLE_ID) is allocated. The type of data collected in the sample is described by the DATA_TYPE field, which for video data, is denoted by the letter "V".

❏ Place the video into the video cassette player and locate the transect to be analysed.

❏ Check the information on the tape cover for any irregularities during videoing.

❏ Open Video Point Table in database. Enter SAMPLE_ID and REPLICATE number.

Video Transect

❏ Open Video Point Table in database. Enter SAMPLE_ID and REPLICATE number.

❏ Locate the start frame from the image on the television monitor - the first frame in which the marker (e.g. star picket) can not be seen, i.e. to the right of the marker.

❏ Identify the benthos occurring under each of the five points on the monitor screen and enter benthic lifeform field code (Table 2.5) and other data into the database.

❏ Advance the tape to the next required frame i.e. advance the tape by the time interval calculated previously.

❏ Continue this procedure until the final marker is reached and the video transect analysis is complete.

❏ Locate the next transect and repeat the procedure until finished.

❏ Save, then check and verify the data.

❏ Backup the database.

❏ Rewind the tape and put it back into its case.

❏ Store the tapes in a dry, secure place e.g. fireproof data cabinet.

Standardisation

❏ Use appropriate camera filters and use the same filters for all sampling. Selection of filters is an important part of image quality.

❏ Regular training of field personnel should be undertaken to ensure high quality video images.

❏ Regular training and cross-checking of video interpretation should be undertaken to avoid observer bias.

❏ Individual observers should regularly calibrate against a known standard video tape to ensure that interpretation remains consistent over time.

Tape Storage

❏ To preserve video tapes and extend their life it is very important that the following notes be observed:

❏ Do not leave tapes in the VCR for an extended period of time.

❏ Store the tapes in their cases, and store the cases vertically.

❏ Avoid storing the tapes in places where there is dust, excessive heat, moisture or magnetic fields.

❏ If possible, store the tapes in a data cabinet designed for magnetic media.

❏ Fast forward the tapes every two years to prevent them sticking.

❑ To protect from erasure, ensure that the 'copy protect switch' on each tape, is placed **ON** after recording.

❑ Make backups of particularly important tapes.

Analysis

❑ Convert the video data to percentage cover data. For each transect the points for each benthic category are summed and expressed as a percentage of the total number of points in the transect.

$$Percent\ cover = \frac{Total\ number\ of\ points\ for\ lifeform}{Total\ number\ of\ points\ for\ transect} \times 100$$

References

Anderson P.K. (1994). Dugong distribution, the seagrass *Halophila sinulosa*, and thermal environment in winter in deeper waters of eastern Shark Bay, Western Australia. Wildlife Research **21**: 381-388.

Carleton J.H. and T.J. Done (1995). Quantitative video sampling of coral reef benthos: large scale application. Coral Reefs, **14**: 35-46.

Christie C.A., D.K. Bass, S.J. Neale, K. Osborne and W.G. Oxley (1996). Surveys of sessile benthic communities using the video technique. Long-term Monitoring of the Great Barrier Reef, Standard Operational Procedure Number 2. Australian Institute of Marine Science. 42pp.

Davidson J. (in prep). Optimising a video transect technique for monitoring and rapid ecological assessment of tropical benthic communities. MSc. Thesis, James Cook University of North Queensland.

Harriott V.J., P.L. Harrison and S.A. Banks (1995). The coral communities of Lord Howe Island. Marine and Freshwater Research, **46**: 457-465.

Leonard G.H. and R.P. Clark (1993). Point quadrat versus video transect estimates of the cover of benthic red algae. Marine Ecology Progress Series, **101**: 203-208.

Osborne K. and A.A. Thompson (in press). The regional relationship between damsel fish communities and habitat on selected reef slopes of the Great Barrier Reef. Proceedings Eighth International Coral Reef Symposium. Panama. June 1996.

Ryan, D.A.J. (in press). Sampling strategies for coral reef video transects. Coral Reefs. Available from AIMS.

Ryan, D.A.J. and J. Davidson (in prep). Optimal sample size determination for estimation of coral cover from video transects. Coral Reefs. Available from AIMS.

Video Transect

Video Database Structure

Video Point Table
XXCRVDAT

Name	Type	Length/ Decimal	Description
SAMPLE_ID	C	9.0	The standard sample identification. This links the sample table to the data files. Format XXGGGNNNN. See sample table in Section 2.9.
REPLICATE	N	2.0	Replicate transect number strarting with 1 (i.e. number for each 50 metre transect).
BENTHOS	C	3.0	Coded benthic lifeform encountered under the sample points. See Table 2.5
FRAME	C	11.0	Frame number from the video tape. Format AA:BB:CC:DD. Where AA = hours BB = minutes CC = seconds DD = 00-24 (25 frames per second)
TIME_SEC	N	7.2	Time from start of the transect (seconds)
POINT_NO	N	2	The point number on the screen. See Fig. II.2 1 = top left 2 = top right 3 = centre 4 = bottom left 5 = bottom right
FIELDCODE	C	40.0	Code assigned to the taxonomic entity by the field researcher (suggested codes listed in Section 2.11). The code must link uniquely to one taxonomic entity. Description of the entity (binomial name) must be given to the database manager when a new code is created. This information is maintained in ALLTAXON
NOTES	C	20.0	Additional notes observed by the recorder (e.g. type of other fauna)

GLOSSARY
OF TERMS

The meanings given in this glossary are for the use of words or phrases in an ecological context.

active gear nets or devices that are moved through the water (by boats or by hand) to capture fish/prawn.

ambient surrounding.

anthropogenic produced or caused by humans.

artisanal (in fishing) small-scale, non-commercial or subsistence.

assemblage a collection of individuals, usually of different types.

autotroph any organism for which environmental carbon dioxide is the only or main source of carbon in the synthesis of organic compounds by photosynthesis.

basal area the total area of the ground covered by trees, measured at breast height.

baseline study first assessment of a situation against which subsequent changes are measured.

beach intertidal beaches (sand, gravel, stone).

benthic living on sea bottom.

benthos animals and plants living on the bottom of the sea.

camera lucida drawing tube attached to a microscope.

carapace a bony case or shield covering the back or part of the back of certain animals with external skeletons, e.g. crustaceans.

catch per unit effort catch statistics standardised for variable units of effort, e.g. hours of fishing.

cod-end rear end of a net where the catch is concentrated.

clay sediment particles between 0.002 mm and 0.004 mm in diameter.

commercial gear refers to sampling gear with the characteristics of gear used by a commercial industry.

communities any group of organisms belonging to a number of different species that co-occur in the same area and interact through trophic and spatial relationships.

creek drainage channel from forest to the main stream; usually less than 20 metres wide, and usually less than 2 metres deep at low tide.

cryptic concealed.

data dictionary a description, usually written, of the structure and functioning of a database.

data sheet a paper form used to record field data in a set format.

database (computer) a computer-based system for storing, manipulating, and retrieving data within a defined structure.

database field a column within a database field.

database record a row within a database field.

database table a structure made up of fields and records, for storing data in a database.

demersal living on or near bottom of sea, but able to swim actively.

demographic study study of growth rates, turnover and age structure of populations.

depth contour horizontal line joining points of the same depth.

diel daily, 24 hour intervals.

digitate a colony shape composed of short finger-like branches.

disturbance change caused by an external agent, could be natural (e.g. weather) or human-induced (e.g. pollution).

diurnal behavioural rhythm with a cycle of 24 hours; active during daylight hours.

diversity variety, often expressed as a function of a number of species in a sample, sometimes modified by their relative abundances.

duplicate a repeated measurement made from the same sample.

ecosystem a dynamic complex of plant, animal, fungal and micro-organism communities and the associated non-living environment interacting as an ecological unit.

epibenthic fauna larger, mobile animals living on the surface of the substratum.

epifauna animals living on the surface of the sediment, or other organisms.

epiphyte   plants growing on the surface of other plants.

fissures   deep groove or furrow.

flat file database   a database structure where the data is stored in large tables with all the data about one topic in the one table.

foliose   thin and leaf-like.

fringing reef   reef surrounding emergent land.

Global Positioning System (GPS)   satellite-based navigation system.

gutters   the smallest drainage unit (approximately 1 metre wide) draining mangrove forests and mudflats; also used for deep grooves in underwater habitats.

infauna   bottom-dwelling and burrowing animals living within the sediment.

larvae   a developing embryo that is independent of the parents, but has not yet assumed their adult characteristics.

leaf area index (L)   a measure of the area of photosynthetic surface expanded over a given area of ground (m^2 leaf area m^2 ground).

leeward   side protected from the wind.

lifeform   external appearance of organisms resulting from the interaction of genetic and environmental factors.

macrobenthos   the largest living components of benthic communities.

macrofauna   the animals retained by a 0.5 mm sieve.

mainstream   main drainage channel.

meiofauna   animals retained by a 0.1 mm sieve, but passing through a 0.5 mm sieve.

messenger   weight (usually brass) used to release sampling gear at depth.

methodology   collection of methods used in a particular activity.

microfauna   animals less than 2 mm long (the limit of comfortable visibility with the naked eye).

motile   mobile.

monitoring   repeated observation of a system, usually to detect change.

mudflats   open expanses of intertidal mud, usually at the entrance of the estuary to the sea, but may occur as accreting banks of sediment in the estuary.

multivariate analysis   a group of statistical techniques for the simultaneous analysis of more than one dependent variable.

Glossary

nearshore close to the coastline.

nekton actively swimming pelagic organisms.

nett remaining after all necessary deductions

nett photosynthesis apparent photosynthesis measured as the nett uptake of carbon dioxide into the leaf, and equal to gross photosynthesis less respiration.

nocturnal active at night.

okta the unit of measure for the amount of cloud cover.

parameter a measure used to describe some characteristics of a population.

passive gear nets or sampling devices that do not require movement to capture fish/prawns.

pelagic pertaining to the water column of the sea; used for organisms inhabiting the open waters.

photo-quadrat sampling of flora or fauna using photographs to record the quadrat.

photocomposite a number of individual photographs of a subject that have been joined together to make one larger image.

plankton drifting or floating forms of organic life, usually microscopic, found at various depths in aquatic habitats.

population all individuals of one or more species within a prescribed area.

population structure the composition of a population according to age and sex of the individuals.

post-settlement after the transition, when larvae have exchanged pelagic for benthic habits (see settlement).

primary key (database) a field common to 2 or more relational database tables which is used to link the tables.

primary productivity the productivity (see below) of autotrophic organisms.

pristine natural, uncorrupted state.

productivity (1) the potential rate of incorporation or generation of energy or organic matter by an individual or population per unit time per unit area or volume; rate of carbon fixation; (2) often used loosely for the organic fertility or capacity of a given area or habitat.

quadrat a fixed unit of area, usually rectangular, used for sampling.

qualitative descriptive, non-numerical, assessment.

quantitative numerical; based on counts, measurements or other values.

recruitment a measure of new individuals (recruits) arriving in a population.

redox potential (Eh) oxidation-reduction potential, a measure of the tendency of a given system to act as an oxidising (electron acceptor) or reducing (electron donor) agent.

reef crest the highest point at the seaward edge of a coral reef.

reef slope the face of a coral reef extending seawards from the reef crest.

refractometer optical instrument used to measure salinity.

relational database a database structure where the data is stored in many small tables that are linked by common fields.

replicate a repeated sample from the same location and time.

salinity measure of the total concentration of dissolved salts in water.

sample any subset of a population; a representative part of a larger unit used to study the properties of the whole.

sample size the number of observations in a sample.

sand cohesionless sediment particles measuring 2.0-0.0625 mm in diameter.

SCUBA Self-Contained Underwater Breathing Apparatus.

Secchi disc device used to estimate the transparency of water.

secondary indirectly caused.

sedentary restricted in movement but not necessarily sessile.

sedimentation process of deposition of particulate matter.

sediment load amount of particulate matter suspended in the water column.

sediment trap apparatus used to measure sedimentation.

sessile attached to a surface; fixed position as opposed to free-living or motile.

settlement a transition in the development and growth of an animal in which pelagic larvae or juveniles colonise and take up residence in benthic habitats.

slate rigid surface for writing on when underwater.

sledge a collecting device towed over the benthos on runners.

software all the programs, programing languages and operating routines used with computers.

soft coral animal consisting of anemone-like polyps with eight feeding tentacles surrounding the mouth.

Glossary

spatial pertaining to space.

spur formations radiating ridges in the upper reef slope dissected by deep regularly-spaced grooves.

standard length measurement of fish length from snout to hypopural bone in the tail.

Standard Operational Procedure (SOP) a written guide detailing the steps required to complete a task, often called a 'user guide'.

standing stock instantaneous measurement of the density of a population.

standing crop instantaneous measurement of the biomass of a population.

subsistence activity at a level just permitting survival; no excess production for commercial profit.

substratum the base to which a stationary animal or plant is fixed, but can be any benthic surface.

subtidal beneath the low watermark.

survey organised inspection.

tailings refuse material separated as residue in the preparation of various products.

temporal pertaining to time.

thermocline a boundary region between 2 layers of water of different temperature.

transects a line or narrow belt used to survey the distributions of organisms across the given area.

trophic group individuals grouped by the way in which they obtain food; similar relative position in the food chain.

turbulence non-linear motion.

vagile freely mobile; able to migrate.

variable any measurable aspect of a sample that is not constant.

visibility distance at which objects may be sighted during a survey.

warp rope or wire for towing sampling gear.

weak link wire or shear pin designed to break if equipment (dredge) gets caught on the seabed.

water column a volume of water between the surface and the bottom.

windward side exposed to the wind.

zenith angle (θ) angle of the sun from the vertical.

Index

4. Soft-Bottom Communities

5. Seagrass communities

6. Coastal Fisheries

7. Sampling Design and Monitoring